MW01037739

To Gary & Jill:
The result of
following your dream
is a good life
Enjoy the story.

B R Steinberg

THE
WIDOW'S
SON

Bruce Steinberg

© 2001 Gardenia Press

The Widow's Son
Copyright © 2001 by Bruce Steinberg

Library of Congress Number: 2001092254
ISBN Number Casebound: 0-9678895-6-1
                    Softcover: 0-9678895-7-X

All rights reserved. No part of this book may be reproduced or transmitted in any form or by any means, electronic or mechanical, including photo-copying, recording, or by any information storage and retrieval system, without the written permission of the publisher, except in the case of brief quotations embodied in critical articles or book reviews.

This is a work of fiction. Names, characters, places and incidents are either the product of the author's imagination or are used fictitiously, and any resemblance to any actual persons, living or dead, events, or locales is entirely coincidental.

This book was printed in Canada.

For inquiries or to order additional copies of this book, contact:

Gardenia Press
P. O. Box 18601
Milwaukee, WI 53218-0601USA
866-861-9443 www.gardeniapress.com
orders@gardeniapress.com

DEDICATION

To my father, Allen, whose life lives on, etched in the
memories and conduct of his children; and to my mother,
Joyce, a winner by any standard—
may this novel make them both immortal.

To Peggy, who proves every day that the past
can be survived because I have her for my wife.

The Dreamer's valuation of a thing lost
—not another man's—
is the only standard to measure it by,
and his grief for it makes it
large and great and fine,
and is worthy of our reverence in all cases.

Mark Twain
"My Boyhood Dreams"

MAY 31, 1966

WHEN I HEAR THE NEWS I want to jump on the dining room clock and make time go backwards. Golden spikes wave from the clock's face, like a sun rising on the east wall. *Stop, go back,* I order in my mind, then pray, squinting my eyes to show I mean business.

The skinny second hand reaches the fat minute hand. For a moment, time stops. With my heartbeat, the second hand reappears and I'm lost.

In our living room, nothing more than the other side of the dining room, Mom says again, "His heart stopped and he died."

"But I'm twelve," I say, as if my age makes her news about Dad sound silly. And I think, Cheryl's eight and David's only seven, 'cause that makes it impossible.

"Jeremy," Mom says.

"What?" I say.

"We saw what we saw."

Mom's not wearing her glasses, her butterfly wing glasses. Her face seems so blank, and her voice becomes so soft I can hardly hear her. "You're staying home from school today."

With a hop beside Mom, David cheers, "All of us, Mummy?"

Cheryl plunges her fingers into her moppy brown hair,
and kicks David in the knee when Mom turns around.

David whines, "Hey!" and pities his eyes up for Mom to
see.

"Take David out to play pinners or something," Mom
says, and she doesn't touch any of us. She runs to her bedroom and slams the door shut.

"Mummy said you have to play pinners with me," David
boasts like he's won some big argument.

I press my hand against Mom's door and hear her fall
hard on the bed. She's crying so loud. She cries, *What am I
going to do? Al, what am I going to do?* My throat feels like
food's stuck and won't go down, and I swallow hard to get
rid of it.

"Can I play pinners, too?" Cheryl says, tapping my shoulder. I see Dad's face in hers, surrounded by all her brown
curls. Her question makes me wonder, *Am I the only one who
heard what Mom just told us?*

The morning my father dies, I play pinners with Cheryl
and David.

•   •   •

In pinners you take a rubber ball, a hard one not a blow-
up one, and it's got to be the size of a major league baseball,
and you throw it against the porch steps for players standing
down the front walk to try to catch the rebound. I don't play
pinners as much as I used to. I've gotten too big for it and
the ball really flies, sometimes into Loblolly Avenue, and
mean Missy Grossman comes stomping out of her house
across the street complaining we're all gonna get run over
one day. Often the ball goes the other way. It skips up the
steps and slaps against the screen door. Mom says it sounds
like somebody's sneaking up behind her saying *Boo!* while
banging frying pans over her head. That's why I call it pinners, that sound it makes when it hits the screen door. *Pin!*

David's White Sox hat spins about his head each time he

throws the ball. Dad gave him that hat, and he gave my sister and me one, too. Our father grew up in the Old Neighborhood, on the South Side of Chicago, so he was always a White Sox fan. Becoming a Cubs fan just 'cause a person moved north to Skokie was nothing but disloyalty. He also said the Cubs hadn't been in the World Series in a million years and he wasn't expecting them to be in the World Series for another million years. The Cubs would sooner flap their arms and fly before taking the field in the World Series, that's the way Dad said it.

Skyler Jenner sits on his lawn wearing his Cubs hat and uniform, watching our pinners game. Skyler lives next door, to the right as we play, in a house the same as mine, only reversed. His side door faces my side door, and every room in his house is flipped around, like there's a mirror reflecting our houses back at each other. Although he's nine and only a bit bigger than David, Skyler's the kinda boy that can get away with being named Skyler and not get beat up all the time. He's almost pretty, like a girl, but unafraid and bossy, and talks about everything as certain as a dictionary.

"My father's a lawyer," Skyler says more often than he says "hello." He warns us all the time how easy he can sue us for this or that, for coming on his property without permission, for pulling grass from his lawn even by accident, for breaking one of his toys, or for not letting his team bat first in a game he's named himself captain (which he's always doing). "Yep, I can sue for that," he likes to say to the rest of the kids on Loblolly Avenue. "Go ask my father." But nobody's asked yet 'cause he might sue us for not trusting his father.

In spring and summer, Skyler dresses ready to play for the Cubs and he's autographed, shoes to cap, by Ernie Banks. Whenever the Cubs win, he pretends he's Jack Brickhouse and shouts *Hey! Hey!* a hundred times then interviews himself about the game. "Great game, Mr. Banks," he says. "Shucks, Jack," he says. "Great for America, Mr. Banks," he says. "Call me Ernie," he says.

Every fall when the Cubs are a hundred games out of first, Skyler puts on his Dick Butkus shoulder pads and his Dick Butkus jersey, and his Chicago Bears football helmet, pants and thigh pads. We can hardly see him, his face-masked face sunk low between armored shoulders. That's fine with Skyler, "'Cause I'm just like Dick Butkus," he says, autographed cleats to helmet.

Skyler's got a lot of sports stuff. His dad's a lawyer. My dad drove a truck for a living. Now Skyler Jenner wants to know what was going on with the ambulance this morning.

"Dad died," David says. David grinds the ball in his leather mitt. "We're not going to school today."

"You know I can sue you if you're lying," Skyler says crinkling his eyes up all serious. "He's not dead."

"He is too!"

As if to prove it, David winds up and whips the rubber ball against the steps harder than I've ever seen him do it before. "Line-drive!" David screams diving to the sidewalk.

It's only a soft pop-up that falls with a hollow thump on David's head and bounces away. David's hat spins a quarter way around, slides down, and catches on his ear. I can't see his face through the hat, I just hear him shoot back at Skyler Jenner, "My dad is too dead! Don't call me a liar!"

Cheryl's been waiting all pinners game for David to get the ball to her. With her jaws crunching something, she walks to Skyler Jenner. She takes her baseball glove off and whacks Skyler on the head with it, knocking his Cubs hat and official hat-brim-attached flip-up sunglasses to the ground.

"Damn you!" she says like a cannon going off.

At first Skyler freezes up, his lips squeezed to a circle the size of a Cheerio, but then he runs toward his house, tattling to the sky, "She's cursing! Cheryl Rosenberg's cursing! She said *damn* . . ." Skyler stutters at the end of his own curse word and covers his mouth, his nervous eyes looking out for lightning bolts. He runs away, shouting back, "For sure I'm gonna sue!" then darts into his house. He's telling on us to his mother, his father, his living father, in his house built the opposite of mine.

Cheryl growls over David, "Don't talk like a brag about it."

"Don't hit me," David says, then warns something stupid— ". . . 'cause I'll tell Dad."

It's hard to tell if Cheryl's going to clobber David 'cause she looks like she wants to, and is about to, but she pounds her mitt instead and hisses, "Good thing for you I have a rule against whacking dumb animals." She stomps to our house, pounding her mitt and feet and the door, and David's shoulders twitch with each angry thump as if Cheryl's whacking him for real.

Whispering "Daddy" over and over, David sits curled up, hiding his face inside his White Sox hat. I don't think he's crying. I don't know what he's doing.

My God, this day isn't nearly started and we can't play pinners anymore.

•   •   •

So many people in my house, and I know Mom wishes we were alone. But we can't stop it. As far as I know, a dead father has never happened before on my block.

Ben and Ida Lipshilts from next door are here, the other next door, not the Jenners' next door. Even though they've been here a million times before, today they're standing so stiff and quiet in the dining room, like they're too afraid to move or say anything.

Ida Lipshilts is pretty short and she smokes her cigarettes all the time. Kinda like an extra finger, she's always got a cigarette. She wouldn't be the same without one. She talks holding it between her lips and it flicks up and down with each word not much different from Lawrence Welk conducting his orchestra. She motions with it, handles it all different ways, as if she's saying particularly important news. *Watch my cigarette, it shows what I mean.* She's really good with it, a huffing and puffing little putt-putt engine.

Everybody I know calls Ben Lipshilts *Big Ben*, even Ida
Lipshilts. I didn't know he was so nice at first 'cause he had
fun scaring the crap out of me when I was younger. He
makes all the kids in the neighborhood think his lawn is such
a big deal so we don't look at it the wrong way let alone step
on it. His lawn doesn't look different from any other lawn,
but just the same, if a ball lands there, it's best to leave it and
get another. Even Skyler Jenner, with his Cubs stuff and
lawyer dad, won't get his baseballs or footballs off Big Ben's
lawn. Skyler figures if a ball lands on Big Ben's lawn, it's as
good as Big Ben's, and we are as good as dead if we go and
get it. We know without ever trying that if we sneak one off
his lawn he will sniff us out, *What sorry pipsqueak stepped
on my lawn? Fe fie foe fum!* Like Skyler Jenner says, "You
can't sue if you're dead."

A couple years ago, Big Ben came to my house with a
laundry basket full of balls. Some were mine. A lot were
Skyler Jenner's. Big Ben gave them all to me and told me he
was kidding about the lawn and that Ida wanted him to get
rid of all the balls he'd collected. He didn't want Skyler
Jenner to get any back. Big Ben called him a snotty kid. "You
look like Dean Martin," I said taking the balls, which he
does. He liked that and told me to come on his lawn any time
I wanted. "But don't tell the other kids," he said winking. "I
still like scaring them a little bit." It's kinda like we've had
this secret between us ever since.

The Waxbergs, Ruth and Mr. Waxberg, are here standing in the living room. Some adults don't seem to have first
names, like Mr. Waxberg. We just know him as Mister. Their
kids have Hebrew names now, Mookie, Hannah, and
Dahveed. Dahveed is *David*, like my brother, but in Hebrew
it's pronounced *Dah-veed*. Mookie's my best friend but he's
been getting really Jewish lately. His whole family is. They
want to move to Israel soon. Mookie used to be Mitchell and
I laughed when he changed to Mookie. He's skinny and
kinda long in the face like the Spy versus Spy cartoons in my

Mad Magazines. He looks like a Mookie and he doesn't like it that I sometimes can't keep from laughing about it. Mookie. What a name.

Grandpa Rosenberg slumps on one of our yellow-cushioned wooden chairs. We've got eight of those chairs, although only four are out around the dining room table on any regular day. Grandpa Rosenberg's drying his eyes and squeezing his nose in a handkerchief. I like Grandpa Rosenberg. He's an ice cream man, so who wouldn't like him? He's like the Good Humor man, but he doesn't sell his stuff in Skokie since he still lives on the South Side. But when he visits, which hasn't been too often, he comes with his ice cream man truck packed to the ceiling with ice cream bars, drumsticks, pushups, double-sided popsicles with three colors in them, and Dixie Cup ice cream, plain vanilla and some with chocolate swirls.We've got a freezer in our basement and he stuffs it full for free. Besides the summer ice cream visits, we just don't see him much.

As much as they like Grandpa Rosenberg, David and Cheryl seem to like Grandma Rosenberg a lot more, even if she doesn't sell ice cream. She's sitting on the arm of the living room couch, arms folded, not looking at anybody. Seems kinda nasty. But she curses a lot, and I guess that's funny, and my brother and sister hang around her just to listen to what they're not allowed to say. Dad was always trying to get her to stop cursing and Mom shooed us out of whatever room Grandma Rosenberg was in. "Goddamn lazy sons-of-bitches . . ." she'd start to say, and then she'd go on and insult the Italians or the Irish or the Negroes. Last summer, I told her our teachers at Eisenhower K-8 were trying to get us to say "Blacks" instead of "Negroes," and she said they were lucky she didn't call them something worse. I don't think people care much about what Grandma Rosenberg has to say. She's just old, fat, gray, and rickety and sits around all day insulting people. She's my grandma, I know, but I'm glad she stays in her house most of the time so nobody but Grandpa Rosenberg has to hear her.

Grandpa Erwin and Grandma Elaine sit close together on the end of the couch away from Grandma Rosenberg. They're the Finkelwitz side of the family. I realize how easy I know their first names. I don't know my Rosenberg grandparents' first names. I see my Finkelwitz grandparents almost every Friday night, in a place Cheryl calls Grandmaland. It's just past the Skokie border on the far east side over a drainage canal, into Chicago, where the streets are narrow and crowded with one-story brick and glass shops, mostly kosher delis and pastry bakeries. Dad said it's officially called Rogers Park, but he laughed when he first heard my sister call it Grandmaland. A lot of grandparents seem to live there.

For as far back as I can remember, Fridays have been our get-together days in Grandmaland, unless someone's sick. We eat Grandma Elaine's cooking until our stomachs get as tight as drums, and Grandma Elaine beats our little drums harder by stuffing a scoop or two of Neapolitan ice cream or Jell-O down our throats. She doesn't force us, but we don't say no, we wouldn't think of it, and Grandma Elaine never sits down. She's running constantly from her kitchen to her dining room table, making sure there's enough for everyone to eat. Her eyes dart around beneath those old eyeglasses of hers. The lenses are bulgy and set like reverse microscopes so her eyes shine through them as big as shooter marbles. When she spies something running low, she darts into her kitchen, returning as quickly with another plate of boiled chicken wings right as one of us is biting into the last one.

"For cry'n' out loud, sit down, Elaine!" Grandpa Erwin always says. She doesn't sit down. She doesn't seem to eat. But I know what's going on. She's chewing in the kitchen — taking bites of this and that on every trip to the stove or refrigerator. Grandma Elaine is efficient that way.

I like the way Grandpa Erwin talks. His two favorite things to say are *For cry'n' out loud* and *Ahch*. He says *Ahch* like you say *Ah* to a doctor looking at your throat, and then gurgles spit in his mouth at the *ch*. His *Ahch* comes with a downward flick of his hand while his head turns away. He means with his *Ahch*, "Take that bullshit away from me," like how Grandma Rosenberg curses, only polite. He rhymes a lot, too: *cats shmatz, dog shmog. You got a cat? Cats shmatz! You got a dog? Dog shmog!* I tell him we're studying the Gemini space program in school, and he says, *Gemini shmemini.* Mom calls it fake Yiddish. Grandma Elaine really knows Yiddish and Grandpa Erwin just likes to replace the first letter or two in a word with *shm*. Fake Yiddish. I don't know what he means by it 'cause he likes cats and dogs, and he can't wait until America gets a man on the moon, but it sounds like he doesn't like something, whatever he has *shm*'d.

We like to see if Grandpa Erwin will drink his glass of Manischewitz wine after each Friday dinner. It's a big deal to see how red his bald head will turn, and how quick. He looks at me, winks, then raises his wine glass. *Shall I?* Of course he does. He drinks his wine and his noggin starts to glow in about ten seconds. After Grandma Elaine's Friday dinner, we watch Frasier Thomas on TV talk about the Family Classics movie that's gonna start. Grandpa Erwin keeps his chair pointed right at the TV. Grandma has her seat on the couch closest to Grandpa's chair. The rest of us find a spot to slouch about and fall asleep.

This afternoon, nobody says much of anything. Everyone's sniffing. As mean-looking as ever, Missy Grossman's got my mother serving deli trays from Kaufman's Bakery, and her husband, Arnold, yells at her to go easy on my mother. Mom's wearing her black stirrup pants. Dad said he liked her in those. "You look just like Laura Petrie," he said when she wore those pants.

As we all know, Laura Petrie is really hot. That's what Arnold Grossman always says. "Nice *tuchas*, really hot. Why can't the women around here have a *tuchas* like Laura Petrie, that's what I want to know?"

Arnold Grossman's not talking like that now. Mom's dropped the deli tray and cries in front of everybody. Mr.

Grossman says something first. "Grace, his insurance will pay for the funeral," and he hugs her. He's so short and has to stretch his head up to rest his chin on Mom's shoulder.

"Be more tactful," Missy Grossman scolds.

While the Grossmans help my mother pick the lunch meat off our floor, I walk to the living room picture window. Outside, Skyler Jenner plays catch with his dad, and his mom watches them like it's the greatest thing in the world. They're all dressed in matching Cubs outfits. As father and son throw the baseball, Skyler Jenner steps backwards onto my front lawn.

My nose pressed against the window, I hear, "Good throw, son."

Cheryl and David sit on our pinners porch, watching them toss the baseball. Their White Sox hats lie on the ground upside down.

JUNE 2, 1966

Today's funeral day. Everyone's whispering about how Mom was supposed to get this done within twenty-four hours after Dad died. That's tradition. Mom's let tradition down. I hate this, all this whispering by the adults like I can't hear what they're saying.

Poor boy. He's the man of the house now.

I hear what they're saying, not all of it, but enough. I hate this place, Shalom Memorial Park. It looks like a big lawn, like Chick Evans golf course on Simpson Street. Dad's being buried in a golf course, but this is where people from the New Neighborhood are supposed to get buried, I guess.

How much is this costing her? What about the mortgage?

I hear them. All of them. This place where they're burying Dad is so crowded with people I've never met before. They're all probably glad they're not me, that's what I see. I don't know why I'm here. Dad's not here anyway.

My father told me many times that we used to live in Chicago, the South Side, on Lawndale Avenue. He called it the Old Neighborhood. I've seen pictures of the place, my room, my crib, my tricycle. It was an apartment in a large building with big trees in front. I can't remember much of it. But Dad liked to say, *Jeremy! Jeremy! You're a Rosenberg!* He had this joke— we have the most Jewish-sounding name in

America. Take the first part, *Rosen*. Standing alone, that's definitely Jewish. Now take the second part, *berg*. Can there be any syllable in the English language more Jewish-sounding? Now put them together, Jewish plus Jewish. We're the Rosenbergs, the Jewish-Jewishes.

I guess that's all right. From the way Dad talked, everyone from the Old Neighborhood was Jewish, so what was wrong with a name that announced it twice? Nothing at all. And in our New Neighborhood in Skokie, almost every house on Loblolly Avenue has a Hanukkah menorah burning in the window in December. A few houses have Christmas trees, but not many. I feel sorry for the Christians. Christmas is only one day. Hanukkah lasts eight days, and every one of those eight days is a celebration of lighting candles and getting presents. Lighting candles is so easy, and watching the Christians set up all those lights and trees for weeks on end, well, it seems like a lot of work for one day of presents. The Jewish-Jewishes had it good in December.

Dad's motorcycle made warm days good for the Rosenbergs, and not just any motorcycle, but a 1949 Harley-Davidson Hydra Glide, with its Twin-V Panhead engine. It's black and silver and looks like an adult bicycle with absolutely all the gadgets. Dad sat me right up front, his belly pressed against me, kinda wrapping around my backside. His arms reached out to the handlebars and I leaned over the gas tank, all big and black, and a painted eagle spread its colorful wings across the bottom of the windshield. When we rode, Dad's breaths mixed with the Hydra Glide's roar. One sound couldn't live without the other.

Missy Grossman told Dad he was reckless giving children rides on a motorcycle. Missy Grossman has her hair screwed on too tight, all black and curled under like a bad try to look like Laura Petrie. I bet her hair would hurt my knuckles if I hit it. Arnold Grossman chased her back to their house, yelling, *Get your tuchas out of their business!* I like the way Mr. Grossman says *tuchas*, all juicy and spitty from the back of his throat. It's like how my Grandpa and Grandma

Finkelwitz say most of their words.

Mom didn't mind the Hydra Glide a bit. She drove it with Dad, and the neighbors came out to send them off. As far as I could tell, we were the only family who took motorcycle rides with their father, and Mom was the only mother on the block who could drive a motorcycle. Some of the other mothers went for a ride with Dad, but Mom could drive it almost as good as Dad. Our rides were like parties with all the neighbors crowding around, setting up barbecues and buckets of ice filled with pop bottles. Everybody but Missy Grossman asked for a turn.

"After my children," Dad would say.

Missy Grossman scowled, "Don't blame me when something happens."

I rode tucked under him as we sped down Church Street into Morton Grove to Rural Beckwith Road, my favorite 'cause of the curves and turnabouts. I loved to feel the way Dad leaned to turn the Hydra Glide, especially when he did it fast — my body pushed to one side even though it felt like it should push to the other.

Riding the bridge over Edens Expressway, back into Skokie, there was that brown sign, *Welcome to Skokie, Illinois — The World's Largest Village.* We entered the New Neighborhood, so bright and full of brick houses and young parents and children for me and my brother and sister to play with. The largest village in the world, and we lived in one of the new brick houses, all young and fresh-looking, the Jewish-Jewishes.

This morning, I've learned to think of the past. I know it wasn't the Hydra Glide that killed my father. It was innocent, cold and quiet in the garage.

Somebody yelps and halts Dad's funeral. It's David. Cheryl's whacked him one in front of everybody. There she is in her dark blue dress, all frilled up with ruffles and a lacy scarf, none of which slows down her right hook a bit. David's on his knees.

"Dad's not a plant!" Cheryl squawks. "He's not gonna

grow back out of the ground!" She stands over him, "You idiot! You stupid idiot!" and runs to the limousine.

David's crying, looking at the grass, pulling a few blades up then more and more at a time, his clip-on tie on the ground. My mother hugs me, squeezing harder, her fingers digging as if searching to find something to hold on to. I can't stand any of this. I'm wondering about the whispers — *How will they survive?* That's enough, I'm not thinking about it anymore. The rest can have this funeral. I'm pretending it's tomorrow.

SUMMER

It's only seven-thirty and David's already getting on my nerves. I wish we had another bedroom to put him in.

"You snored again," he's saying from his bed all baggy-eyed.

"Did not," I say.

"You snored all night. One day, I'm gonna tape record you and prove it."

Great, that's all I need is our clunky recorder spinning under my head. My brother on the prowl, Mr. FBI, Snore Detective Division. His bed is on the wall opposite mine. Last week, it was by the closet. A week before that, it was by our windows.

David likes rearranging his side of the bedroom. Ever since the neighbors started getting their shag carpeting put in, David's been doing that with his bed. I think he's trying to scratch up the wood floor so Mom will get us some shag carpeting like the Lipshilts', the Grossmans', and the Jenners'. The Waxbergs got shag carpeting put in even though they're talking all the time about moving to Israel.

"Why can't we get shag carpeting like everyone else on the block?" he says. This upsets Mom, especially when he says it more than once when she comes home from work. So he's pushing that bed of his around our bedroom to prove the Rosenbergs are redecorating, too.

Our hallway isn't long and I hear Cheryl talking to Mom in the bathroom.

"Why do you have to go to work all the time now?"

"It's my job."

"But why?"

David starts getting out of bed and I try to listen through his noise for Mom's answer. If she said something, I didn't hear it.

"You do too snore," David says in my ear, "loud, loud, loud!" He leaves our bedroom wearing his Batman pajamas and turns to the kitchen.

Mom's coming down the hall. It leads from the bathroom straight to my bedroom door. Her shirt has some small ruffles on it and her jacket's the same dull brown as her skirt. Man, it's been hot out. She won't be comfortable wearing that stuff. She's all straight and business-like, her hair cut short and up a little like those women with the beehive hairdos I'm starting to see on TV commercials. They all look like they have balloons growing out the top of their heads. Mom's isn't so bad, but I miss the way she used to look in the morning.

"You're in charge again," Mom says, sitting on my bed. We had our talk, our man-of-the-house talk. "Be a good example for Cheryl and David," she says.

"Can I use the wooden spoon on them?"

We have this wooden spoon Mom goes for when we're bad. When we deserve a spanking, we hear the kitchen drawer open up, and that always sends us diving for our beds, under the covers, shouting, *Sorry! Sorry! Sorry!* We know Mom has the wooden spoon. She comes in holding that spoon over her head and starts like she's about to go at us. And then she lowers it to our bodies and tickles us with it. A little poke in the ribs here, a little poke there. I can never keep from laughing until my eyes tear up. It works that way for all of us. It helps Mom, I guess, to have ticklish kids.

"You can't use the wooden spoon," Mom says. "If you need help, Ida will be home at noon. Just make sure Cheryl and David get on the Camp MaSkokie bus by nine. You don't need the spoon."

"Camp MaSkokie starts today?"

For three weeks, every day but Saturday, Cheryl and David will be at day camp until four. I'll be on my own. I rest my head on my pillow and relax. It'll be like my own vacation from work.

• • •

Mom's taking off in our blue Chevy Bel-Air. Mom and Dad bought it new in 1962. It's a deep blue, not like the color of the park district swimming pool, but blue like a blueberry. It has no fins, but Dad said fins were going out. I'm not sure what "going out" meant back then, but I knew Big Ben's black Oldsmobile had big pointy fins that came out at least a block or two behind the rest of the car. It looked like a car Flash Gordon would drive, all chromy with fins sweeping back as if million-mile-an-hour winds were streamlining the metal backwards. Big Ben's Oldsmobile could leave and turn the corner, and those rocket ship fins would take forever to leave, too.

Dad called Big Ben's car a fake Cadillac. That didn't sound good. Now Big Ben owns a real Cadillac, a light yellow one, and it doesn't have much in the way of fins. Nobody's new car has fins, so I guess our old car isn't "going out." Don't think Mom's going to be getting a new car soon anyway.

"It's an ugly car," Cheryl says looking out the picture window as Mom drives away. Even from the window I see the tear in the top of the back seat and a little stuffing poking through. "I'm going to do something to make it pretty," she says.

Cheryl's wearing baby blue short pants and her white cotton shirt with the horses, like merry-go-round horses. She's got her black and white shoes on. They're hard and leathery with hard bottoms.

"Why don't you wear your Keds gym shoes?" I say to her. "You'll be running around a lot at camp."

"Annette Funicello wears these shoes," she says in her snotty voice that means to tell me I'm stupid and she can correctly say *Funicello.* "They're saddle shoes," again meaning I'm stupid. "Annette Funicello wears them all the time," meaning I should already know that. "Sally Jenner wears them all the time, too, even when she was on Bozo's Grand Prize game," meaning that I'm the oldest child in the family, but not nearly the smartest. My sister, with her groans and moans and tsks and tongue clicks, says a lot more with her noises than with words.

"Sally Jenner missed bucket number three," I say. "A lot of good those saddle shoes did her." Cheryl sneers at me. "Besides, all those Mouseketeer shows with Annette Funicello are on Channel Nine. They're reruns. They're a hundred years old. Annette Funicello died a long time ago."

"She's not dead," Cheryl says. "She's on TV."

"You don't see anyone on our block wearing Mouseketeer hats, do you?"

"So ...?" she draws out to let me know I'm wasting her time. "Mom says I can wear these shoes," meaning I cannot challenge the authority and word of Mom, gone to work, unavailable to set this right. Cheryl stomps her saddle shoes on the wood floor, making the sound of horse clops, meaning the topic is over. I could not challenge the saddle shoes.

•   •   •

Ugh-ah-boo, ugh-ah-boo, ugh-ah-boo ugh-ah
That's the call of Chief MaSkokie.

Skyler and his sister, Sally, are trying to teach David and Cheryl one of the Camp MaSkokie songs. "There's a lot of them," Skyler Jenner says. "You'd better learn them real fast before the bus comes." *Ugh-a-boo, ugh-a-boo . . .* It looks like David's worried and going to cry. Cheryl doesn't seem to care and plays hop-scotch on the sidewalk.

Where should I stand? With the campers or their moms?

The campers slouch about at one corner of Loblolly Avenue and Ellerson Street, moping and whining how unfair it is to go to camp so soon after school's over. Skyler's upset 'cause his mom won't let him wear his Cubs clothes to day camp. Sally is two years older and half a foot taller than Skyler and tells him to shut up.

"Who you gonna sue?" Charlie Grossman says to Skyler, covering one nostril and blowing gunk from the other to the sidewalk.

Charlie is Karl's younger brother, and Karl is my age, like Mookie, and too old now for MaSkokie Day Camp. Although Mookie and I went until we got too old this year, Karl Grossman never went to Camp MaSkokie. "Didn't want to," he said. But everybody knew Camp MaSkokie didn't let him go 'cause, as Charlie likes to say, "I'd get rid of him, too, if I could."

"No booger-blowing on the sidewalk!" Dahveed and Hannah Waxberg cry. "I might faint," Hannah says.

"I might pick it up and throw it at you," Charlie says.

Hannah gags and runs to stand behind Sally Jenner.

Bobby Kinder laughs with Charlie. The two of them look like Laurel and Hardy standing next to each other. Charlie's kinda plump and has an odd-rounded face, like a potato. Nobody makes fun of his weight 'cause his dad has all these magazines called Playboy that give our dickie things Mr. Stiffies just by looking at the pictures. Charlie lets us in his house and we go right for the magazines. There are so many under Arnold Grossman's side of the bed, and when we're done looking at them, we have to wait a while and talk about sports stuff until our Mr. Stiffies relax.

Bobby Kinder is the one Christian MaSkokie day camper at the corner. He's Charlie's best friend and skinny, like me, with thick dark hair that kinda gathers in clumps and sticks up. His parents have a picture of a woman wearing flowing robes painted right to the wall in their living room. Bobby calls her Mary and stops to cross himself at the chest whenever he passes by her. Other than that, I guess he's like the rest of us. He has no problem looking at those magazines. Sometimes I catch him squeezing his pants right at the zipper when he does, and he crosses himself when he leaves Charlie Grossman's house.

Nobody's paying any attention to Bup Miller. Bup stands away from the other campers, kicking at stones in the gutter. Bup's pretty big for a ten-year-old, and he's still got that crew cut even though the rest of us started growing our hair like the Beatles two years ago. He lives in the house at the corner, the smallest house on the block, two over from mine with Skyler's in between. Although she won't come out and stand with the other moms, Bup's mom watches from her picture window to make sure Skyler's leaving Bup alone.

We all started calling Bup an ass to his face ever since last summer when he sawed halfway through the branches of our favorite climbing tree, which grew next to Bup's house. Who knew what Bup was thinking when he did that?

One day last fall, Skyler started slapping Bup around and kept at him like a windmill 'cause Bup was threatening to beat up Dahveed, who's about half Bup's size. Bup had no good reason to fight Dahveed. Skyler Jenner looked all confident slapping Bup in the face. A smaller kid slapping around a bigger kid, it didn't look good for Bup. So Bup tried to run away and Skyler chased him. Up his own tree Bup goes. That tree forked out with four trunks at the ground, and kept forking out branches every four or five feet. It was a shady tree, too, good enough to hold twenty kids, and Bup had ruined it making those half-cut-away tree branches. But Bup snapped a sawed branch first and fell to the ground, breaking his arm and, according to Mr. Waxberg, his ass.

That tree's gone now. The World's Largest Village widened Ellerson Street and had to take it down. I guess it was dangerous anyway, thanks to Bup. I think everybody wanted to sue somebody, but nothing happened that I know about. All I know is nobody talks to the Millers unless they have to.

Icks-biddly, ootn' -tootn', bo-bo, skah-deetn'-dot'n'
Hah-chah, wah-nah, MaSkokie!

David's struggling with that one and now can't remember the *Ugh-ah-boo* one.

When Charlie and Bobby decide to see who can blow a throat hocker the farthest, I decide to stand with the moms. Maybe it might help me be the new man-of-the-house if Cheryl and David see I'm with the adults. After all, Bup looks like he can beat me up, Skyler beat Bup up, and Cheryl whacked Skyler and got away with it. That's not good for the new man-of-the-house.

Mr. Waxberg's walking toward his white boxy Rambler. The top of the car is shiny and comes to a slight point, just like him. My grandpas are bald, but Mr. Waxberg's head looks polished and egg-shaped. He's waving at Mrs. Waxberg as he gets in his car. When he drives away, Loblolly Avenue seems opened up, nothing but street. All the fathers have gone to work, and my mom.

"Well, look who we have here!" Mrs. Jenner says as chirpy as a bird.

She's always so cheery and friendly with her round smile and eyes that curve upward at the outside and inside corners, smiling along with her mouth. She has the best Laura Petrie flip on the block, just like on TV, but with bright blonde hair. I've noticed there's always a line drawn dark right where her hair comes out of her scalp, as if a cartoonist made it to show where her head is. I stand next to her 'cause she's like a living television show, a happy one, always on and upbeat, never a bad thing to say to anybody.

Mrs. Grossman's got her arms folded, and although she's a bit taller than Mrs. Jenner she somehow seems shrunken up and tight. Mrs. Grossman's wearing a brown bulky bath robe while Mrs. Jenner's got her stirrup pants on, white ones, with a pink V-neck shirt. Mrs. Jenner's just one big happy mom, I think, and Mrs. Grossman looks like thunderstorm clouds.

"Good morning," I say to the moms.

Mrs. Waxberg smiles at me. The best thing about Mrs. Waxberg is her voice, so soft and reassuring. She's not very pretty, even Mrs. Grossman might be prettier, it's a kinda weird thing to compare. Mrs. Waxberg is the tallest mom on the block, taller than the men, except Mr. Waxberg and Big Ben. Her face balls up at the cheeks when she's smiling, and when she's talking, she's always smiling. These things make her prettier than Mrs. Grossman.

"Good morning, Jeremy," Mrs. Waxberg says. "Are you in charge today?"

"He's being a man, I think," Mrs. Jenner says. Mrs. Jenner stands closer and gives me a hug with one arm around my shoulder. "He sure feels like a young man to me." She smells really good, as if flowers bloomed under her skin. I feel myself beginning to get a little bit of a Mr. Stiffy, but I'm tucked in the up position in my jeans so nobody can see.

"How's your mother doing?" Mrs. Grossman says. "I saw Mr. Yellen leave your house the other day."

Mr. Yellen is the other lawyer on the block. He's even shorter than Arnold Grossman, and he's bald and kinda wimpy looking, like Tim Conway on *McHale's Navy*. I don't know Mr. Yellen very well, but he started coming over every other evening a week after Dad died.

"Mom's fine," I say. "Mr. Yellen works on some papers on the dining room table."

"How much is she paying him?" Mrs. Jenner says. "Maybe my husband might charge less." Mrs. Jenner looks as happy as Laura Petrie dancing around the living room for Sally Rogers and Buddy.

"I've never heard Mr. Yellen charge Mom anything," I say.

"Nothing?" Mrs Jenner's constant happy face eases a bit.

"I swear she's never given him money. Mom thanks him a lot and he leaves. Sometimes Mrs. Yellen comes over, too, and brings cookies."

"Izzy Yellen comes out of her house?" Mrs. Jenner says.

Mrs. Waxberg looks kinda sharp at Mrs. Jenner. "Well, *I* never see her," Mrs Jenner says.

We stand quiet at the corner, Mrs. Jenner's arm still around me. "For free?" Mrs. Jenner says, whistling. Her eyes aren't looking at anything except generally over the top of Mrs. Waxberg's head, which is a bit high up in the air.

The MaSkokie Day Camp bus rolls down Linwood Street to Ellerson. It arrives at Loblolly Avenue and slowly makes its turn. It's a school bus, full size, and David grimaces just as the bus pulls in front of him. A faint rush of air wooshes when the bus door closes and the wheels begin to roll. As the bus pulls away, Cheryl's still at the street corner, standing behind a bush.

"What're you doing?" I shout.

"I don't want to go!"

I run across the street and grab her by the arm. Even if she can beat up Skyler, who can beat up Bup, who is bigger than me, I'm putting Cheryl on that bus. I drag her along and she leans backwards, her saddle shoes clopping away at my heels. Mrs. Waxberg makes it ahead of the bus and flaps her arms to stop it. It isn't as if the bus can drive off fast, not like a motorcycle.

"I don't want to go!" Cheryl says again and again. Mrs. Waxberg walks over and leans down to Cheryl, bending low like a tree discussing something with the grass.

"What's wrong, honey?" Mrs. Waxberg says.

Cheryl makes every muscle in her face tug her forehead toward her chin. "I don't want to go!"

"But camp has got everything there, everything. You name it."

Cheryl looks at Mrs. Waxberg and smiles, against her will, I think. It's hard not to smile at Mrs. Waxberg when she's talk-smiling at you.

"My daddy says I don't have to go to camp."

"You've been talking to your daddy?" Mrs. Waxberg says real serious.

Cheryl stomps one of her shoes.

"When?"

"At night when I go to bed. He says I don't have to do nothing I don't want to."

"Oh, honey." Mrs. Waxberg's hand almost disappears into Cheryl's hair. "Before your daddy left us, did he always let you do everything you wanted to do?" Cheryl isn't answering but her frown weakens. "And didn't your daddy leave your mommy in charge when he had to drive his big truck?"

"Yes, ma'am," Cheryl says looking into Mrs. Waxberg's big smile, smiling a little herself.

"And I know you always listened like the good lady you are, even when you had to do something you didn't want to do." Cheryl's nodding her head. "Now you talk to your daddy all you want. I have, too."

"You have?" Cheryl says, beginning to cry.

"Ever since it happened, I go to synagogue and talk to your daddy. It's okay to talk to him in your room at night, he's there, too. When I talk to him, I tell him everything's all right and we're all looking after his family. But I also know he would never tell you to disobey your mommy. And when Jeremy's in charge, your daddy expects you to listen to him, too."

Cheryl looks at me with her muscled-up face. "Does Daddy want me to go to day camp?"

"That's what he told me," I say.

"All right then," Cheryl says, picking up her lunch box. "I guess that's what he told me, too."

Mrs. Waxberg takes Cheryl by the hand and walks her to the bus. This is going to be tough. I had no idea about talking the way Mrs. Waxberg talked to Cheryl.

Mrs. Grossman's shaking her pointer finger and screeching something mean to Mrs. Jenner as they stand more than ten feet apart at the street corner. I hear only, " . . . do something for them . . ."

Mrs. Jenner's still smiling the happy way she always does, looking pink and white and as pretty as can be. Mrs.

Grossman stomps away, her robe flopping about like the uniforms on the Wicked Witch of the West's soldiers as they march to the Witch's castle.

• • •

I've never been alone in the house before.

That sunburst clock keeps ticking. Funny how it's quiet normally but when I'm home by myself it's the loudest thing. *Tick, tick, tick,* like a bomb.

Mom's left the photograph albums out on the coffee table. She's always doing that, looking at those old black and white pictures like there's nothing new to take a picture of anymore. That skinny album with the flip-up pockets, I've looked at the pictures in there a hundred times at least.

The first picture is my favorite. There's Dad on the Harley-Davidson Hydra Glide, a side shot, straddling it with his black boots on the ground. Dad looks large in his black jeans and black leather jacket. With eagle wings and a white brim, Dad's riding cap looks like the one Colonel Hogan wears on *Hogan's Heroes.* I once thought Dad was Dick Van Dyke and President Kennedy all rolled up into one. They all had that thick hair that looked soft and stiff at the same time, parted on the side. Dad looks tough in this picture, and he's peeking back toward Mom. She's sitting sidesaddle all skinny in her boots, black jeans, and leather jacket. Smiling hard like someone just told them a joke, they look like they would have fun forever.

Mom and Dad rode the Hydra Glide all the way to Niagara Falls for their honeymoon. Don't know anyone else with a mom and dad who did that for any vacation.

I hear a loud noise, like squealing brakes, and I walk to the picture window. There's a truck in front of the Jenners' house. Out comes a new couch, orange and leathery, matching orange chairs that look more like butterfly wings, some boomerang-shaped end tables, and a TV in a cabinet, all sleek and modern. The workmen carry a couch out of the

Jenners' house that looks like the one I just got off of. Mrs.
Jenner is obviously motioning the men to get rid of it, shoo-
ing it away.

In my house, nothing's changed since Dad died — bare
wood floors, vinyl couch with the popped and lost buttons,
the bulky dining room tables and cabinets, and the 1964
World Book encyclopedias. My house looks as still as a
photograph.

•   •   •

I'm kinda surprised Karl or Mookie haven't come over by
noon. It's Ida Lipshilts at the front door with her amazing
cigarette and a peanut butter and jelly sandwich on white
bread on a plate.

"Have you eaten yet?" she says, that cigarette bouncing
around like it's out of balance and ready to fall.

Don't care for grape jelly, especially when it's soaking
through the bread like the sandwich Mrs. Lipshilts has. "I ate
two sandwiches already," I say.

"What were they?" she says, taking her cigarette out of
her mouth, dropping it on the pinners porch.

"Fluffernutters."

"Fluffernutters? That's nothing but marshmallows in a
jar. That's no lunch." She walks through the front doorway.

"Frasier Thomas would never advertise anything bad on
TV," I say.

Mrs. Lipshilts flicks her wrist down. "They'll sell anything on TV. You eat these sandwiches. The bread is Wonder
Bread, guaranteed to build your body twelve ways, they say.
If you believe Frasier Thomas about Fluffernutters, you'll
believe in Wonder Bread."

She lights up another cigarette without letting go of the
plate. How'd she do that? Like she's got three hands. Mrs.
Lipshilts gives me the plate with the purple sandwiches and
sits on the couch, pulling me lightly by the elbow to sit next
to her. She tosses a cloud of smoke out her mouth and the

smoke balls up and hovers over her head then drifts toward me. I like the smell of her cigarette at first, the smell of the match being lit and the first puff. Then it gets to be too much and my nose feels like it's falling in and itching from the smell. She's watching me watch her smoke and laughs.

"It'll go away before your mother comes home," she says, smushing her cigarette on the edge of her plate, ashes tumbling near the sandwiches. "So how are things going?"

"Fine."

"That's all you kids say — *fine*. The roof could be falling in and all you would say is 'fine.'" She's got her left hand tucked tight under her right elbow, and her right hand's twitching like it can't figure out where the cigarette went.

"When did you start smoking?"

Mrs. Lipshilts looks at me kinda surprised. "Don't even think about starting. It's a dirty habit."

"But you and Big Ben smoke."

"I was nineteen when I started. I was a showgirl in a circus. Can you believe it?" I'm sure my eyes tell her I can't believe it. "It's true. Big Ben gave me my first cigarette. He's a little older and I wanted to impress him, so I smoked it. He kept feeding me his cigarettes and I kept smoking them. Finally, he had only one left and he let me have it, and I fell in love."

"What was Big Ben doing in a circus?"

Mrs. Lipshilts tilts her head back and looks kinda wishywashy at the ceiling. "He was hired to fix electrical wiring and spent the time trying to pick me up."

Although our couch is low and sags in the middle, Mrs. Lipshilts' feet barely touch the floor, her toes tipping down to reach. I guess she must've been easy on the horses and easy to toss around by trapeze artists, so I can believe she was a circus showgirl and that it was pretty easy for Big Ben to pick her up.

Her fingertips squeeze at the outline of a pack of cigarettes in her pants pocket. Maybe I should let her go.

"Thanks for the peanut butter and jelly sandwich," I say.

"I'll probably be hungry again in an hour or so." Mrs. Lipshilts leans over and kisses me on my forehead.

"You're welcome," she says standing up. "You can return the plate whenever you like."

She walks to the door quickly, jerks her hand to wave like she meant to do it but almost forgot, and leaves my house. I see her through the picture window, hunching low as she walks, working a lighter and a cigarette. She stops and blows smoke in the air like she's heaving a big sigh of relief.

Grape jelly oozes through the Wonder Bread turning the slices into purple mush. Karl and Charlie Grossman won't eat Wonder Bread 'cause they've seen their mother squeeze slices into a ball and press it into the corners of her floors to clean out the gook.

The sandwich trails purple across the plate and lands in the kitchen garbage pail with a slurp. But Ida's cigarette stays stuck to the plate on a dab of jelly. When I pick at it, it seems to vibrate, saying, *C'mon, smoke me!* Suddenly it looks like a key to adulthood, something adults do but don't want kids to do, so I've got to try.

Should I? — the tip is bent over, but there's enough.

When it was Ida's turn to ride the Hydra Glide, she always had trouble finding a place to rest her feet. "You used to be taller before you smoked," Dad said, and Ida laughed but didn't deny it. Maybe she's lying about being a circus girl.

I want to ride the Hydra Glide one day, and I need to reach the pedals, so I bury Ida's cigarette beneath the jelly sandwich, just in case Dad wasn't kidding.

•   •   •

I've read two Superman comic books, a Batman, and my *Mad Magazine*. They had one story in *Mad* about *Star Trek*. Mad called it *Star Blech* and Captain Kirk drove around in the Starship Booby Prize. Besides these things, I've pretty much wasted my day so far. With only two hours left before the Camp MaSkokie bus returns, I call Mom.

"International Minerals. How can I help you?" The woman's voice sounds businessy, like I better know something or she'll hang up.

"Mrs. Rosenberg, please," I say.

"Just a moment — three Mrs. Rosenbergs work here. Do you have a first name?"

Wow, three Rosenbergs! How about that? "Mrs. Grace Rosenberg, please," I say.

"I'll connect you."

The line clicks and hisses at me. Finally, I hear, "This is Grace Rosenberg. Can I help you?" Her voice sounds like the one that first answered.

"Mom?"

"Jeremy?" she says, sounding more like Mom. "What's wrong?"

"Nothing."

"I can't talk now. I'm pretty busy."

"Do you think I can come over? I can ride my bike. It's not that far."

"This isn't my old job, Jeremy. You can't hang out here."

"So whatcha been doing?"

"Listen, it's not that I don't want to talk, but I can't right now." A deep voice rumbles through the phone. "I've got to go," Mom says in a hurry. "See you at seven."

I hear the click through the phone. Seven. She promised five-thirty when she left this morning. What could she be doing at International Minerals until seven that's more important than saving me from Cheryl and David?

At Mom's old job, the Morton Grove Animal Hospital had a green parakeet named Luigi that must've weighed twenty pounds. Luigi knew my mother's name — *Grace, Pretty Grace.* Is Mom pretty? Dad made up songs about her "sky blue eyes" and "ruby lips" and "auburn hair" until I had to fake-choke to get him to stop. "It makes perfect sense," Dad said, "that 'She's my Grace with the pretty face' rhymes."

I thought my family was as fun as the Petries on *The Dick Van Dyke Show.* We didn't dance around the house like the

Petries did, but Dad's motorcycle rides made us popular, and Mom was home most of the time 'cause her part-time job at the animal hospital was three days a week and only till noon.

It's beginning to feel like Mom's part-time job now is our home.

I hear *The Dick Van Dyke Show* isn't coming back on the air next fall. I don't know what we're going to do for television shows.

•　　•　　•

Looking through the living room picture window, I see they're home— the monsters are home. Cheryl steps off the bus, then David. She's walking fast to get away from him and he says something to her. She turns and stares at him, and he stops, taking a step back, and flinches his arms up. I bet she pounded him at camp today. She's got those saddle shoes beating the ground like she weighs a whole lot more than she really does, and I hear her pounding clip-clops through the window. The sunlight's shimmering in the glass and it makes Cheryl and David look smoky, dark, and dangerous, like they're gunslingers and I'm a sheriff without any ammo left, and they know it.

"I didn't pick my nose!" David hollers when they come in.

Cheryl's saddle shoes track in mud. There's no white showing anymore.

"You picked it and you ate it," she says like it's a well-known fact, refusing to look at him. "I'm gonna change my name. If I'm going to camp I can't be known as the sister of the booger-eater."

I say, "David Rosenbooger-eater?" which makes him explode.

"I didn't! I didn't! I didn't!" David says stomping his Keds. He drops his lunch pail on the floor with a clang.

"Any boogers left in there?" Cheryl says. "Peanut butter and boogers?"

David's face puffs up to cry. He kicks his lunch pail and runs to our bedroom, locking the door with a slam and a click.

Sitting on the couch, Cheryl touches her toes to the floor the way Mrs. Lipshilts does it. She swings her feet and flakes of dried mud chip off each time her heels strike the couch. Her hair turns curlier like it always does when it's hot out, and she looks like she's wearing a pile of brown spaghetti on her head.

"Did you really see him pick his nose?"

Cheryl turns on the TV just in time to show the Cubs beat the Cardinals by three runs.

"Don't lie to me," I say. "I'm in charge and I report to Mom." I hesitate a second and decide to say it the way Mrs. Waxberg did— " . . . and to Dad, tonight." Cheryl looks at me, angry, like I wouldn't dare.

"I'm sure he picked his nose and I'm sure he ate his boogers. He's such a booger-eater."

I turn off the TV. "Did you say anything on the bus?"

Lines of dirt stick to her skin at her mouth and eyes, like sad clown makeup. Cheryl tsks and tongue-clicks, and skips to her room, slamming her door.

The lock on my bedroom door isn't much. All I need is a point of some kind to stick in the little hole at the center of the handle and it opens. Guess it would slow a robber down a second or two, but that's about it. I stick a pencil in the hole and open the door. David's on his bed. He's pushed it to the middle of our bedroom and he's lying on it, listening to records on my Wildcat record player.

As usual, he's gone into my Beatles records again, stacked eight or more of them on my adapter. He sees me and leans down to the floor to raise the volume on *Eight Days A Week*. I pull the plug out of the socket and the Beatles' voices slow to grumpy men groans, like they're dying from being poisoned. David glares at me with his hands behind his head.

"You didn't eat your boogers?"

"No," he says pouting. "I ate *nobody's* boogers."

"Did Cheryl say anything on the bus?"

"She sang *Ugh-ah-booger-eater, Ugh-ah-booger-eater* all the way home over the back of my seat. She had everyone doing it, even the bus driver."

He looks the most like Dad, more than Cheryl or I do. "I'm sorry," I say.

"Why'd you laugh at me?"

"I guess it sounded funny."

"It's not funny being called booger-eater on a day camp bus."

"I said I'm sorry."

"Does Cheryl hate me? I don't hate her, why does she hate me?"

"I'll clean out your lunch pail," I say.

David says as if he has to, "There's no boogers in it."

Cheryl's in her bedroom, door shut, dropping stuff on her floor. Probably her muddy saddle shoes. I go to the bathroom and close the door.

Sitting on the toilet I hear somebody at the door, not loud or obvious, but real quiet-like. It makes me stop my business and listen. Nothing. I start doing my business. Then Cheryl on the other side goes *bloop bloop* and laughs, and goes *bloop bloop* again. Skyler Jenner's voice carries from somewhere outside into the bathroom, *Cubs win! Hey! Hey!* and my sister again with her *bloop bloops* at the bathroom door. My insides freeze up and I can't go anymore.

●   ●   ●

It's Wednesday night — *The Dick Van Dyke Show* night. It comes on after *Green Acres*, which comes on after *The Beverly Hillbillies*, which comes on after *Lost In Space*. Will, Penny, Judy, that other guy (the pilot, they hardly ever say his name), Mr. and Mrs. Robinson, Dr. Smith, and the Robot are still stuck on a planet with no plants but plenty of breathable air. Everyone's laughing at Mr. Douglas behind his back down at Sam Drucker's store in Hooterville. Ellie May beat up Jethro down by the see-ment pond, again. Sometimes Mom will watch *Ozzie and Harriet* (yuck), or *The Patty Duke Show* (more yucky), or *Gidget* (don't even ask how yucky) on Channel 7 on a small black and white TV in her bedroom, but when eighty-thirty rolls by, we're watching Rob, Laura, Ritchie, the Helpers, Sally and Buddy, Mel, Alan Brady, right there in our living room on Channel 2. I like it when they do the flashback stuff: Rob in the army, getting lost in the jeep, slamming his combat boots on Laura's toes. That's how Rob and Laura fell in love.

Mom and Dad met when she was thirteen and he was fourteen. They ran into each other going after a tennis ball. Mom said Dad asked her for a date sitting there on their sore butts. She said yes, but they lived so far apart, so Dad stole a motorcycle from an older friend named Burt from the Old Neighborhood. I've always thought we'd make a good television show.

A little past eight tonight, Mom finally comes home from work. She makes some Kraft Macaroni & Cheese and leaves us in the kitchen. "Mr. Yellen's coming over," she says going to her bedroom to change. She looks tired to me. Cheryl and David go to their bedrooms to eat. I turn on the TV and find a show called *Gomer Pyle U.S.M.C.* is on instead of Rob and Laura Petrie. I knew it was coming, but I still can't believe it.

My sister likes to pick a record and play it on her own Wildcat until she doesn't feel like playing it anymore. That can take over a week. Last week she played *Monday Monday* for five days straight. Tonight she starts playing *Paperback Writer*, and she'll never play *Monday Monday* ever again. I expect *Paperback Writer* will go on for at least a few days. Mom tells her to keep it down, but I can hear it as I hide in the hall. I've got a spot to listen in secret while Mom and Mr. Yellen work over papers in our dining room, to see if she pays him anything like Mrs. Jenner asked. Maybe Mr. Jenner might charge less. I wish Cheryl had the record turned down a little more.

"So how much do I have left?" Mom's saying. Mr. Yellen

speaks kinda soft and I can't tell if he says anything back. But I hear him cough a little, like the fake cough David does to convince Mom he's sick and can't go to school.

"You don't have anything left," Mr. Yellen says.

"What?" Mom says.

"In fact, you owe."

"How much?" Mom says even softer than Mr. Yellen.

"Seventy dollars a month." They're real quiet, except for the chair legs squeaking on the wood floor. "Yeah, it's that much," Mr. Yellen goes on. "Seventy dollars a month." His voice sounds real sad. "He didn't have much insurance as an independent trucker. His medical bills took it all." After some silence and more paper shuffling, Mr. Yellen says, "Can you ask for a raise?"

"But I just started my job."

Is that Mom's voice? So weak, it rattles me, like there's a stranger in the house.

"They're paying me fifty cents an hour more than my part-time job paid." I hear a pen click-clicking again and again. It sounds like clipping toenails. "I'm a secretary. They're not paying more than two-fifty an hour."

"Grace, after federal and state taxes, your monthly mortgage, your average monthly bills, utilities, phone, property tax, car maintenance, clothes for the kids, food bills, if you live as you are you will be about seventy dollars short every month."

I listen closer now. Mom's short of money.

"But we don't *do* anything!" Mom says, and she starts crying over the seventy dollars a month she doesn't have. "We haven't been on a vacation. I haven't bought a stick of furniture. I just fed my kids a dinner that costs nineteen cents a box."

I'm gripping my jeans in my hands at my ankles, pulling hard on the material. My knuckles are turning white. Mom's a secretary with three kids and a mortgage. I've never thought about my family this way — I haven't — I haven't! How can my family live in the same neighborhood as the

Jenners, in a house just like theirs only theirs is run by a
lawyer? It's impossible. Mom's crying in front of Mr. Yellen.
I can't take this. I can't.

"Jerome . . ." she says. Mr. Yellen's first name is the same
as mine, only formal, and I feel like she's talking to me. "I
can't even afford to buy a new bed. I'm sleeping in the same
goddamn bed my husband bled to death in."

Oh, God - oh, God! I don't want to remember that day. I
love you, Mom, I'm thinking. Please stop crying. She's crying, and I feel so empty. I just thought things would go on as
always. I never knew it'd be this hard to stay where we are.
My lungs feel so full of air, and my throat is so wide open,
and the air tastes dull and hopeless. I sneak into my bedroom
and close the door behind me. David's pushed his bed into a
new corner, to the side of the window. He's sitting there at
the foot of his bed drawing a picture on a blank piece of
paper using a blue crayon.

"I'm gonna ask Mummy to get us some shag carpeting
like everyone else has," he says like words to a nursery
rhyme. He says it like the shag carpet has to appear now.
Mom only has to say yes.

I don't know what's happening. I'm walking over to
David and I'm watching myself do things from the outside,
that's how it feels. I see I'm angry, and I'm gonna do it. I
know I shouldn't, but I backhand slap David across his face.
I stand there at his bed, his head turned away, and he slowly
looks back at me with a big red mark on his left cheek. He's
stunned, and his mouth and eyes droop open. I didn't want
to do it, and I'm back inside me, mad at myself, and sorry I
hit him, and so hard. David's the bottom of the totem pole in
this family, the youngest, the weakest, and everything gets
dumped on the bottom, that's what I'm thinking as I watch
him tense his face up for a good cry.

"Hit me," I say before he starts bawling. His eyebrows
crunch in the middle a bit, like he's frozen himself right
before he goes into a full wail. I think I might have to say it
once or twice more, but David hauls off with a fist to my

chest. It stings like a mosquito bite and not a bit more, but I wince hard just the same like it hurts me so bad, so he won't cry. I grab him by the shoulders. I say to him, "We're broke, David. Do you understand what it means to want a toy and you have absolutely no money? That's the way Mom is right now."

"But . . ." he starts to say.

"Please," I say again. "If you love Mom, never ask about shag carpeting."

Like the little spy he is, David watches my face, figuring out something. In a matter of a minute, he's been whacked, he's whacked me back, and he's hearing that Mom can't even buy a toy for us. His face still has that look, the moment before a good bawling, but it eases back a little, and his eyes stare off to someplace uncertain, moving over my shoulder, then down to the floor, our bare, shagless, wooden, scratched up bedroom floor.

"Should I never ask for anything again? Will that help?"

If it weren't for all the things Cheryl keeps saying about him, I would think David's pretty smart for his age. He shows me his piece of paper. It's a square box like an architect's drawing, a box house like our house, with lines for walls and doors and drawings of furniture and a staircase reaching up to someplace our own house doesn't have. He's got little blue dashes all over the inside of the box. Shag carpeting, I'm guessing.

"You can rip it up," David says. "We don't need shag carpeting right away if Mummy can't buy us a toy."

"I'm sorry I hit you," I say.

He's kinda looking weird at me, grinning like it's cool to have your big brother say he's sorry to you all the time. That's all right. He's not a booger-eater, not that I can tell, and I shouldn't've hit him. He's just at the bottom of the totem pole, that's all.

•   •   •

You know how when you're sleeping, you know you're

sleeping and you can make yourself wake up when you want to? That's where I am. I can feel that it's kinda early, but I want to wake myself up to see what that flapping sound is. It's a noise in my dream and I see a bird flying with one wing. I wonder how it stays up in the air. It's a large bird, with red, blue, and yellow feathers. But the bird looks straight ahead and it's flying all right. It's flapping that one wing every few seconds, a floppy, lazy flap.

I squeeze my eyelids tight and the bird fades away, but that flapping's still there, kinda quiet, but there. Opening my eyes, I see morning sunlight circling around the window shade. Little bits of dust float in sunbeams, some moving in a certain direction like they're alive and have some sort of purpose, some kinda lazy and just hanging there — and there's that flapping.

A sliver of light sneaks around the far edge of the shade and lands on David's feet. He's asleep with the covers kicked off of him and one of his pinkies stuffed to the knuckle in his mouth. Only kid I know who sucks his pinky — and there's that flapping. I lean over my bed and see our old reel-to-reel tape recorder circling a finished tape around and around. Every time it goes, about two inches of the end of the tape slaps against a small metal spike that's supposed to keep the tape in place. A wire stretches from the recorder to under my pillow where I pull out the round microphone.

David only hit the play button and forgot to hit the record button along with it. Even if I snored the way the bunch of old geezers do sitting in the back row of the syna- gogue during Sabbath services, and that's pretty loud rum- bling, he's not gonna get a thing on our reel-to-reel recorder.

I thread the tape through the empty reel and rewind for about half a minute. David's still asleep, sucking that pinky. I whisper, *This is what I think of the snore detective*, and I reach to my butt and fart into the microphone.

I stink it up a little, but I smell coffee and it reminds me of Mom, not the fart smell, just the coffee. Mom always made a cup of coffee at five in the morning when Dad was

going on one of his interstate truck jobs. He didn't drink coffee. She made it for herself. I make sure I don't tip the
recorder over when I get out of bed, and I open my bedroom
door and peek around the corner.

"Come on over," Mom says to me. She's in her pajamas,
her white ones with the small blue dots. Mom's got the
kitchen chair swung around facing the window. There's a
second chair next to her turned around the same way. With
the curtains pulled aside, I can see the sun sitting orange on
the point of the Levins' house across the stone alley. Mom
pats the seat beside her. "Come on," she says.

Mom's smiling a bit, looking out the window. It's as
though Mr. Yellen's news about the seventy dollars never
happened at all. Her eyes are bright blue and her face seems
rested and clear. Her dark hair is a little mussed up, as if she
just pulled her leather motorcycle helmet off her head, and
it's a lot better looking than her puffed-up beehive do.

"You like living here?" she says. To tell the truth, I don't
know of any place else but here, can't imagine any other
place to live, not even the Old Neighborhood. "You gonna
answer?" I let out a hiss like a snake 'cause Mom wants an
answer, but I hardly know what to say. "I like it here," she
says.

"I like it here, too."

"You've got a lot of kids to play with on this block, don't
you?"

"I guess so." The sun rises off the Levins' roof.

"Your father and I liked to watch the sunrise whenever
we could." I'm not sure what to say to Mom, so I say nothing. I figure I'd probably say something that might make her
cry. She's smiling at me and I want to keep it that way.
"When you grow up and become a millionaire, promise me
you'll be good to every secretary that ever works for you."

That's weird, I think. Why wouldn't I? Mom leans back
in her chair and I lean a little into her.

The sunrise makes different colors in the kitchen window
and I watch them change from purple to violet to orange to

yellow. Finally, I hear a slamming in my bedroom and a click of the tape recorder buttons and David saying, *Oh! Now that's really crummy!*

"Time to get ready," Mom says. "The monsters are rising."

She'll take a shower, put on a businessy outfit, and force her hair back into its hair spray, beehive prison. I think her millionaire bosses should be nice to her considering how she can't finish watching the sunrise with me.

•   •   •

Mrs. Waxberg's knocking at my front door. She's got the MaSkokie Day Camp bus waiting at the corner, at least thirty kids stopped on the bus. "Jeremy?" she says calling in, her voice muffling through the door. "Aren't David and Cheryl coming?"

Cheryl and David hide with me under the dining room table.

"I don't get it," Cheryl says.

"Shh," I say pulling her shoulders down. She was about to step out and ruin it. One stomp of those dirty saddle shoes might give us away. Mrs. Waxberg rings the doorbell.

"I thought you said Daddy wanted me to go to MaSkokie Day Camp."

"Daddy's got different orders for today," I say.

"What are you guys talking about?" David's saying. "How are you talking to Dad?"

"Shh," I say loud enough to send some spit flying. Mrs. Waxberg leaves the door. I see her through the picture window walking toward the corner. I lose sight of her and in a minute the bus is revving up and moving down the street. "Okay. Get up."

Cheryl rises with me from under the table. David stays there muttering about how I talked to Dad. Cheryl pulls on my T-shirt like it's a lamp string and says, "Mrs. Waxberg told us she talked to Dad, too. She said Dad's telling her I should go to camp. How can Dad be telling you something different from Mrs. Waxberg?" Cheryl's eyes peer ice blue at me, and her lips smash into each other, like she's wanting to chew me up if I don't answer this one to her satisfaction. Her IQ must be as high as the moon, and it's gonna kill me one day, maybe right now.

"Mrs. Waxberg talked to Dad last Friday. Today's Thursday. I've had new talks every day since then."

"You're lying," she says, and tsks at me. "I talk to Dad every night and he's not saying anything to me about new plans."

David bumps his head hurrying now to get up from under the dining room table. "How're you guys talking to Dad?"

"We just do, David," I say.

"But why is he talking to Mrs. Waxberg and not me?"

David and Cheryl want answers about talking to Dad, and Cheryl's gonna hit me — David, well, he'll hit me, too, once he sees Cheryl doing it, that's what I know's gonna happen.

"Mrs. Waxberg's like Gladys Kravitz from *Bewitched*," I say. "She's always spying through windows, checking out everybody's business. Dad doesn't tell all our business to Mrs. Waxberg, only enough to keep her busy and that's all."

"I don't think Mrs. Waxberg's like Gladys Kravitz," Cheryl's saying. "Nuh-uh. She's like Millie Helper. Kinda ugly, but nice, and she doesn't dance too well at Rob and Laura Petrie parties. Gladys Kravitz is ugly and not nice at all."

"Mrs. Waxberg's like Aunt Bee," David says.

"You think *all* the Moms are like Aunt Bee," Cheryl says with a tongue click at David. "They can't all be like Aunt Bee. Think of somebody else."

"Mrs. Drysdale," David says.

"No," Cheryl says.

"Jeannie from the bottle."

"Definitely not. You can have Hazel."

"I don't want Hazel," David whines. "She's not on TV anymore!"

David and Cheryl yabber, trying to come up with a TV woman to be Mrs. Waxberg. Maybe they're not so smart after all, that's becoming pretty clear.

"The Petries aren't going to be on TV anymore," I say. Cheryl and David stop yapping and start frowning and pouting as if I had just told them school was starting a month early. "Millie Helper's not going to be on TV anymore. None of them are. There's not going to be any new *Dick Van Dyke Shows*. They're putting Gomer Pyle in an army show marching around with a gun."

David gives me his "Nuh-uh — isn't Gomer on with Sheriff Andy Taylor and Barney Fife?" Sneering at Cheryl, he adds, "And Aunt Bee, too? Gomer pumps gas at the filling station with Goober, and he's stupid. Who'd give Gomer Pyle a gun anyway?"

"Channel 2 did."

David watches me like he's waiting for me to apologize to him again, like yesterday. I nod my head and tell him it's true, and cross my heart so he has to believe me.

"There's nothing good on TV anymore," David says. "Not like there used to be."

David's whining sounds a lot like Grandpa Erwin's *TV, shmee vee*. But Grandpa Erwin doesn't care for Dick Van Dyke. He's mad 'cause they took *The Danny Thomas Show* off the air. "Last good thing on *shmee vee*," he said, and none of it was as good as the old radio stuff, except for Walter Cronkite and the space launches, that's okay for Grandpa Erwin.

"Why'd you make me miss the MaSkokie bus?" Cheryl says. She's tapping the toes of her saddle shoes, sounding like typewriter clicks — *And now for the news,* her shoes are saying, *tap'a tap'a tap, big brother Jeremy to announce today's plan.* David's waiting, too, but at least they're off the Dad-talking stuff. TV talk gets their minds to wander.

"We're cutting lawns today," I say.

"Whose lawns?" Cheryl says.

"I don't know whose lawns. There're lots of lawns to cut around here. We're going to march down the sidewalk until we find some long grass, and ask to cut it."

Cheryl's good at lawn-cutting and likes it 'cause David's never done it. She does ours half the time, before I can get to it, and likes to cut the lawn to chase David away, from a pinners game or the swingset, or where he's standing. She raises the mower up and growls after him until he runs off. She makes weird patterns in our grass chasing after David, but she gets it done.

David's eyes work inside as much as outside. "Why do we have to cut lawns?"

"'Cause I've talked to Dad," Cheryl says, and she nudges David toward the hallway. Her saddle shoes tap'a tap the news — *Time to cut lawns 'cause Dad says so*, and David's soft Keds pad along, and his hurried voice says, *Okay, okay, if Dad says so.*

Really, though, I know Dad's not talking to Cheryl. He isn't talking to me, and I've been trying. And he wouldn't be talking to Mrs. Waxberg instead of David, that's for sure. Dad's not talking to anyone. We're alone, and I've got to make money. Our house isn't big at all and Cheryl's room is right up against the dining room where Mom cried to Mr. Yellen about owing seventy dollars a month. Cheryl must've heard them, just like me. It's not like Cheryl to give in so fast to do something I want her to do.

I follow Cheryl and David out the side door and see Mrs. Jenner heading down to her basement, carrying a white double-layered cake of some kind. The top of her blond head bounces along with her as she walks down the steps. The Jenners have a finished basement with a real tiled floor and wood paneled walls and furniture like a living room's furniture, bright and orange and yellow, with a big black bean bag chair. Dad had been building wood frames in our basement, set up so something could've been put over them. They're like skeleton bones waiting for skin, and the basement cement makes the wood look so hollow.

The people in *this* house, I think turning to look at the steps leading to the gray cement of my basement, need to cut lawns. I pass by the Jenners' back door, and I can't help feeling how much I wish to live in that house. I wish I could be a Jenner.

• • •

We're having quite the fight over what we should take, not a fistfight, but a lot of staring and growling, like tomcats. Cheryl wants to take the electric lawn mower.

"It's got two blades," she says. "It'll cut faster."

"We can't go expecting people to pay us to cut their lawns with their own electricity," I say back. "And it's older than the gas mower."

Cheryl clicks her tongue at me and says, "But that old gas mower stinks." She tsk tsks as I pull the gas mower, and stomps her saddle shoes out the garage.

I have to drag David off the Hydra Glide in the corner. He's pulled back the dirty tarp and climbed on the seat, squinting his eyes like the wind was blowing in his face. I couldn't help but see that he sat forward, on the edge of the gas tank, the way we always had to do it with Dad in the back. I hand David the lawn edger and tell him to find Cheryl, but not to hit her with the edger.

"She'll get you back with the rake," I say, and he nods knowing that she would.

As I pull the tarp back over the Hydra Glide, I feel Dad's motorcycle tug at me like we're magnets and metal, but I can't stop to think about it. Making sure that three is faster than one cutting people's lawns will keep me busy enough considering the other two are Cheryl and David.

Cheryl's riding the rake down the alley after David like the Wicked Witch of the West, cackling, and David drops the edger, its heavy-spiked circle end clunking into the stones. He runs away and disappears beyond the Millers' house, screaming all the way like he's a girl who's just seen Paul McCartney.

•   •   •

I've got my train heading down Linwood Street, I'm in the lead, David's in the middle, and Cheryl's swatting David in his legs with the rake, denying doing it right after doing it. We're all in our blue jeans and white T-shirts, like a team. I thought that might make a difference, but it hasn't so far.

"Cut it out!" David says swinging his arm behind him at Cheryl's rake.

"Cut what out?" Cheryl says all sweet and pouty. I let it keep going that way so David doesn't wander off, which I'm figuring he would.

Heading north on Linwood, away from the school playground, is like going into enemy territory. There are kids here I see only in school, their pointy heads not at all like the heads of the kids on my block. I have no idea who the bad kids are here so I think they're all bad, and the houses look unfriendly even though they're basically the same as the houses on my block. But they're different somehow. It just smells different here, but I can't offer to cut our neighbors' lawns. The neighbors might ask questions.

I tune in WCFL on my transistor radio strapped to the lawn mower's handle and Barney Pip is laughing away during the news: *It's Thursday, July twenty-first, at ten-oh-two in the morning!* Pip's laughing at that. *Get ready for the A-OK landing later today of Gemini 10, deepest into space ever . . . except for maybe myself.* He's really breaking up over that one. *These Gemini men are really something. They are groo-vah. And they're gonna be groo-vin' when they get back to find Tommy James and the Shondells still a Hankying-and-a-Pankying away! How 'bout it! Groo-vin' at number one on the Pip charts, Hanky Panky. It ain't barely more than two minutes long, so let's play it twice! Groo-vah!* He's laughing about something, I don't know what, but I imagine Grandpa

Erwin is turning Barney Pip off his radio in Grandmaland with his fake-Yiddish *radio shmadio.*

Hanky Panky is a song twelve-year-old boys aren't supposed to like. It's a girl song and it's stupid. It just says over and over again about a baby doing Hanky Panky, that's it. So this guy's singing about how his baby's crapping in diapers, and it makes it to number one over the Beatles. I can't believe it. But I admit that I kinda like the drums, but that's as far as I'll say it. My steps start walking to it, and I can tell from Cheryl's saddle-shoe clip clops that she's walking to it, too. David's kinda skipping to keep Cheryl from swatting his legs with the rake, and it adds a nice little beat to it. So here we are, in blue jeans and white T-shirts, me pushing a lawn mower, David skipping and swishing his hand back at Cheryl's rake, and Cheryl tapping the sidewalk with her saddle shoes, all to *Hanky Panky.* I've got them under control and we're all heading the same way, like a real family, and I'm hoping Pip plays *Hanky Panky* till the day's over.

All the houses on Linwood are one-story brick boxes, reddish, brownish, yellowish, and some have sandstone chunks built into them in spots. They all look like lock boxes, with cement walks that form the front lawns into the shape of a pair of green, square pants pockets. These houses are little fortresses, only Superman could break in. And every house has one tree planted in front, a honey locust or a maple, like everyone got together and made an agreement about it. Some houses have a tree in the back, but again, just one. The trees aren't big yet, maybe rising as high as a few feet over the roof gutters at most.

With red, white and blue tassels dangling from his handlebar grips, a boy on a tricycle rides down the sidewalk from a front porch a lot like my own pinners porch. His house's bricks are light yellow with sandstone around the front door, and the grass is long enough to start falling over in places.

"Watcha guys doing?" he says, milk dried at the corners of his mouth. He's about two years younger than David, I think, wearing a buzz crew cut and a funny eyebrow on the right that goes up at the end like half a Mr. Spock.

"We're looking to cut some lawns for five dollars each," I say. "Your grass looks pretty tall." David, standing beside me, drops the edger on his foot. He winces then smiles at me. Cheryl's hair forms a brown spaghetti outline around David's head.

The boy eyes me, raising that Mr. Spock eyebrow higher and squinting down the other. "That your lawn mower?"

"Right," I say.

"Don't look too clean," the boy says, pedaling back an inch, then forward an inch. "Does it work?"

I lean over the motor and pull out the choke, grip the rip cord and pull back. I don't even get a putter.

The boy says, "Don't sound like it works to me."

"Let me try," Cheryl says. That's all I need — my little sister showing me up in front of some strange kid that's smaller than David.

"I'll do it," I say to her. But she's coming over anyway, dropping the rake on the sidewalk. I grab the rip cord and start pulling fast so Cheryl can't get hold of it. The motor sputters a little bit, but it still doesn't start.

"It ain't gonna work," the boy says turning his tricycle to ride down the walk. I stand up and catch my breath. Cheryl steps in for a few pulls and gets nothing.

"Should've tried it before we left," she says. She's looking at me like I'm not that smart of an older brother. A smart older brother would've tested the mower before setting out to cut people's lawns.

The front door to the house opens and a man in a white T-shirt's standing inside the screen door. He's smoking a cigar and his face is puffy and kinda hairy, but not a lot, like he can't decide whether to grow a beard. "Watcha got there, young man?" he's saying like I'm trespassing.

"My lawn mower won't start."

"Probably a spark plug," he says.

Mom used to tell Dad it was probably the spark plug

every time the Hydra Glide didn't work right. It's kinda the thing to say about an engine when you don't know what you're talking about, that's what Dad told Mom. But he'd change the spark plug and sometimes that fixed whatever wasn't working. "Be back in a second," the man says like he's ordering me to stay.

"What're we doing?" David complains. "When're we gonna cut a lawn?" He starts tapping the edger on the cement. Laughing at us, the boy on the tricycle sings — *It's probably the spark plug, probably the spark plug.*

"I'm going home," Cheryl says.

"You're not leaving," I say. "We're gonna cut some lawns. We have to cut some lawns."

The puffy-faced man comes out the door, shrinking as he walks down his porch. He can't be more than an inch or two taller than me, and he's shaped like a bowling pin, a bowling pin smoking a cigar. When he gets up close, I see his cigar isn't lit. He's just been chomping on one end for a while, making it all soggy and tore up.

"Let's try this spark plug," he says. His voice sounds rough coming around his clenched cigar.

The sides of his stomach pour over the outside edges of his pants, and he reminds me of one of those pear-shaped balloons all blown up and about to pop from too much air being inside them — one more puff and *poof!* He's changing the spark plug and chomping on his cigar, and he's got sweat on the back of his neck just from doing that. There's no guy on TV looking like that, I'm thinking. "Try it now," he says, and he stands slowly. It's hurting just listening to the creaks and pops coming out his knees as he rises. I bend over the rip cord and pull it once. The mower putters a bit. I pull the cord twice more and the engine turns over. It sounds like it might stop, but a pop and a burst of black smoke comes out like a small firecracker, and the mower starts to purr. "The spark plug needed changing," he says, raising his voice over the lawn mower's rumblings. "That's all." He's talking like he did some brain surgery or something.

"Cut your lawn for five dollars," I say as businesslike as I can. My talking has to be raised up a notch, the talk people do over a running lawn mower, like talking to hard-of-hearing people.

The man looks like he's about to drop his cigar. His belly starts heaving the way they do on fat people when they're laughing. "Five dollars?" he's saying loud, and not much at all like a question, more like he's accusing.

"We rake up the cuttings and edge the lawn."

"I can do it myself in under thirty-five minutes, on a day a lot hotter than this one." He's looking over my shoulder, at David and Cheryl. She's been swatting the rake at David again and David keeps whining about it.

I order, "Cut it out," and Cheryl sticks a hand in her armpit and pumps her elbow down.

"I'll pay you three bucks," he says, his lawn mower talk a whole lot louder than mine. A step closer and he places his cigar and angry stare inches away from me, like a pie in the face. "And I want a dollar for the spark plug."

"I thought you were doing us a favor."

"I want a dollar for it or I'm taking it back."

"It doesn't cost a dollar for a motorcycle spark plug!" I'm yelling, not just lawn mower talking. I'm yelling at somebody's dad. "I'm not paying you no dollar for a crummy lawn mower spark plug!"

"Labor," the man says. "You owe me for the plug and the work I did changing it."

"But it took thirty seconds!"

The man pokes his cigar at my nose and his eyes disappear into one Cyclops eye. I grip the lawn mower handle. I need to hold onto it, feel it vibrate and hear it roar. It keeps me there. I'm not moving.

"All right," he says. "I'll pay you two bucks to cut my lawn, and you can keep the spark plug." His puffy, half-furry face pops out veins, like wormy, crooked roads.

"Goddamn it!" I curse, and Cheryl's rake clunks to the sidewalk. "That's nothing but the same thing. Three bucks minus one buck, two bucks minus nothing. It's the same thing."

He's so close, there's nothing but our breathing between us, and his cigar pointing at me like a bazooka, none of it smelling like anything good. He could grab me and hit me, but I'm not gonna run. I stare back at him and try to make veins pop out on my forehead.

"Three bucks, then," he says, smiling out the side of his mouth. He's laughing, like how Mr. Ed laughs when he pulls a trick on a human. "Who'd know a boy would know how much a spark plug costs? That's good, really good." He places his hand on top of my head and rubs my hair. "Smart kid," he says. I can tell he wants me to laugh with him. But I won't laugh. What kinda father tries to cheat a kid out of money? No man on TV I've ever seen.

"We'll get started right now," I say, and I push the lawn mower over the grass and ask, "Is that length okay?"

"Fine," the man says still laughing his horsey laugh. He turns to the boy on the tricycle and orders him to keep an eye on the little rip-off artists. I don't care much for that. Maybe Mom has to go through this type of thing as a secretary with her cheap, mean millionaire bosses. The man walks up his sidewalk, the flabby sides of his stomach pouring over his skinny black belt. He pulls some mail from the mail slot by his front door and turns to sit on the cement stoop. Kinda looks like he's getting on a toilet to do some business, but I'm thinking that 'cause I'm mad, so that's what he looks like to me just then. He's reading his mail and looking up at us. The boy on the tricycle pedals up to me and orders, "Hop to it," his one eyebrow cocked up, the other eye squinting.

•   •   •

It starts out pretty well. First I cut the back lawn so the man can't sit on his porch and watch me. But I'm back in front and find out that David's rather useless. He couldn't use the edger, dragging it up on the sidewalk or deep into the grass many more times than getting it straight. And now there's something about him, like I can't run over any bug with the lawn mower, so he's using the rake to stir things up in the lawn in front of the mower instead of piling up the cut grass behind me like he's supposed to. He yells at me to stop as if there's a big emergency, and he bends over and pulls a worm from the grass and puts it under a bush next to the cement porch. David's got his fingers out like he's making to pet the worm.

"Rake up the cuttings behind me," I say.

David looks a little confused. "But by then it's too late. The bugs'll be run over."

"That's not what the rake's for. You use it to pile up the cut grass."

"What good does that do? The bugs'll be chopped up."

"We're not here to save bugs. We're here to cut the grass and clean up the clippings, and make some money."

David drops the rake at his feet. "That's no reason to kill the bugs!"

My God, he's starting to cry.

I look around to find Cheryl and I can't see her, but I hear the rasp of the edger, pumping away, sounding like it's supposed to sound, like pulling masking tape off a roll in quick tugs. She's left a good half-inch trim space between the sidewalk and the grass in front, and she's finishing up in back. If only David could rake, we'd be done with this yard in less than half an hour, but he's crying full out now, sniffling away over saving his bugs.

"Just let the cuttings alone," the man shouts from his porch. Still sitting, like he's got box seats at a ball game, the man's laughing at us, a row of his tiny teeth showing at the corner of his mouth, zippered right up to the cigar. "I haven't raked in years."

David searches again for bugs to save, and the man's laughing harder like we're some sort of clown show. Happy finding another worm before it gets chopped up, David stops crying as quick as he started, as if he never cried in the first place. I don't understand how he does it, his instant emotions, here then gone. He's smiling a bit, keeping his eyes on the ground in front of the mower, stepping back as I step forward. I wonder how many bugs he's stepping on? Can't tell David to turn around 'cause he might realize he's been stepping on bugs the whole while, and that will turn on his instant-cry, so I let him be. I can't help but feel sorry for him 'cause he's making the man on the porch laugh hard enough to choke.

Soon Cheryl's edging the lawn along the sidewalk leading from the side of the house. She's tearing up a sliver of turf as easy as slicing cake. Muscles in her arms work away, her tongue poking at the inside of her cheek. Pushing forward, one saddle shoe stomp at a time, Cheryl shoves the edger ahead twice with each stomp. The edger rasps away, shooting trimmed grass out to the sidewalk. I turn off the mower as I cut the last strip of lawn, and the *stomp-rasp-rasp, stomp-rasp-rasp* is like a drum in my ear. With David kneeling by the bushes saying, "There you go, worm," and Cheryl's *stomp-rasp-rasp,* my wimpy brother and tough sister send the man into another laughing fit.

"Well, I have to say I've had a good time watching you stooges cut my lawn."

I turn to him with my hand open. The boy sitting on his tricycle kicks at a sliver of grass Cheryl's edged out. "Three bucks, Dad," he says.

"I'll pay 'em," he says reaching into his pocket as he steps off the porch. I wave Cheryl and David over to stand near me. With the money appearing in the man's hand, all I can think about is that Mom's missing seventy dollars each month divided by three dollars is about twenty-four lawns. I figured that out in my head while cutting the backyard.

Twenty-four lawns a month!

I breathe in deep and smell cut grass and gasoline. I don't think I can take mowing lawns like Mom can take being a secretary, not at all.

Making to give me the three dollars, the man freezes up

and his cigar falls from his mouth. He leans, teetering, on the backs of his heels.

"Goddamn it!" he says a whole lot angrier than before. I thought he might fall, but he kneels down and rubs the grass right where I finished the last strip, then stands and sniffs his hand. "Goddamn it! Your mower's leaked gasoline all over my lawn!" All red-faced, he shouts to the boy on the tricycle, "Get the goddamn hose, kid!" He glares and steps toward me, but stops to pick his cigar off the ground. He grunts shoving the cigar in his mouth, working it with his teeth and lips like he doesn't care where it's been. "Get the hell outta here! You've killed my lawn!"

"I have not!" I say. But the gas smell gets stronger.

"Look down at your shoes!" he orders, and I do as he says.

A stream of dirty gasoline flows from under the mower, across the sidewalk, and around my Keds. I look back up at the man, not knowing at all what to say. He's got his hand gripping around those three dollars and they're heading back into his pocket. I'm not getting it. Mom's not getting it. "Get the hell outta here with your damn lawn mower before I light a match!"

David's shrieking now and Cheryl's telling somebody, probably everybody, to shut up. I yell at them, "Go home!" They're not moving. "Now!" I shout. They're standing there, looking stupid with their yappers hanging open, as if the man meant it about dropping a lit match on the ground loaded with gasoline. Spraying the hose on his lawn, the man's not paying us any attention and I know he's not paying us any money. The gasoline puddles at my Keds. I can't believe it. I've killed the mower. I haven't helped Mom a bit and that man starts yelling again.

"Get that goddamn mower off my sidewalk!"

He lets David have it in the face with the hose spray.

•   •   •

When we reach Ellerson Street, the gas stops dripping. Ran out, I guess. If I had a match, I could light our trail and blow up Linwood Street. Cheryl and David walk behind me pretty quiet. They're arguing about something, though, I just got it tuned out. Maybe it's 'cause of lawn mower noise, or that man's growling, but I can't hear them too good. Whatever they're saying, I'm sure it's about nothing. I feel my radio bounce against my thigh and I turn it on and the volume dial as far up as it will go.

Barney Pip says, *I feel like playing it again and again until the astronauts do come home. Oh, boy! Somebody stop me, I love the Hanky Panky!* For sure Cheryl's gonna start playing *Hanky Panky* for at least three weeks straight. But *Hanky Panky* kinda drowns out the bad things I'm thinking about myself, how I can't get things quite right, about failing most of the time, how I'm failing being the new man of the house.

My feet again move along to the *Hanky Panky*'s drumbeat. And I don't know why, I just do it, I start wiggling my butt at my brother and sister, and it gets them laughing. We turn the corner to Loblolly Avenue, and there's our house, and there's Mom's Bel Air parked a bit on our lawn, and a police car right behind it. I'm not surprised it's a crime to dribble gasoline all over somebody's lawn, and I'm not surprised at all that the man would call the cops on me. I can't figure how he knew where I lived.

•   •   •

Mom's got me in my bedroom, and Cheryl and David are at the Waxbergs'. Mom's not happy about having to come home from work at eleven in the morning. I'm lying on my bed, hearing the policeman ask her questions in the kitchen, always leading back to, "Who's watching the kids while you're gone?" Guess the policeman isn't impressed with me, stinking of gasoline and walking right into the house with it all over my shoes. He wants to know if I was causing trouble, like starting fires or something. Kinda wish that man on

Linwood would call just so the policeman would believe me about the mower, even if he's probably gonna ask for money to fix his dead grass.

"My oldest watches the others," Mom says. "He's a good kid."

I've got that feeling in my stomach again, like the night before, only not as bad. It's good to hear Mom say that about me in spite of everything. But it's not so good that she's saying it to a policeman 'cause it means he isn't believing anything good about me at all.

"We can't have a twelve-year-old responsible for an eight-year-old and a seven-year-old," the policeman's saying.

"I can't afford a full-time baby sitter. I'm a widow." There's something strange in the way Mom says *widow*. Not at all weak, but strong like she's demanding understanding from the policeman. "I'll work it out," she says. "I don't need you to tell me how to run my life." I sit up and I can't help but smile a bit. Mom's giving it to the policeman, and he's wearing a gun!

"There are rules we have to follow, ma'am."

Mom's pointy secretary shoes clip along the kitchen floor tiles. "What are the rules for a widow with three children, a mortgage, bills, and woman's wages?" I lean against my bedroom wall to hear better 'cause the policeman doesn't seem to be saying anything. I hear his heavy-booted feet stepping a bit.

"All right," the policeman says, a bit more friendly. "We just got a call from a neighbor saying she was worried something was wrong with your children. It appears it's just a misunderstanding at this point. Don't get mad." The policeman's boot-steps bang down the landing stairs toward the side door. "Try to come up with a better plan, that's all."

Amazing. The screen door slams shut and nobody's under arrest. *I'm* not under arrest. I lean back against my pillow and wait for Mom. It doesn't take a minute before my bedroom door's opening.

"You got the wooden spoon on you anywhere?" I say,

looking around her.

"Should I get it?" Her beehive hairdo is collapsing a little, which is good 'cause I don't like it anyway.

"No," I say. And I ask her, "What are woman's wages?"

Mom leans her back against my door and sighs, "It's all I get."

"I heard Mr. Yellen last night. And the seventy dollars a month."

"I see." She wipes her eyes and some black streaks along her face. "How much were you going to charge to cut a lawn?"

"I tried for five dollars. I could only charge three dollars. I broke the gas mower."

"Three dollars each means a lot of lawns. What were you going to do in the winter?"

"Shovel sidewalks."

"And is it going to snow every day in the winter?"

"I'd think of something."

Mom walks to my bed, whispering, "He's so like his father." I can't believe Mom would think Dad was a goof. She sits on my bed, her face so full of different expressions that it's impossible to pick out any one. I wait for her to say something, but she only keeps mumbling about how much I'm like Dad. So I say something to remind her I'm not.

"Did the man with the lawn I gasolined call to sue us?"

"So much like your father."

I don't believe her.

"This was sticking out of the mailbox when I came home," she says pulling a white envelope from inside her suit jacket. She hands it to me and tells me to read the envelope and then open it. I take it and read, *Loblolly Avenue loves the Rosenbergs. Every month. Let Jerome Yellen know when it's no longer necessary.*

"What does this mean, Mom?"

"Open it."

I flip open the little flap and find a stack of five dollar bills inside.

"Fifteen fives," Mom says, "and there's two ones in there. Seventy-seven dollars."

"Who gave it to us?"

"It says what it says."

I can't tell what I feel exactly. It's hard hearing your mother say things about sleeping in the same bed your father died in. But I don't want to leave this house, not yet.

"It's charity," she says. "We can't keep taking it forever. I'm in the mood to demand a raise." She smiles. "If I quit my job, the boss would fall apart."

"I bet he would," I say, and I'm sure of it. Mom puts her hand behind my neck and kisses my forehead.

"All of you look so much like your father," she says stroking my hair. "Please don't ever think I don't love you no matter what happens to me. I'm a widow now."

She goes back to work in the blueberry blue Chevy Bel-Air with the tuft of stuffing coming out the back seat backrest. Holding the envelope, the fifteen fives, the two ones, and its promise to love us, I wonder what it's really like to be a widow. I've lost my father. I'm a widow's son. But watching Mom leave the house, her shoulders slumped, I suppose I have no idea what it means to be her now. I'm no better than the policeman.

I add the money up three more times, to be certain. From the living room picture window, I see Mrs. Jenner coming out of her house, her house built the opposite of mine. She stops at her front walk and stares at my house, and she's so sharp-looking in her dark blue pant suit. Just watching and smiling, that's all she does.

Of course, I think, squeezing the money. It had to be.

• • •

Another envelope shows up in our mail on August first with the fifteen fives and two ones inside. Mom's been after Mr. Yellen to find out who's dropping it off, but he won't tell. Says it's a secret and all that. She tells Mr. Yellen that she's making fifty cents an hour more now. Mom found out the mail clerk, the m-a-l-e clerk, Mom says, was making forty cents more an hour than she was, and he's lazy, sitting around doing nothing half the time. So she marched up to her boss's desk, sat down and let him know it.

"Do you think your m-a-l-e clerk can type eighty-five words a minute?" she said with a pile of unfinished work on her lap. "I'm the head of my household, treat me like one." And she sat there, refusing to move.

She got the idea watching Martin Luther King Jr. on TV and his thing he's calling *civil ain't-obeying-dance*, like a friendly way to say *nuh-uh* to people who aren't treating you right. Grandpa Erwin started to say *King Shming* one day over the telephone and Mom cut him off. "Don't ever say anything bad about that man to me," she said.

Mom says she thought she might lose her job, but her boss gave in. He guessed it probably wasn't right paying the m-a-l-e clerk forty cents more an hour than a professional, lightning-fast secretary like Mom.

"Not such a hard guess," Mom said back to her boss.

But she doesn't want her boss to think she's getting anything more than she deserves. It doesn't count as a raise, she just got her salary to where it should have been in the first place.

We hear about this at bedtime, not at all like Dad's old bedtime stories about the Hydra Glide. Since I'm twelve, I shouldn't be needing bedtime stories anyway, but these new ones are fun 'cause they're real. Mr. Yellen tells Mom at our living room table that the envelope's gonna stay at seventy-seven dollars at least for the next several months, "Just in case," he says, which makes me both nervous and glad about the money envelope.

I think I saw Mrs. Jenner deliver the August envelope, but it might've been the invitation to Skyler Jenner's birthday party.

• • •

Next week is the last week for Camp MaSkokie. David

and Cheryl leave me alone these days, but they're still going after each other pretty good. I think I've got them figured out now. Cheryl's like Wednesday from the Addams family, real scary and devious, but she's never done anything to really hurt anybody. She's got some ideas in her head that only she understands, and there's nothing anyone can do to make her happy or like you. I look at her blue eyes, and I can't tell if she's hating or liking something just then. And she's tough and says she's happy I swore at the man on Linwood Street. Says she went back to the fat man's house and found nothing wrong with his stupid lawn. I don't believe she went back there, but she gives me two bucks and keeps one for herself. Got it out of the man's pocket by standing there and shouting good and loud that he was cheating little kids until he gave up the money. She keeps one dollar for herself 'cause she feels she earned it, and David gets nothing 'cause he's just a queer little faggot. That's what she says. I ask her what she means and she says, "He just is."

Cheryl doesn't want to be anywhere near David. At the MaSkokie bus stop, David's standing as far from her as he can 'cause he knows she wants it that way. And being as little as he is, there's nothing he's able to do about it. I know he's been eating a lot of Wonder Bread 'cause it says it builds bodies in twelve ways, whatever that's supposed to mean, and he figures it will make him bigger faster so he can beat Cheryl up one day. But all that Wonder Bread eating makes him go to the bathroom a lot more, and there's Cheryl outside the bathroom door, torturing him with her *bloop bloop* thing again while he does his business until he's crying.

David goes into my *Superman* and *Mad Magazine* comics, and he's still trying to tape-record me snoring. But he's seven years old, so I tolerate him. Cheryl can't seem to tolerate much at all when it comes to David.

I know he sneaks into Cheryl's bedroom. She's got all these *Archie* comic books and Beatles posters, and David likes to examine them. And Cheryl knows David's been in her bedroom even if he's put things back exactly right. She knows it for fact even if she's had a sleep-over at Hannah Waxberg's house. Cheryl comes home and immediately starts to yell, "David's been in my room!"

David denies it and says that he touched nothing and wasn't in there, but she turns to him like Wednesday Addams about to cast an evil spell on him, and she hisses, "Oh, you were in my room all right. I can smell it!"

Mom's not dealing with it. She's too tired most of the time. Now that she's got her raise at International Minerals, her millionaire bosses have her working like she should be making twice more. Mom leaves at eight and comes home at six-thirty, or later, and she's too tired to do much of anything. She watches the little black-and-white TV in her bedroom and falls asleep to it. I know she doesn't like *Man From U.N.C.L.E.*, but I hear it Friday nights through my bedroom wall. She watches *Mr. Roberts* first and just sleeps into *Man From U.N.C.L.E.*, and then the news and Johnny Carson.

Exactly when Mom started collapsing after work, letting the housework go undone, is hard to say. Now it's just the way it is. No more watching the sunrise out our kitchen window, no more watching the living room TV together, no more sitting on the pinners porch after dinner — it all kinda ended. We eat macaroni and cheese on paper plates, or maybe cereal when I feel like washing a few bowls from the pile in the sink.

She tried at first, I think, but the millionaire bosses keep her too busy at work. When I open her bedroom after dinner, she's asleep, sometimes before eight, and it's kinda embarrassing for me to see her sleeping in her work clothes. There's no mom on TV acting like that, so I close the door and try to forget about it.

David's pretty much on his own with Cheryl and he's losing really bad. I'm not much help 'cause, to tell the truth, I don't get David. He's always out in the backyard and alley, saving flies from spiders and worms from birds, telling me he can't let anything die. And he comes in with his dirty hands and gets them all over my comics. I stub my toes on that reel-

to-reel recorder almost every morning and I want to throw it
at him, but I promised never to hurt him again. So I ignore
him and let Cheryl do what she wants to him. It's not as if
anybody could stop her anyway.

• • •

Our first Friday night dinner drive to Grandmaland since
Dad died. Grandma Elaine insists we start it up again. Mom
doesn't want to 'cause she doesn't feel like driving, but she
gives in, finally, when Grandma Elaine threatens to bring
over her pots and pans and porcelain bowls and boiled chick-
en and chicken soup and *schmaltz* and the farfel and matzo
balls, and — so Mom gives in 'cause it's easier to drive than
clean the house before and after Grandma Elaine and
Grandpa Erwin show up with their entire kitchen.

Cheryl's put a six-inch flower sticker on the Chevy Bel-
Air right in the middle of the hood, although it's off to the
left about an inch. Says she's gonna get more from someone
she knows at Camp MaSkokie, and Mom says she'll let her
do it. It's flower power and it means peace and love and all
that, and we're riding in the flower power Chevy Bel-Air on
the way to Grandmaland while Cheryl does her best to annoy
David.

David's in the back behind me and Cheryl's behind Mom.
Pressing herself against the door as much as possible,
Cheryl's letting David know she's trying to be as far away
from him as the Bel-Air will allow. She thinks the trunk
would be a good place for David, but that isn't going to happen, so she's put her right hand up against the right side of
her face, like some sort of vision shield to block David's ability to see her and her ability to accidentally see him.

"Quit sucking that candy," she says, and David freezes
up, holding his hard candy on his tongue. The spit builds up
in his mouth until he dribbles a drool drop, which, of course,
Cheryl can hear like it's a firecracker exploding in the back
seat. She turns and tsks and tongue-clicks and drops her

hand shield to turn and sneer at him — "David's a stupid idiot" — and he's too scared to do anything about it. Mom says to cut it out, but that's like telling the sun to stop shining when it comes to Cheryl. David's still the bottom of the totem pole. He takes his losses and saves the bugs.

If Mom didn't blink and turn the steering wheel every now and then, I'd swear she's just a robot sitting there. She's driving down Church Street all the way to the edge of Skokie, to the far east side, and since it's the World's Largest Village after all, it does take some time. Church Street only lets you go thirty miles an hour, which seems kinda slow considering how wide Church Street is. Maybe it's so you have to go slow and look at all the new buildings going up and all the pretty brick houses. The newer ones are getting bigger all the time, and the apartment buildings are made of colorful bricks and have large sandstone chunks in them. It's like each building says to the next, *You're nothin', look at me!* It kinda makes me wonder why they built all the houses on my block like little square boxes if they can do all this fancy stuff.

When Mom gets us to McCormick Street, though, all the fancy stuff is over. She takes us to Touhy Avenue and makes a left there, and we're not in Skokie anymore. Once we cross over the drainage canal into Grandmaland, the wide streets get narrow and have lots of cracks in them, like the sidewalks. Crossing over that canal is kinda like watching *The Wizard of Oz* movie go backwards, like the canal's the tornado and it blows us back to the gray ugly place with all the bent and shabby buildings. And I don't want to go there 'cause it's all in black and white, and where we come from's in color.

The Grandmaland people are old and short and wear dark jackets and hats even though it's August. "Grandmalanders," Cheryl calls them. They walk fast and pull carts behind them as big as animal cages rolling along on two wheels. With their carts stuffed full of white paper packages and white boxes with gold string tied around them, the

Grandmalanders hurry out of shops and rush down the sidewalk like there's some deadline they have to make, or else. And the shops seem to close as we drive by. We pass a synagogue right there on Touhy Avenue, across the street from the Bernard Horwich Jewish Community Center. It's supposed to be like the YMCA, but it's Jewish. I can't imagine these little people in hats and coats in August stripping down to bathing suits to swim laps.

Grandmalanders gather outside the community center and the synagogue, talking in small groups. It's kinda weird, but you can't see their carts and packages anymore, like they vanished. They look at us kinda funny 'cause we're the only car in the street moving at sunset, and the start of Sabbath service is so near. They're all Jewish, really Jewish, and I feel sorry for them 'cause they don't live in Skokie, where there's no such thing as looking really Jewish, not like how it is in Grandmaland. I don't want to be *that* Jewish.

Mom parks the Bel-Air in the secret spot behind Grandma Elaine's and Grandpa Erwin's apartment building, in the cement alley where the garbage men come to pick up the weekly trash. There's an old sign that says no parking, but on Sabbath in Grandmaland, there's no place else to park, and I bet the policemen and tow truck guys are walking around the synagogue and community center or the shops, pulling carts behind them as the shops close for Sabbath, so there's no reason to worry. It took us a half hour to get here, and besides Cheryl's "David's a stupid idiot" and Mom's "Stop it, quiet down," nobody said anything the whole ride over. When David gets out, he's got his hard candy in his hand, all melty and sticky, and he tosses it to the ground.

Grandma and Grandpa Finkelwitz' apartment building looks like a castle to me. It's a block long and made of brown brick, only the bricks are larger than Skokie bricks, and there are no chunks of sandstone or colorful bricks stuck in the sides anywhere. It's three stories tall and the bricks at the top are shaped into small castle peaks, like teeth that have big gaps between them. Trees make their way up over the third story by a long shot, and the branches from all the trees disappear into each other so it's hard to tell which tree owns which leaves. They're thick and the bark is rough, like face wrinkles, all the way up, not at all like the smooth honey locusts in Skokie.

The whole thing says *old* to me, especially when we go in the front entrance. It's got a wood archway with plates of colorful glass, and the air inside smells like it's been breathed by millions of other people for a hundred years before it got to me, like there's almost not enough oxygen left in it to keep me awake. Cheryl's saddle shoes make the long, tiled entrance hallway echo as if some other person we can't see is walking toward us to leave the building. When we stop in the middle at the mailboxes, the footstep echoes stop, and my back becomes cold and all tingly. I sense an invisible man standing behind me, watching to see what we're doing.

Mom pushes a button near the top of a row of buttons for the third floor apartments. They're built into a metal plate with little doors and keyholes and the words *U.S. Mail* across the top. In a few seconds, Grandma Elaine's voice comes over the speaker.

"Grace?" It's kinda funny hearing it 'cause it sounds like Grandma Elaine's on the radio. Just once I'd like to hear Grandma Elaine announce over this little speaker, "Let's play *The Hanky Panky*," in her Grandmaland voice. It'd kill me laughing.

"Yes," Mom says. The inner door buzzes, but it stops before any of us can get to it. Mom goes back to the button and speaker. "A little longer, Mom," she says, and the inner door starts buzzing again. Cheryl pushes the door and we follow. Through the buzzing, I hear Cheryl's saddle shoes on the tile floor leading to the staircase, and the echo steps are there again, but going the other direction. I turn to look back, expecting the outer door to open somehow. It doesn't, of course, but the steps seem to leave us and fade into the outside air.

Grandma Elaine keeps her finger on her buzzer until we're almost up to the second floor. I smell the boiling chicken coming from every door we pass on the way up, wet and thick in the air. It's in the walls and the stairway carpet, and even if everyone stopped boiling chicken forever, it would take a hundred years before the smell would begin to go away.

The apartment door is already open and Grandma Elaine's waiting a step outside for us. She's wearing a pale blue dress that goes to her ankles and ruffles around her like curtain pleats. Her hair's as white as a dandelion right before the seeds blow away, and it's shaped like that, too, only her hair won't blow away under what must be a good minute's worth of hair spraying. She's looking right at me as I'm the first up the stairs, and her eyes explode their gray-blue at me through her reverse microscope glasses.

"Lookie who's here!" she says as if she's surprised to see me. Grandma Elaine's hug feels like it has no top or bottom. It's like pressing into a big comfy pillow, with a few odd lumps here and there, and she smells like a pillow stuffed full of plump chicken feathers. Her arms spread across my back, pressing my head to her shoulder, and it's all one big mush.

Grandpa Erwin's in his chair at the farthest end of the apartment to the left of the door, wearing his white, button shirt and gray slacks hitched up at the knees, the way he always has them when he's sitting down. He's got his remote control in his hand and it rings out a *ping* as he presses a button. He raises his hand with the remote and starts pressing and pressing, ringing out those pings, but I can tell from the commercial for Lux detergent that keeps playing without a hitch that the remote isn't working. And he lets out a loud, *Ahch! Remote shmote!* He leans back in his chair and swings his body forward, pressing his arms down on the chair to get up. His body balances there half up, like it might go back down, but he tucks his head forward and straightens. I can remember Grandpa Erwin back to maybe when I was four or five. I've never known him to get out of a chair without making it a big production.

"Hello, Grace," he says to Mom. They kiss quickly on the lips and then hug. It's kinda uncomfortable 'cause we haven't been together like this since Dad's funeral. There's a point when I know we're supposed to ask how everyone else is, and then everyone's supposed to say, "Fine, fine." And then, "What's new?" And the answers are all, "Nothing, nothing." But that point is here now and none of us says these things.

"Let's have some eat," Grandma Elaine says in her Yiddish way of talking English.

We know where our places are and the dining room table is set with everything Grandma Elaine owns, enough for twenty people. David takes his seat at the head of the table in a yellow chair made for a two-year-old. But he fits in it and sits as high as the adults, his butt kinda bulging through the spaces between the seat cushion and rail. Cheryl's sneering at him and attacks with a rat-a-tat-tat of tongue clicks and tsks and rolling eyes. She sits to the left of Mom, where Dad used to sit, where she doesn't have to look at David unless she wants to. At least Cheryl isn't saying anything and David's ignoring her — he's probably figured out that when it comes to Cheryl, Grandma and Grandpa Finkelwitz' apartment is like a goal in a tag game.

I'm next to Grandpa, across from Mom, and Grandma Elaine begins wearing out the rug waiting on us. "First helping of chicken soup," she says. "You going to break your k'naidel record tonight, Jeremy?"

Grandma Elaine calls matzo balls *k'naidelakh*. It's *k'naidel* if she's talking about one *k'naidelakh*. Matzo balls and *k'naidelakh* are the same thing. Not even Grandpa Erwin says *k'naidelakh*. It's a funny word, like *Clem Kadiddlehopper* from the Red Skelton Show— *K'naidelakh, Kadiddlehopper* — they're words that make me laugh just hearing them.

When I was nine, I chewed down eighteen of Grandma Elaine's matzo balls. Everyone was amazed 'cause I'm so skinny. Grandpa Erwin bought me clothes that were way too

big for me 'cause he was certain that wearing them would
make me grow into them. But it didn't work. Only Grandpa
Erwin thought it would work and only Grandpa Erwin was
surprised that it didn't. Everyone wanted to know where
skinny nine-year-old me put those eighteen matzo balls.
Grandpa Erwin told Cheryl to look under my chair and Dad
said to check my pockets. Then Grandma Elaine came from
the kitchen and leaned over my shoulder and said in her spitty Yiddish, "Have more eat? Another *k'naidel*?" Then everyone knew where those *k'naidelakh* went 'cause when I was
through having my laughing fit, about three of them came
out my nose.

I can't eat watching the Red Skelton Show 'cause I never
know when Clem Kadiddlehopper might show up, and I
can't eat Grandma Elaine's matzo balls 'cause she's gonna
say *k'naidelakh*, I know she will.

The matzo balls sit like hand-sized bald baby heads in a
white bowl at the center of the table, next to the gefilte fish.
It's easy to get matzo balls and gefilte fish mixed up 'cause
they're about the same pale white color and size, and Dad
called the gefilte fish albino turds, so everyone would know
the longer ones were the gefilte fish. The soup starts coming
one bowl at a time 'cause Grandma's got the soup filled to the
edges and she's careful not to spill. She brings mine to me
after everyone else has theirs and the liquid swirls at the
edges. It's a clear liquid and I see the little flower patterns on
the bottom of the porcelain bowl. Grandma Elaine's chicken
soup is not much different from tap water. Every drop of
water that's run over Grandma Elaine's chicken is saved in
her biggest pot. She'll be giving Mom a few gallons of it in
empty milk bottles and Mom will water the houseplants with
it when we get home.

We take turns with the salt shaker until it's almost empty
and we slurp our tap water, with a thimble of chicken drippings, into our mouths. Grandpa Erwin does it with us. None
of us tells Grandma Elaine the truth about her chicken soup
'cause we all like the way she looks standing there at the

doorway to the kitchen, beaming her super-magnified eyes at us, her hands folded over her dress, wearing a smile that stretches her lips thin. She's waiting for us to finish our soup so she can bring out the first piles of boiled chicken.

I don't think I'd ever tell anyone outside my family what Grandma Elaine serves us to eat. She doesn't cook much beyond what chicken and water can do. Chicken that's boiled forever mushes off the bones kinda boogery, and the skin falls apart in your mouth like soaked paper. Grandma Elaine cooks everything a chicken has to offer, and she serves up a plate of boiled chicken feet and a chicken neck that looks like a long, bent *kishke*. Nobody eats that chicken neck stuff except Grandma Elaine at the end of dinner. Although it all tastes good, even the chicken feet, it's kinda embarrassing to admit. But I'm never ever gonna put my mouth anywhere near the chicken necks or *k'naidelakh*.

After dinner, we're all ocean ships beached and rolling on shore in the living room, spread out on the floor and couch, Grandpa Erwin in his chair all slouchy. He's on vacation for the rest of his life. He used to be a plumber. Now he sits in his chair whenever he wants, keeping track of his free time by looking at a gold watch his bosses gave him for getting old. I sit by his chair, on the couch, burping. My burps smell like the chicken air I breathed coming up the stairs to the apartment. David's sitting on the floor, leaning up against the couch. I hear Grandma Elaine in the dining room with Mom, clearing up. I know Grandma Elaine's eating leftovers off the plates 'cause she doesn't try to hide it, nibbling her way to the kitchen. Grandpa Erwin looks at me and says with a shrug, "It's because of the Depression." I nod at Grandpa Erwin 'cause he's looking at me like I know what he means, which I don't.

It's a special night on TV 'cause Frasier Thomas is on with a special edition of his *Family Classics* show. He's showing *Journey to the Beginning of Time* all at once. Usually he shows it in episodes on his *Garfield Goose and Friends* after-school show. It's pretty good 'cause it's about

boys going back in time, paddling along in a rowboat, visiting cavemen caves and dinosaurs, and every inch the boys
row their boat, the further they go back in time. But each
episode's only as long as a commercial and it's over just
when it's barely started. You gotta wait until the next day
before you can see the next few seconds of it. But tonight,
Frasier Thomas is showing *Journey to the Beginning of Time*
from beginning to end, and it's supposed to be an hour-and-
a-half long instead of two months of Frasier Thomas saying,
"Tune in tomorrow for the next episode of — *Journey to the
Beginning of Time.*"

"Mom, it's starting!" Cheryl yells from her spot in front
of Grandpa Erwin's chair.

"In a minute," Mom says.

"For cry'n' out loud," Grandpa Erwin says. "The downstairs neighbors can hear you."

"But Mom's gonna miss it," she says.

"*Ahch!* Miss shmiss, it'll be on a hundred more times."

Frasier Thomas is wearing a nice, dark suit on *Family
Classics* instead of his Garfield Goose Show navy admiral
uniform. "On *Garfield Goose,*" David says, "he always looks
a little scared, like he might have to drop a bomb or something."

Frasier Thomas talks like he's chatting with you at the
dinner table, like he's everybody's uncle. The TV's showing a
book on a desk, and the camera moves in on it until it fills
the entire screen— *Family Classics Presents, Journey to the
Beginning of Time.*

"Mom! Starting!"

"For cry'n' out loud," Grandpa Erwin growls. He's got
his hands resting lightly on Cheryl's shoulders. We don't say
much when we're watching TV. We're all trying hard not to
fall asleep.

The four boys going back in time start out at a museum,
looking at a mean-looking dinosaur skeleton. Their eyes
kinda glaze over and, before you know it, they're heading
down a river in a boat toward a dark tunnel. When they go

through it, everything's gone but them, their boat, and the river, no buildings and no other people. The river's turned a little icy and they pull the boat to shore and look around to see what's happened. There's not much talking going on in the movie, just some hiking through woods to a cave. I hear Grandma Elaine's and Mom's voices in the bedroom leak through the wall. The couch I'm slouching on is right up against it, but the wall's real thick and solid and I can't make out what they're saying.

David rolls away from the couch on his belly and brings his face within five feet of the TV. The youngest boy is about to find some caveman drawings on the cave wall, but nobody's gonna figure out what it is. "What if one of the cavemen shows up this time?" David says.

"It's not gonna change from the last time you saw it," Cheryl says, tsk-tsking.

"You don't know that," Grandpa Erwin says to Cheryl. "Maybe one of them will show up. I'd like to see what one of the cavemen looks like, wouldn't you?" David peers over his shoulder at Grandpa Erwin and smiles. Poor Grandpa, I'm thinking. He's got no idea what Cheryl's like anymore. She's watching the movie knowing it's just a movie, and nothing in it is gonna be different no matter how many times it's on TV.

A woolly mammoth walks along the river and one of the boys in the rowboat calls it a hairy elephant. But the oldest boy in the boat knows something's wrong 'cause he knows it's a woolly mammoth, and they haven't been around since before radio.

"Erwin!" Grandma Elaine shouts from the bedroom.

With a thump against the wall, Mom says really loud, "Oh, Mom! I can't believe you did this!"

Grandma Elaine shouts again, "Erwin! I need you in the bedroom!"

Letting loose an *Ahch,* Grandpa Erwin begins his production of getting up, leaning back and pushing himself forward.

"Erwin! In the bedroom!"

"Ahch!" he says to me with a little smile. "Bedroom shmedroom. What could she want with me in the bedroom? I haven't done anything good in there in years." He winks at me and smiles like a smiling pumpkin face shrivelled a week after Halloween. Grandpa Erwin turns toward the bedroom and disappears behind a wall. I hear the door open and Grandma Elaine says, "Shh, close it quick."

"Here's where those dinosaur birds come along," David says.

"I can see it," Cheryl snaps back.

The one pterodactyl's being kinda stupid, flying so close to the land dinosaurs. It's not hard to figure out what's going to happen even if I hadn't seen this at least three times before. I guess I should be more interested in what's going on in the bedroom. There's some feet-stomping and voices loud-whispering at each other, like yelling with a hand over your mouth. They're grumbling in there and I can make out "Take it" and "I can't believe you did this." I'm also trying to watch the Tyrannosaurus Rex bite the pterodactyl's wing. Watching the movie gets harder for me with all the adult arguing going on through the wall.

"I can't watch," David scolds the TV. "Let the bird go!"

"You idiot," Cheryl says. "You already knew it was gonna happen."

The banging and stomping and Mom's repeated "I can't believe it" make their way toward the bedroom door. Mom's talking good and clear, and Grandma Elaine's saying, "Grace, please, you need to take this and do something about it. You can't let it go."

Just a little bit, so Cheryl and David don't notice, I lean my ear near the wall. Grandpa Erwin's not giving any advice. Both Mom and Grandma Elaine ask him to make the other one stop. He's telling them both to quit their yelling, letting out his *Ahchs!* when they keep yelling anyway. The bedroom door's opening.

"Everyone get ready to go home now," Mom says. Her face is red and hot-looking, and I can tell she's been crying.

"But Mummy," David whines, "the Tyrannosaurus Rex and the Stegosaurus haven't fought yet."

"The Stegosaurus dies again," Cheryl says.

"You don't know that," David says.

"I'll bet you anything."

"Grace, please," Grandma Elaine says. Her face never gets red, but she's gripping some large envelope, big enough to hold a schoolbook report, and she's trying to get Mom to take it.

Mom turns away, saying, "Mom, please." Grandpa Erwin's standing behind Grandma Elaine, looking down. I know he's hating this. He just wants us all sitting around and dozing in front of the TV.

"Jeremy," Mom says, expecting me to help her. I get off the couch and kiss Grandma Elaine.

"Cheryl, David," I say. Cheryl stays on the floor with her eyes telling me what she'd say if no adults were here— *Who made you king of the world?*

"You need to take this," Grandma Elaine says, raising the envelope.

Seems like it's poison to Mom, and she winces away and snaps her fingers at David and Cheryl. "You heard your brother. Let's get going."

"I'm never gonna see this whole movie at once," David says getting up as rubbery as a Gumby doll. Cheryl pops up, darts in front of David, and kisses Grandma Elaine. I'm sure she didn't want any of David's leftover spit coming off of Grandma Elaine's lips.

I can't say I've ever seen Mom and Grandma Elaine argue before, not like this, and not in front of everyone. Mom once told me how she couldn't get a whole stick of gum, only half at a time, until she was eighteen years old. If Mom didn't yell about that for eighteen years, there must've been something really going on in the bedroom.

On the way out, Grandma Elaine sneaks the envelope to me, whispering, "Take this," like it's a super-secret formula for chicken cooking, so I'm stuck trying to hide it from Mom walking down the stairs. Grandma Elaine knows I'd never refuse anything from her, except her *k'naidelakh*, but that's all. Maybe it isn't fair that Grandma Elaine gave it to me 'cause she must've known Mom would find out. It's kinda hard hiding something like a big yellow envelope. Mom holds the downstairs inner door open for me and sees me holding the envelope behind my back. All I can do is shrug.

"It's all right," she says, and takes it from me, folds it in half like she's not caring about it, and puts it in her purse. I gotta say my fingertips are burning a little 'cause I want to see what the big deal is inside that thing. But I'm not getting it and I doubt Mom's gonna keep it long before the garbage-men take it away forever.

Cheryl's ahead, walking in the hall past the mailboxes. Her saddle shoes start clopping again on the tile and the echoes bounce off the walls behind me. We're being followed, that's what I feel, but the echo-steps grow louder and head toward Mom and that envelope. I call out in my mind — *Dad?* If Dad is walking with us, he can hear a thought-out cry for him as good as a shouted one. I'm too old to be calling out for ghosts, but I do it 'cause I need to do it just to be sure.

I don't hear anything back. When Cheryl goes out the front door, the echo-steps stop.

•   •   •

After Friday night in Grandmaland, Grandma Elaine's envelope disappears. Grandma Elaine and Grandpa Erwin don't talk about it the next Friday, at least nothing I overhear. It never shows up in the trash so I pretty much figure out it's a lot of money that Grandma Elaine and Grandpa Erwin want Mom to have. I'm not surprised Mom keeps it. We need it.

•   •   •

Saturday mornings are a kid's best friend, even in the summer when there's no school, and August thirteenth is no exception. We're allowed to be lazy, get up late, watch too much TV, and hang around doing nothing. With his hair poking in every direction, David's hopping around the bedroom in his BVDs saying that he finally got me. He hits the rewind button on the reel-to-reel recorder and then the play button. "Listen," he says to me baggy-eyed and smiling. I close my eyes and pretend not to pay him any attention, but I have to admit, I'm interested in what my snoring might sound like. "D'you hear that? D'you hear that?" I can't hear anything but static. "Told you so!" He plops his BVD'd butt on my bed and folds his arms real bossy-looking.

"I don't hear a thing."

"I'm taking it to show-and-tell the first day of school," David says, hopping off my bed. He skips once to the recorder, rewinds it, and listens again. He starts laughing and says, "Gotcha!" I'm not sure what he's got unless I snore out radio static, but I'm not going to say anything more about it 'cause I'm glad it's over. Maybe I'll finally stop waking up with a microphone under my pillow. So far, Saturday is going just fine.

Of course there's nothing like Saturday morning cartoons. Even in the summer, they're better than weekday cartoons. We get to watch Johnny Quest, and Rocky and Bullwinkle, and the Warner Brothers stuff is coming up. It's the only time Cheryl leaves David alone 'cause she never watches any of it. She stays in her room and plays her records. She's been playing *Wild Thing* by the Troggs for the last four days, every chance she gets. It kinda fits her like a shadow fits to a person's feet. When I'm watching her, I'm thinking of that song.

David's a little upset right now 'cause President Johnson's breaking in with some news about Vietnam. One moment Yosemite Sam's getting shot in the face with his own shotgun, and the next moment there's a deep-voiced man saying, "And now, the President of the United States with an important message to the American people."

I think it's all right 'cause it's just like watching a cartoon.

President Johnson's got these big ears. I don't want to leave it at that, big ears, 'cause they're so much more than that. They hang down to his jaw and wiggle like cow tongues. It's hard to believe they're real. Dad used to say that's where Lady Bird Johnson keeps all her earrings at night, and he'd tap the TV screen right where those big ear tongues were flopping around. Between them is a big honker of a nose. When President Johnson talks, he's so serious-sounding, but his ears jiggle and wiggle, and that nose looks like it's flying off the TV set right at you. So it's like I said, we're still watching cartoons. He's saying something about how a Communist takeover in South Vietnam was no longer possible, and he's thanking all the American soldiers.

"Where's Vietnam?" David says to me. I shrug. David's watching the TV all blank-faced, his lower lip hanging down a little bit. Then he turns to me and says he knows something I don't. "Mr. Yellen's son is starving himself so he doesn't have to go there. Dahveed said at camp that Brian Yellen doesn't weigh over a hundred pounds now. He's supposed to be turning eighteen and going to Vietnam. I've never heard of an eighteen-year-old weighing under a hundred pounds."

I can't remember what Brian Yellen looks like. He's an older kid, a high school senior, and has nothing to do with us. David keeps rattling away. "Dahveed told me he's skinny, like a skeleton. I guess he hates Vietnam to do that."

And now, back to our regularly scheduled broadcast... Yosemite Sam is just fine after being shot up a hundred times and is busy stuffing dynamite down Bugs Bunny's hole in the ground.

I get a lost feeling watching all the cartoon shows. The next thing I know it's past ten-thirty, but I keep on watching. Mom's bedroom door opens and she comes out looking as though she's trying to look awake, blinking hard, forcing her eyes to open wide, and clenching her lower jaw to keep from yawning. But her clothes are all rumply and her beehive is a little knocked over to one side, away from the smush marks on her face. I know she's been sleeping straight through the morning. She's reminding us that Skyler Jenner's birthday party starts at one, and she wants us to get ready. It's too bad 'cause the Batman movie just opened up at the Skokie Theater, but now we can't go 'cause of Skyler Jenner's party. He's invited everyone on the block. I mean, I'm twelve, David's seven, and Cheryl beat him up, but he's invited all of us. He's even invited Bup Miller, who nobody else ever invites to their birthday parties, and who always has his own birthday parties out of town. It's not like Skyler Jenner will miss me if I don't go. But Mom's insisting and it's a reason to turn off the TV.

I don't understand Skyler Jenner. He's outside playing catch with his dad, and every time he throws the ball, he shouts out the name of a player on the Cubs. They're taking up the sidewalk in front of their house so a person would have to ask permission to get by.

Mookie Waxberg's fresh from a walk home with his family after Saturday morning Sabbath, still wearing his Sabbath *kipah* cap on his head, sitting on my pinners porch with me, strumming his guitar. Smelling like balsa wood, it's a big guitar with steel strings, and it's got a white circle around the hole in the middle. A polished brown wing beneath the hole shines at me. Mookie adjusts his *kipah* and explains what a pick guard is and what the hole's for.

As round as his guitar hole, Mookie's smile is made up mostly of his two top front teeth, and his hair is combed straight down to the tops of his black eyeglass frames. But he looks so cool sitting on my pinners porch with that guitar on his lap, even with his Sabbath *kipah* bobby pinned to his hair. He keeps playing this one chord, a *G* chord he tells me, sometimes down-stroking it, sometimes up-stroking it. As wimpy as Mookie is, he's just so cool right now.

"Ernie Banks!" Skyler Jenner shouts, tossing his major league baseball to his dad. His dad catches it and says nothing. He slowly winds up and tosses it back to Skyler. "Strike one!" Skyler Jenner shouts. And they look so good together in their matching Cubs jerseys.

"That ball was *so* outside," Mookie says. "I can't believe they're rooting for the Cubs anyway. What place are they in?"

"Glen Beckert!" Skyler Jenner bounces one through his dad's legs.

"Last place," I say.

"They're worse than the Mets," Mookie says with a snort. "Can you believe they're rooting for a team worse than the Mets?"

"Don Kessinger!"

"Skyler's got the lineup for a last place team memorized." Mookie strikes his one chord and sings out, "Why that's just stupid."

"Ron Santo!" The ball goes flying over Mr. Jenner's head.

Mookie downstrokes then upstrokes that one *G* chord again and again. He's singing his own song. The *Stupid* song, Mookie says, snickering secretly in my ear, for Skyler Jenner.

"Billy Williams!"

Mookie keeps on strumming, down then up, ringing out that one chord in two directions. It sounds like an Indian chant, humming along at one tone and not changing. Mookie sings, "Stupid, Skyler's stupid. He roots for the Cubs so he's stupid."

"Adolfo Phillips!"

"Stupid, Adolfo Phillip's stupid. He plays for the Cubs so he's stupid."

My stomach starts hurting from keeping the laughing going on inside my gut quiet so the Jenners can't hear, and Mookie's got his eyes closed and scrunched the way the guys in the groups on American Bandstand do it.

"Byron Browne!"

"Stupid, Byron Browne's stupid . . ."

Skyler Jenner knows every one of the players on the Cubs, and every one of them gets into Mookie's song except for some guy named Jonathan Bocabella, which is too long a name to fit, and they're all stupid.

"Stupid, Skyler Jenner's stupid . . ."

We're going to Skyler's birthday party in an hour and we're singing that he's stupid. I think different things about the Jenners. I wish just once that Skyler and his dad would ask me to play catch with them, and I get mad 'cause they never do. Mr. Jenner's not at all like my dad. Mr. Jenner's real formal looking, even in that Cubs jersey. It looks like a tuxedo on him somehow, like he could wear it to a wedding and everyone would say, "Hey, look at that spiffy Jersey!" And when he's with Mrs. Jenner, they're holding hands and smiling and kissing the air near the other's cheeks in front of anyone who's there. I think they could have so much time for me, and I wish they'd invite me to be with them, but they don't. I know they're giving us that money envelope, so there's no way I'm mad. I just wish they'd give me more than their money.

Mrs. Waxberg calls for Mookie and he takes his guitar by the neck as he crosses the street. He plays the accordion, too, and knows lots of notes, but this *Stupid* song on his guitar, I'm thinking, might make him a rock star.

Mr. Jenner takes a pipe out of his pants pocket and puts it in his mouth. He tells his son to bring the baseball to him. I watch them shake hands like businessmen, and they walk together to their house. They never look over to me, like I don't exist, and I keep imagining I'm walking right beside them into the house built the opposite of mine.

The whole block smells like it's getting ready for Skyler Jenner's birthday party. I guess it's a big deal turning ten when you're a Jenner.

•   •   •

Haven't been in the Jenners' house too much, but I recognize the inside right away. As long as I think of my house backwards, I know where everything is.

The moment I go in the front door, I see the tan shag carpeting vacuumed so it looks like a freshly cut lawn, perfect, with the tracks made by the vacuum cleaner all in a row. And

I see the deep orange couch I had watched being brought in, and the matching double seat, and even another chair made up just like it, and I smell the leather like it's a new Cadillac sitting right there in their living room. The TV set's in a stereo console with big black speakers built right in at the ends, and the TV's all folded up inside and put away so it looks like a fancy cabinet hiding a mysterious record player and TV gizmos. But they have the center lid up so everybody can see it's in there and the Jenners own it.

The windows seem so big and airy inside the Jenners' house, and the curtains aren't like our heavy ones at all. They're light and flowing, and the sunshine makes them glow as bright as white neon lights. The dining room is lit up by the glowing curtains, and the tables glisten their beige wood at me, polished like a whole can of wax has been used up.

Mrs. Jenner's guiding me, Cheryl, and David through the upstairs, and Cheryl asks why we didn't use the side door to go to the basement. Mrs. Jenner must've heard her, but she keeps smiling. "The party's *downstairs*," Mrs. Jenner says as if "basement" is a curse word.

I hand her the box Mom wrapped up. The paper's blue and white, and it's got Hanukkah candles in groups of nine on it, with the center candle in each group raised a bit, but they're small so I'm hoping everyone will think it's birthday wrapping paper showing birthday candles. The card is taped to the outside with Mom's handwriting on it— *To Skyler, From Jeremy, Cheryl, and David*. Mrs. Jenner takes it and I'm hoping she doesn't think we're cheap bringing one birthday present from three kids wrapped in Hanukkah wrapping paper. I'm sure Mrs. Jenner doesn't want Mom to take the Jenners' mystery money and spend it on toys for Skyler. It would be like giving it right back, so I'm sure everything's all right.

Karl Grossman's coming up the stairs from the *downstairs* and he blocks our way.

"Gotta use the bathroom, Mrs. Jenner," he says.

"There's one downstairs."

"My brother's been in it for the last five minutes." Karl's looking really worried at Mrs. Jenner, and he's stepping on his own toes.

"Come with me," Mrs. Jenner says, and we let him pass to go with Mrs. Jenner to the *upstairs* bathroom.

Downstairs, Skyler Jenner's wearing a shiny silver tie over a dark blue shirt that's tucked into pants as white as new snow. His hair's combed back and shines its deep brown at the sides, and he's got a thick pompadour up front like a motorcycle windshield, and one thick loop of it curled down so it almost reaches his right eye. He looks like Elvis Presley, sitting in the big black beanbag chair in the middle of his downstairs.

Skyler sees us coming down the steps and he gets up to walk over. "Hi," he says with his hand out. "Thanks for coming." Kids don't shake hands to say hello, but Skyler Jenner does on his tenth birthday.

The Jenners' downstairs is a play land. Its walls have a covering like they're made out of hula girl dresses. And the support beams are boxed in with the same stuff and have a golden twine built in, swirling up like the lines in a barber shop pole. The floor is tiled in large, brown and tan squares, and there's a couch, like a half circle, facing a TV built right into a shelf along the wall lining the staircase, where they have their Dick Van Dyke parties and their Dick Van Dyke conversations. The light in the white ceiling tile makes it feel like we're in afternoon sunshine, and there's no trace of the furnace or washer and dryer machines. They're tucked away behind the hula skirt walls.

Mr. Jenner's in the far corner behind a drinks bar, a curved padded shelf that's got bottles of pop stacked up, and piles of ice in buckets, and there's a countertop behind it with a sink in the middle, and fancy silver faucets arching out of the wall. It's like having a giant lemonade stand right there in the downstairs. Mr. Jenner's holding his pipe, watching Cheryl and Skyler shake hands.

"Have a good time," Skyler Jenner announces to us, and he goes back to the beanbag chair, which Dahveed immediately gives up without Skyler Jenner having to say so. Everything in this place makes me think that this is what my house could've looked like if my father were alive, and I'm thinking opposite things at the same time, that I want to run out right now, and I never want to leave.

The parade of kids never lets up. Bobby Kinder is already here with Dahveed, and the Grossmans, Karl and Charlie, though there's something wrong with Charlie 'cause he keeps going to the bathroom. The Bower twins are here in matching jean jump suits with some kids I don't know and won't bother to find out. Bup Miller shows up right after Cheryl, David, and me, and he's grown at least an inch since summer began. Mookie comes, without his guitar, and Hannah follows to join Dahveed already standing by Skyler Jenner. Sally Jenner's helping her dad serve drinks and there's some teenagers over there. One of them's a girl, big and beautiful enough to be in one of Mr. Grossman's dirty magazines, but she's completely dressed, of course, but I'm thinking like she's not.

Mrs. Jenner's organizing a line of kids and refuses to tell us what's going on. Skyler's next to her with his hands on his hips looking like the all-important birthday boy. Sally's messing with a record player on a shelf and music starts coming from the ceiling, but I can't tell from exactly where.

"Dance contest!" Mrs. Jenner shouts.

The Mamas and the Papas start singing, *I saw her again last night* . . . Mrs. Jenner's telling us all to dance and she starts doing the Pony. She's tapping out with one toe and then the other, and she's got her arms out in front with her wrists all limp. She's smiling away, and Hannah Waxberg starts giggling and running in place. "That's it," Mrs. Jenner says. "In ten seconds, Mr. Jenner and I are going to start judging who's dancing the best, and we're going to tap the losers and tell them to sit down. Ten! Nine! Eight...!" She's counting down so seriously, like she's launching a space ship while she's hopping around doing the Pony to the Mamas and the Papas. Mr. Jenner comes over and takes Mrs. Jenner by the hand and starts doing the Pony with his pipe in his mouth and his eyes looking at nobody in particular.

I get caught standing still in the line of kids, doing nothing, and Mrs. Jenner taps me on the shoulder, directs me to sit on the half-circle couch and Ponies away with Mr. Jenner. Mookie and Dahveed start running in place like their sister, and Bup Miller and Skyler Jenner stand in one place trying to outjump each other. "I can hit my head on the ceiling!" Bup Miller says. "I just don't want to." Skyler calls him a liar and they keep on jumping. Charlie Grossman makes his way to the bathroom again and Karl Grossman gets tapped on the shoulder by Mr. Jenner. I can't figure that out 'cause he was hopping higher than Bup and Skyler put together.

"I don't know why they even invited me," Karl says, dropping himself next to me on the couch. "I only play baseball with Skyler. That's probably why I got tapped out." Karl pulls his blue jeans up at the waist and then leans to me, his big chin with the cleft in it sticking out like a little *tuchas*. "Did ya' see Bobby Kinder's sister?" I look at the line of kids jumbled about, hopping and running in place, being circled by Mr. and Mrs. Jenner, who hold hands and do the Pony. "There she is, Kelly Kinder, by Sally Jenner behind the bar. Woo, she's hot. I'd like to see her dance."

"That's Bobby Kinder's sister?" I say.

She's wearing a full-length, colorful wrap-around dress, and her hair's up, showing her tanned skin going all the way down her back until the material shows up again about six inches above her hips. Not even Mrs. Jenner has that kinda body.

"Well, I do certainly dream of Jeannie," Karl cranks to me out the side of his mouth. "Blink me into your bottle."

The Jenners aren't tapping anyone else on the shoulder, just me for standing there and Karl for not playing with Skyler. "Almost everyone's a winner so far!" Mrs. Jenner calls out, and she claps her hands to applaud everybody except me and Karl. "Play that song again and this time," she says, warning us like a policeman, "this time, we'll be tougher."

The Mamas and Papas begin again, but then the needle scratches across it. Everybody turns to look at the drinks bar, and there's the top of Cheryl's moppy hair behind it. She disappears completely, and then the sound of a record needle thumping on a record kinda startles everyone.

The Troggs start singing, *Wild Thing!*

Cheryl comes running from behind the drinks bar, her arms out like airplane wings. When the Troggs shout *Wild Thing!* — Cheryl screams with her eyes closed, something maybe a chimpanzee might understand. She starts spinning her arms about and everyone moves to give her room. She stops and stares right at a point in the air where nobody's standing. *Wild Thing!* Cheryl screams, and starts doing the Pony a little bit, but then starts jerking her hips like it's a whip every time the drums pound. Her hair's flying every which way, and her elbows jam into her sides like she's flapping to take off. All the other kids just watch 'cause they don't know what to do, like it seems silly to run in place and hop around when Cheryl's doing whatever it is she's doing.

"She's lost it," Karl says to me.

"Don't say that."

"Sally!" Mrs. Jenner says over the Troggs. "I told you never to play that record!" But it gets louder, and Kelly Kinder steps out from behind the drinks bar and walks slowly, slinky-like, toward Cheryl.

"Oh, please, let it happen," Karl Grossman hiss-whispers, "...dance."

Kelly Kinder stands beside Cheryl and lowers her fingertips to the sides of her dress. She starts pinching the material and hoists the bottom of the dress up to her thighs. She begins to lower herself to a crouch. Karl's moaning a little. All the eyes in the downstairs look like they're blowing out their pupils, like Orphan Annie eyes, and I think Karl's are gonna pop out completely.

Wild Thing!

Cheryl screams with her eyes shut and whips her hips about. Seems so strange watching her do all that in her blue party dress while Bobby Kinder's sister's doing the same exact thing, and screaming with Cheryl, like they took the same dance lesson or could read each other's mind. Mrs. Jenner's not smiling at all and she's trying to find her way around the kids to get to the record player. But she can't get to it until *Wild Thing*'s about over. Like a dance team, Cheryl and Kelly Kinder whip their hips and arms about the downstairs, eyes closed, jaws clenched tight, the same look on their faces, looking like they're the only people in the downstairs.

Mrs. Jenner finally gets to the needle.

Cheryl and Kelly Kinder raise their arms over their heads, open their eyes wide and shout, "Wild Thing!" Kelly Kinder turns to Cheryl and hugs her, raising her off the floor, and Karl's wishing so much that he could be in Cheryl's place right now, even if it means wearing a blue party dress.

"You're the winner! You're the winner!" Kelly Kinder tells Cheryl. Cheryl's breathing hard and kinda smiling, but her eyes are all about the place, her hair falling over them.

"This is *my* party," Skyler Jenner says, stomping his black dress shoes on the tile floor. He walks up to Cheryl and yells at her. "This is *my* house and *my* party! We're supposed to play the dance contest game *my* way!" Skyler Jenner takes a step toward Cheryl like he's going to do something, but he keeps his arms at his side and sneers at her. "You're not a winner. I'm supposed to win. Why don't you go back to your crummy house?"

Karl Grossman's looking at me like I should do something, so I get up. Making my way around the couch, I have no idea what I'm going to do. But when I come around, I see Skyler Jenner's on the floor, and he's starting to cry.

Bup Miller's standing over him, a fist ready in case Skyler gets back up.

Bup looks large and his skin is flushed right through his stubbly blond scalp. His eyes dart back and forth before he takes off and runs up the stairs. Cheryl's in Kelly Kinder's arms, looking down at Skyler Jenner crying on the floor. My world of neighborhood kids watches me as I place my hand on Cheryl's back, its heat warming my palm.

"Are you okay?"

She turns to me, her eyes blinking fast. "I can't stand it here. Please take me home."

"David Rosenberg!" Mrs. Jenner scolds across the downstairs. "You had better go with them." Mrs. Jenner's voice is an order, to be followed by consequences if we don't leave right away. David appears from behind Mookie and Hannah, and walks quickly to Cheryl and me. His body's moving like he doesn't know what to do, so I grab his hand and take him up the stairs.

Bup Miller's at my side door, sitting on the one step. He stands, looking like the biggest kid on the block, but he's an oaf with his thick neck and crew cut. Raising his chin, he starts to talk, stuttering as though he's not sure what he wants to say.

"My dad's got stomach cancer," he says, tearing up.

Bup's brown eyes are stupid-looking 'cause they're set too close together, like they should be on a smaller face. "Can I talk to you, Jeremy?" he says. He rubs his knuckles where he socked Skyler Jenner in the face. "I need to talk to you."

• • •

I can't believe I tell Bup Miller about my secret hiding place. He says he'll wait for me to come back outside, and I tell him I don't know when I'm coming back outside. Still, he says, he'll wait.

Mom's in our kitchen with Ida Lipshilts when I come in with Cheryl and David. The air inside smells pretty thick of Ida's smoke even though Mom has all the windows open. I try to explain to her what Cheryl did, but I don't understand it myself, and I'm not sure why it made the Jenners so mad. Cheryl was just dancing, kinda wild, but better than everyone else there except for Kelly Kinder. Mrs. Lipshilts sticks her lower jaw out and pulls on her cigarette using the *V* made by her middle and index fingers. A soft, lippy *puh* comes out of her mouth with the cigarette.

"And they kicked you out for that?" Ida says, jiggling her shoulders.

"I swear that's all."

Mom puts her hand on Cheryl's forehead and tells her to go to her room, she'll be in there in a few minutes. David doesn't say anything. He runs to our bedroom, wearing the shock of being ordered out of the Jenners' house in front of all the neighborhood kids across his pouty face, and slams the door shut.

"What's Bup Miller doing on our swingset?" Mom says looking out the kitchen window.

"He just wants to talk to me, that's all."

"Go then," Mom says, waving her hand.

"Those Jenners," Mrs. Lipshilts says, sucking her cigarette until the tip glows hot orange. She thinks it's funny. She has no idea what this could lead to if the Jenners no longer want the Rosenbergs living on Loblolly Avenue.

•   •   •

About two years ago, I found by squeezing behind one of Big Ben's bushes alongside my garage, I could climb on top of an old wooden picnic bench hidden there and pull myself up on the garage roof. The kids on Loblolly Avenue are always having these all-block long neighborhood tag games, where one guy starts out as the it-kid, then tags another, who also becomes an it-kid, and tags another, until there's only one non-it-kid left, who's declared the winner. I climb up on the garage roof and not only do I win, nobody knows where I've gone to. Don't use it all the time, just when I'm feeling lazy. The it-kids slink on by, checking in bushes and behind the air-conditioner, always looking ahead or down at the ground, but they never seem to look up. If one of them did, they wouldn't know how to tag me anyway.

I've shown Bup Miller my secret, and he's sitting up here with me, burning our butts on the hot shingles. He wants to know what it's like to have a dead father. It's a question that goes into my ears, zings me in the gut, and spreads out, until my toes and fingers tingle from feeling all hollow inside. Hadn't thought of it that way before. I've been thinking all this time that I no longer have a father, not that I have a dead father. Why does it feel so different to think about it that way? The first thing that comes to mind is maybe that's how other people think about it— Jeremy Rosenberg has a dead father— something made him dead.

"Don't you want to find out who killed him?" Bup says eyeing a shingle in front of his big black dress shoes. He pokes a small twig at a turned-up corner.

"Nobody killed him. He just died."

"That's not what I heard. I heard somebody killed him eight months before he died."

"That's just stupid, Bup. How's that possible?"

"He was in that truck accident, and he wouldn't have even been hurt except for that. My dad calls it a domino theory."

"What's a domino theory?"

Bup turns to me with his eyes blinking their too-close-together blink. "It's where one thing leads to another. That's all it is."

Listening to Bup on the roof right now is like listening to Bozo teach arithmetic. He's beginning to sweat like a pig in his dressy birthday party clothes, and his face doesn't seem to make sense, like all his face parts are borrowed from other, different-sized kids.

"It's the same with my dad. He's got stomach cancer and that's gonna make him dead. The dominos are falling and they can't be stopped." Bup drops the twig on his dress shoes and rests his bumpkin head on his fists. "I wish I could've stopped that first domino from falling, that's all." He looks at me again and says, "Don't you want to find the guy that pushed over your dad's first domino?"

I don't know what to say. Even if I had an answer to that question, I don't think I'd tell Bup. Knowing Bup Miller, I'm not entirely certain his dad's dying. It wouldn't be beyond what Bup's said or done before. He might be making it up just so people will feel sorry for him. If he's making it up, and I could prove it, I'd push him off this garage roof right now. I'd be Bup's first domino.

"Guess I'm going to be like you, then," Bup says real slow, as if talking to himself. "We might have to move. The doctor says maybe ten months or so." He picks up his little twig and throws it toward the edge of the roof. It hits the gutter and falls in. "Nobody around here likes me anyway, so what does it matter?"

"It's 'cause you lie all the time, Bup."

"I know."

"And you do stupid things like cut climbing tree branches halfway through and fight kids half your size and throw stones at us at the bus stop."

"It's not my fault. You guys hated me before I ever did a thing." Bup's pale skin turns red and his eyes sag like he's wounded. "My dad's as fat as an elephant and he's got B-O and my mom's a bony scarecrow. I don't stand a chance. When I go to the bathroom, I don't even turn on the lights. I don't want to see what I look like. I already know it ain't nothing good looking back at me in the mirror."

It's true about Bup. He's ugly. His fat father and scarecrow mother made him that way, so it isn't exactly his fault.

"My dad's really dying. I'll take you to my house right now and you can go ask him yourself."

"Well, that'd be stupid," I say. "If you're lying, he'd probably beat the crap out of you, and if it's true, I'd feel like a crud."

"Then you're gonna have to believe me."

I think he's smiling. It's hard to tell with Bup. I shrug at him 'cause I'm still not sure if he's telling me the truth. But if it's true, then it must be something to be the son of a future dead father, and nobody likes you 'cause you're ugly and your parents are ugly.

"I feel," I start to say, and Bup watches me like I'm about to say the smartest thing he's ever heard. "I feel like I miss his smell. He smelled like an engine 'cause of his truck and his motorcycle. It's gone and I miss it."

I haven't said any big thought, just one I'm sure of. Feels like a big deal to say it out loud, even if it's only Bup Miller listening. Bup thanks me and tells me he's going to make sure he remembers what his dad smells like, too, even if it's kinda gross. He says when he goes through puberty he might become handsome, that's what his dad tells him. What a thing to be told by a fat, ugly father.

From the garage roof, I see kids leaving the Jenners' house. The party's turned out to be a lot shorter than it was probably going to be. Mrs. Jenner comes out her side door and I lose sight of her as she walks across the sidewalk toward my house. I hear her knuckles rapping on the screen door and my mother saying, "Sure, you can come in."

"There they are!" Skyler Jenner's pointing at Bup and me from his front sidewalk. "Get Jeremy! Make him an it-kid!"

Mrs. Jenner must've closed the party down and sent everyone out to play it-kid tag so she could yell at my mother and say she's not giving us money anymore and we have to move back to the Old Neighborhood. Bup stands up on the garage roof.

"Where're you going? They can't tag you up here."

"Nobody tags me anyway."

Bup turns to climb down to the bench between the bushes and the garage, and I yell at him to stop. But it's too late, Skyler Jenner sees where Bup's getting down. Bup tears around the garage and heads to his house, probably to get a good whiff of his stinky father. Skyler Jenner pokes his head over the gutter.

"Don't think I can't get you, Jeremy!" Skyler Jenner swings a leg over the gutter and starts pulling himself up.

I stand and tell him to quit pulling at the gutter, but he's raising himself on it. Mookie's chasing Charlie Grossman through the alley and catches up with him behind the garage. "Got you! Got you!" Mookie cries. Charlie Grossman points to Skyler Jenner banging his party shoes on the gutter and yells, "What're you doing?"

"Jeremy's up here!" Skyler barks like a combat soldier. "I'm gonna get him!"

Can't lose to Skyler Jenner, don't want to be tagged by him with all the other kids watching. I step to the edge of the garage roof, face my house, and jump. Skyler shouts out, *Crazy.* The ground comes up to whump me, and it takes only a second.

"Stop him!" Skyler Jenner yells at Mookie and Charlie.

My feet kinda buzzing, I raise myself up and run. I run before Mookie reaches me and head down the sidewalk between my house and the Lipshilts' house. Skyler Jenner winds up to jump off the garage and I spin away 'cause I don't want to watch.

Karl Grossman's running at me from the Kinder house, and Dahveed's standing by my pinners porch. I walk a few steps down the sidewalk and wait. Skyler Jenner marches toward me with Mookie and Charlie behind him. Karl's got the front sidewalk blocked off with Bobby Kinder, and Dahveed is making to tag me. I turn about and see that maybe I can get by Dahveed, but Hannah's coming across the street, and she starts to run to keep me from escaping across my front yard.

"I want to tag him!" Skyler Jenner orders the others. The it-kids back off. "I found his hiding place. He's mine. I'll sue anyone who tags him before I do."

I turn to Skyler and growl words that find themselves inside me and come out, "If I ever see you playing catch with your dad on my sidewalk, I'm gonna send my sister out to beat you up — like she did before."

Dahveed starts to laugh and Skyler Jenner tells him to shut up. Skyler makes to run at me, and I take a deep breath.

I raise my leg over Big Ben's lawn.

"You're crazy!" Skyler Jenner shouts, but I keep going. I walk across Big Ben's lawn about six steps to the middle of the forbidden grass. Skyler Jenner's on the edge of the sidewalk shaking his fist. "You ruined my party! You're crazy! Your sister's crazy! All you Rosenbergs are crazy!"

Skyler, Mookie, Hannah, Dahveed, Charlie, Karl, and Bobby — they're all in a row on the sidewalk, refusing to take a step on Big Ben's sacred lawn. Skyler Jenner keeps telling me I'm crazy, and the rest of them start in with it, too. Bup Miller's watching from his front yard, smiling his off-centered smile like he knows I'm learning what it's like to be him.

Closing my eyes, tilting my head back, the sun makes the dark under my eyelids swirl fantastic colors. A door opens and super-scared it-kid voices shriek— *Run! Run! Run!* — and a man's deep voice, *Who's on my lawn?*

Heavy arms — father arms — wrap around me, lift me, and carry me to the sky. It-kids yell over and over, *He's caught Jeremy on his lawn!*

Surrounded in Big Ben's cigarette smoke, I let my imagination make it into the smell of motor engines. He tells me it's all right. He's just playing with me.

His warmth, smell, voice, all around me. I remember now. I remember how it feels to have a living father.

SEPTEMBER

The money envelope comes again on September first. I don't bother to watch for it 'cause I assumed it wasn't coming and we'd be looking for a place to live in the Old Neighborhood.

With my stomach churning at the sight of Ida Lipshilts serving one of her jelly sandwiches, I hear the clink of the mailbox. When I find the envelope in the slot in the front hall closet with the words, *Loblolly Avenue loves the Rosenbergs*, I step out on the pinners porch and see Mrs. Jenner setting up a sprinkler for Skyler and Sally to run through. The water and the Jenner kids come onto my lawn. They must've gotten over things pretty quick. As I count the fifteen fives and two ones, I feel guilty about the things I said to Skyler Jenner and the things I started thinking about his family.

The end of summer has a smell to it, and the first day of school changes everything. It's just as warm and blue in the sky as yesterday, and the trees are still green and the flowers are still blooming. But when I breathe in, there's an expectation in the air, that I have to be in certain places at exact times, *or else*. There's no lying around anymore, no looking around, no thinking things can wait until tomorrow. This morning tells me I've wasted my summer away and it's time to get up.

Mom's up.

For the first time in months, she's making a real breakfast for us, wearing her gray skirt and matching jacket, her hair in beehive prison. Working at the stove quickly, her noises let us know she's late, cooking eggs, sunny side upside downside, she calls them. She manages not to break any yolks, and she's able to get them cooked enough so the egg whites bake white around the yolk, but the yolk remains runny and tasty for Wonder Bread slice dipping. Cheryl's already sitting at the kitchen table, tapping the heels of her saddle shoes against a metal chair leg. Pretty ratty looking, those shoes, for the first day of school, and her plain, powder blue dress is kinda wrinkled around the belt. Her hair's got a red ribbon in it wrapping around the start of a puffy, curly pony tail.

"Who's your homeroom teacher?" I say sitting next to her.

"Mrs. Gasser," she says.

"That's Gastert," I say. "Is she still teaching third grade?" Cheryl shrugs and grunts *uh-huh*. "She's pretty nice," I say. Cheryl dips a half slice of Wonder Bread into the middle of a broken yolk. The yellow leaps into the bread. She swirls it and sticks it in her mouth.

My bedroom door pounds open and David stomps into the kitchen wearing his Batman BVDs. He comes up to me and demands to know, "What did you do to my snore tape?" His eyes are all serious, like it's the end of the world.

"I didn't do anything to it," I say.

"How come Mookie's singing his *Stupid* song on it?"

I forgot about that. Mookie learned two new chords on his guitar. He showed them to me. C and D7 chords that went great with the G chord he already knew, and they sounded like a real rock and roll song all put together. He wanted to *cut* a record, so we used the old reel-to-reel recorder.

"I can't bring Mookie's *Stupid* song for show-and-tell!" David whines. I can't figure how that'd be any worse than letting the entire second grade listen to my snoring.

"It's impossible to eat with you in here," Cheryl says to David without looking up. "Could you leave, please?"

"Cheryl," Mom scolds.

"But I said *please*."

"He's got a right to be here as much as you do," Mom says, setting a plate of eggs down.

"Then I'm done. I can't eat in front of him." Cheryl pushes her chair back and David reaches over her plate. Sitting next to me, David starts finishing Cheryl's eggs. "Oh, how gross!" she says, stomping out.

"I don't know what I'm gonna do for show-and-tell now," David says. "School's ruined."

"These eggs are for you and David," Mom says to me. She's checking her clothes for cooking spots. "I've got to get going."

"Aren't you walking us to the bus stop for the first day of school?" David says. A tiny river of yolk dribbles from a corner of his mouth.

"I'm late. Missy Grossman will be here in about ten minutes to take you to her house until it's time to go to the bus stop."

Like a falling bomb, I whistle, "Missy Grossman . . ."

"Kablooey," David says.

"What's wrong with Missy Grossman?" Mom says. I tell her nothing's wrong, but I'm thinking it's like being with a scary witch who's gonna yell at any moment about things that don't even matter.

Mom leaves me with David in the kitchen. I can't remember if she kissed me before she left. It's just how things are. Mom drives off in the Bel-Air, with flower power stickers stuck on the doors, trunk, and hood, and the tuft of stuffing coming more and more out the back seat.

Except when Missy and Arnold Grossman aren't home and Charlie sneaks boys in to show us the magazines we're not supposed to see, Missy Grossman's house is like having Big Ben's forbidden lawn on the inside. Once we're in the door, there's a passage of white marble tile we're allowed to stand on, and we can go into the kitchen if we're polite, but not a step must be taken on the living room or dining room carpet. I stepped on it once years ago, and I can still remember Missy Grossman's shriek, *What're you doing?* — like I had pushed the destruct button on a Gemini space ship with the astronauts still inside it.

The living room and dining room are off-limits, the living room couches covered in clear plastic. "It's the untouchables room," Karl says. Sometimes he likes to break off a piece from a Frito and toss it under one of the plastic covered couches, just to do it. He says it's gone by the next morning, and his mom hisses at him, *Stop it, I know what you're doing.* "She's got dirt radar," Karl says.

With all three Rosenberg kids in her house, and Karl and Charlie, Missy Grossman looks more worried than she usually does. She's drinking coffee in the kitchen and eyeing us through the steam so we don't sneak out to the living room. My body feels clumsy, like my arm's gonna jerk out and knock over a lamp 'cause it knows Mrs. Grossman would kill me, so I think about it and think about it, and imagine doing it 'cause I know it's exactly the kinda thing Mrs. Grossman thinks kids want to do to her house.

"Why don't you kids go to the basement?" she says. "I'll be ready in ten minutes." We quickly go 'cause we don't want to stand there watching her watching us, and it's a big relief to get away.

In the basement, Charlie Grossman starts setting colored balls in the rack on a pool table that smells like cigarettes. David helps him. Cheryl makes her way to a wooden record album shelf built into the wood paneling. Like he's done it a hundred times, Karl's sizing up a pool stick.

The Grossmans' basement is like everybody else's living room, only better, with deep red and black shag carpeting and a fancy drinks bar that stretches half as long as the basement. Dark, wood-paneled walls, top to bottom, with lights built right into the ceiling tile, like they're ceiling tiles themselves. There's a color TV, bigger than the one upstairs, and it has its own built-in, wood-paneled cabinet.

Arnold Grossman's curly-haired head pokes over the top of the couch facing the TV. He's got some businessy papers on the coffee table, and he talks like W.C. Fields. "No tearing the felt," he says to Charlie aiming his cue stick. "Torn felt, one sorry *tuchas.*"

"Would you like a soda?" Karl says to me from behind the drink bar.

"You've got pop in the morning?"

"I've got Coke," Karl says putting up a Coke bottle, "Pepsi, Seven-up, Ginger Ale, Cream Soda . . ."

"Cream soda?" I say. That's like drinking candy.

"Sure. You can have it."

I listen for Mr. Grossman to say something about drinking pop before school and sorry *tuchases*, but he asks Karl to get a Cream Soda for him, too. I take my Cream Soda and lean over the drinks bar. There's a picture of Ernie Banks shaking Mr. Grossman's hand in front of some hospital. It's autographed. I notice it's not even hanging high enough to see unless you're leaning over the drinks bar like I am. If Skyler Jenner had something like that, he'd be wearing it around his neck.

"What do you do for a living, Mr. Grossman?" Cheryl says sitting next to him on the couch. He tilts his nose back and looks at her, squinting his eyes.

"Why, honey," he says. "Didn't anyone tell you? I'm a crook."

"You are?" Cheryl says, impressed. "Is that why you work at home?"

"That's right. And I'm a darn good crook, too."

"What do crooks do?"

"Different things." He puts his hand on her shoulder. "In my case, when someone goes out of business, I just take their stuff and sell it."

"Really," Cheryl says, looking at me as if scolding— why didn't *you* think of that? "So how're you doing being a crook?" Mr. Grossman laughs like a whole bunch of spit's gonna start flying out of his mouth.

"I'm doing good. Lots of people go out of business."

David shoots at a pool ball and bangs the back end of the stick against the wall. Mr. Grossman raises his head. "I don't care if you're not my kid. I'll take care of your *tuchas* just as easy as Charlie's." Mr. Grossman's smiling, but I guess crooks do that right before they might hurt someone.

From the landing at the top of the stairs comes a voice, like a dog whistle, that makes Charlie and Karl snap to attention. Its shrillness rattles them and makes Mr. Grossman roll his eyes. "Get up here and get going," Missy Grossman says. She's coming down the stairs, talking like an army general, *Now! Now!*

"Park your broom, you witch!" Mr. Grossman snaps at her. She ignores him and continues to call for us. We run to gather our book bags in a hurry.

"Ah, let them stay home. They'll learn more watching me be a crook."

"You just shut your mouth," Mrs. Grossman says, pointing her finger at Mr. Grossman.

I'm the last one up the stairs and I freeze on the landing. I have to see how this ends. Tilting my head around the corner of the landing wall, I see Mr. Grossman walking over to Mrs. Grossman, raising his hand like he might smack her one. But Missy Grossman's not moving. She's leaning her face forward like she's inviting him to just try to smack it. Mr. Grossman stands at the bottom, Mrs. Grossman on the first step, and he reaches his hand behind her and pulls her by the butt into him. He's squishing his fingers into her backside there, and he's kissing her, not like the Jenners with their snappy cheek-pecks. He moves his lips over hers, and they're smush-smushing them together.

And then I see somebody's tongue! — but I can't tell whose tongue 'cause their lips are all tangled up!

I turn and climb the stairs from the landing, real quiet so they don't hear me. Mrs. Grossman comes up from the basement, mean-looking as ever, and she hands me my Cream

Soda. "Don't forget this," she says. "Now let's get your sorry little *tuchases* out to the bus stop." I drink my Cream Soda along the way. It goes down like sweet caramel.

• • •

I don't think there's a more interesting place in the world than the seventh grade at Eisenhower K-8 in Skokie, Illinois. It's got nothing to do with the school itself. Not the teachers. Not the classes. It's the kids. In the gymnasium, seventh-grade boys athletics, Coach Slowick hands out a program schedule of softball, basketball, wrestling, and tumbling, and President Johnson's athletic achievement competition. I've got time to look around.

There's Jeff Schuber. He's the first one everybody notices. He's already got hair growing on his face and, as a bunch of us noticed in the locker room, quite a lot around his dickie thing, too, like he's a real man or something. I didn't look and stare, Jeff Schuber simply dropped his pants by a locker down the row from mine. He had to put on a jock strap like the rest of us, and I saw it, it was there, like a funny sign along the highway you can't help but look at, buried in a pile of curly hair. I turned away real quick so nobody would catch me watching.

Didn't see anything, at least not more than for a split second, and I didn't mean to look, I just noticed. A bunch of kids in my row of gym lockers noticed the same thing, looking, then looking away, just like me. They all had the same shocked frown on their faces, kinda worried about themselves. *What's wrong with me? When's my dickie thing gonna grow man hair? Probably never.* My jock, with its ridiculous straps crossing over my butt, sometimes slipping between my butt cheeks like a self-inflicted hinder-binder, has a lot of room left in the front pouch. I would've had a lot of questions for Dad about this one. I know I'm not gonna talk to Mom about it. I couldn't.

Then there's Jessie Fagan, as short as David, with bones

like a bird's and skin paler than white milk. Jessie's in the seventh grade, too, just like Jeff Schuber. Mookie's next to me telling me Jessie Fagan's jock strap wouldn't stay up and he had to wear his regular underwear with permission from Coach Slowick.

"First Jessie Fagan had to show Coach Slowick how the jock strap wouldn't stay up," Mookie says, " 'cause he's got no waist or butt, and hardly a dickie thing at all. His jock slid down to his ankles in front of everybody. Then Coach Slowick said he could wear the underwear." Mookie isn't laughing about it. He seems relieved it didn't happen to him.

I look at Jessie Fagan, then Jeff Schuber, and wonder how this is possible. Between them are the rest of us. We're like a piano keyboard, with its highest key far to the right squeaking like a mouse, and the key on the far left end thumping as deep as elephant farts. And the rest of the keys are a little higher or lower than the next one, but all on the same piano. We're all in the seventh grade. But we're also different from piano keys. The bigger kids kinda gather together— *We're the big kids, we'll go first at everything.* And the littler kids are collecting together, too— *We're the little kids, peep peep, we'll wait.* I'm kinda in the middle, skinny but not too skinny, and not short but not tall. Average. There's no group of averages gathering up. We kinda fill up the space between the littles and the bigs.

Coach Slowick wants us to line up between the basketball nets. A mass of purple shorts and matching Eisenhower K-8 sweatshirts stumbles about, looking like a bunch of grapes, our gym shoes squeaking along the wooden gym floor so polished up it's like looking into a mirror. There's a smell in this gym, like in the locker room, of new rubbery gym shoes and freshly opened gym clothes with their newly pressed, undamaged Eisenhower K-8 logos. It smells like a spilled chemical experiment and a little bit of Fritos mixed in.

"Tallest to the right," Coach Slowick calls out. "No, no, *your* right, *my* left. God almighty, let's start over. Tallest by the drinking fountain side. All right, move!"

Well, that's easy for Jeff Schuber and Jessie Fagan to figure out. I kinda wait to see what happens, and the boys look at each other's heads to see where they belong. One by one, the line forms, and I make my way toward the middle, between Mookie Waxberg and Karl Grossman.

"You!" Coach Slowick shouts. I raise my hand to my chest. He nods and wiggles his index finger for me to come forward. "Over there!" He points to his right, my left, away from the drinking fountain. He nods his head when I stand between Greg Stein and Jerry Goldfarb, about ten kids down from Mookie and Karl. *Littler than Mookie,* I'm thinking. Mookie's the wimpiest big kid on Loblolly Avenue, next to Bobby Kinder.

It's an interesting place, the seventh grade. We really are a lot like piano keys, and I've been placed toward the one end, to the short side of Mookie.

•   •   •

My name's being called over the school intercom system. Neat.

Melinda Levinberg watches me like I'm a big deal even though Jeff Schuber's sitting in the seat next to her. Most of the twenty-five kids here in Mrs. Gilbert's seventh-grade social studies class are looking at me, but I notice Melinda, with her hair as dark as a Hershey's chocolate bar, and long, down to her waist. She knows how to chew gum. She works it between her side teeth, smiling, the pink goo oozing out and making little popping noises, like blowing kisses at me.

Jeremy Rosenberg. Please come to the Principal's office!

Sounds serious and important, and Melinda's brown eyes gaze at me for a few seconds longer than an accidental glance.

"Jeremy," Mrs. Gilbert says. "Better get going and see what it's about." Melinda's giggling and Jeff Schuber's looking at me like this is so unusual— *Jeremy Rosenberg could never be in trouble. What's up with Jeremy? Maybe he's bad enough to hang out with the big kids, like a mascot.*

As I walk alone in the hallway, my footsteps echo off the gray block walls, reminding me of the echo-steps I hear in Grandmaland in the entranceway hall when we have our Friday night family get-togethers. The footstep echoes don't seem to end anywhere, they just keep going, fading down the long and shiny floors, but never disappearing completely. The echoes make me think of him, my father, hugging me, telling me it's all right— *You'll grow hair on your face, and down there, too, one day soon.* And here I am, a little to the small of average and no father to talk to about it, the dead father boy, the boy Bup Miller goes to, to find out what it's like to have a dead father.

The Principal's office is at the end of the hall and the echo footsteps come to meet me there.

"Jeremy?"

I turn, half expecting to see a miracle standing behind me.

"Mr. Rosenberg? Jeremy Rosenberg?"

Principal Newman looks at me over his small, round glasses hanging out on the tip of his nose. He's bald and rumpled-looking in his suit coat, and, in a nervous voice, he asks me to sit down.

"Hi, Jeremy," David squeaks from the office couch. He's bawling, but trying to smile, looking a little slumped and embarrassed.

"What's wrong?" I say.

Principal Newman says, "Sit down."

I sit on the far end of the couch from David. He looks at me and turns away.

"You shouldn't've recorded Mookie's *Stupid* song," David says with an odd, fake-sounding laugh. He shakes his head.

"What're you talking about?"

"If you'd just let it alone, I could've brought the snore tape to show-and-tell."

"There was no snoring on that tape, just hissing, and you know it."

"That's how you snore!" David cries. I deny it and he continues to laugh, like he wants to get angry, but he can't 'cause something must've happened to land him in the Principal's office.

Principal Newman drags his chair around his desk and sets it in front of the couch. "David," Principal Newman says, "what made you think there would be show-and-tell on the first day of school?"

When I hear Principal Newman ask that, I wish that I had thought to ask it. David shrugs and lowers his red face to his hands. Principal Newman reaches to his desk and pulls an envelope out from under a sheet of paper. The envelope is yellow and big enough to hold a school book report. It looks as wrinkled as Principal Newman's suit jacket, and it has an even crease down the middle.

I face David and demand, "Where'd you get that? That's Mom's!"

David shrinks himself up. Watching us over his glasses, Principal Newman opens the envelope and starts pulling out a paper, a newspaper page, then stops.

"I tried calling your mother at home first, Jeremy," Principal Newman says. His voice sounds fake-calm, like Dr. Singer saying, *This won't hurt a bit,* just before he gives me a booster shot. "I never got through."

"She works now, full time," I say. "Full time."

"I see," he says, sounding like he's disappointed in Mom. He shoves the paper back in the envelope. "I'd like to call her, Jeremy. It's important."

"Please don't call her. They've got rules there, and they get mad real easy." Wish my voice could sound tougher when I say, "I'm the man of the house. Let me be the man of the house."

Principal Newman looks at me like he's sizing me up for man-hair on my face, then slaps his palms on his knees. "As long as I have you here, David brought a newspaper article,

Jeremy. He read it out loud in second-grade math. He hasn't stopped crying since. It's from Atlanta."

I'm swallowing, trying to say something. I don't know what it is I want to say.

Principal Newman gets up from his chair. "I'm going to let you two have my office for ten minutes, or longer if you need it. You can be the man of the house, Mr. Rosenberg. Maybe that's best, I don't know. The school counselor isn't here today." He shakes his head a bit, like he doubts I will ever grow man hair, then leaves me with the battered envelope and David.

"Read it! Read it!" David says through his whimpering. He beams his eyes on the newspaper page I pull from Grandma Elaine's envelope. "Read it out loud, like for show-and-tell!"

The paper's a little yellow, but the photograph is clear enough to show Dad's truck flattened in front. I'm wondering how Dad could've fit in there and still be alive. I read for David, like for show-and-tell.

Yesterday, near midnight, a semi-truck driven by Alan Rosenberg, thirty-six, of Skokie, Illinois, crashed into the back end of an unknown vehicle on an unlit ramp off I-20 west of Atlanta. Mr. Rosenberg's cab was crushed on impact. Police speculate that another large truck had stopped on the ramp and failed to set up warning signals or flares. The debris indicates this second vehicle departed the scene after impact. Police found Mr. Rosenberg in his cab, unconscious and not expected to survive due to severe trauma and blood loss. At last report, he has been hospitalized in intensive care. His condition is listed as critical.

"Keep going!" David says. "More! More!"

Authorities could not notify the family for several hours as Mr. Rosenberg's wallet was found in the

grass several yards away from the collision. His
money and most of his identification were apparently
taken at the scene, making initial identification of
Mr. Rosenberg difficult.

"Who did this?" David bawls. He stands up and waves
his fist at the paper. "Who could've seen Dad like that and
stolen his money and not help him?" His face looks like all
his blood's flowing through it at once and his eyes narrow to
slits as he repeats, *Who?*

"Did you sneak this out of Mom's purse?"

"Her closet," David says. He sits down, breathing heavy.
"I don't know why I read it for show-and-tell. I don't know."

I see black splotches stained through the paper and I turn
it over. In a yellow-white space beneath a shoe ad, there's
writing, a telephone number it looks like, but with an area
code in front I've never seen before, and Grandma Elaine's
handwriting— *Grace, you need to call this number and find
out.*

David looks like he's had it. Wiped out, beaten up, ready
to fall off the couch. I don't say anything, I just sit next to
him, this time real close, and hug him. First time in my life
without being told I had to. I stay that way with him until his
tears finally stop. This is what Dad would've done, and I'm
the new man of the house, for real, I'm thinking, man hair or
not. I don't hear footsteps. I hear, and I feel, David's heart
beat near mine.

•   •   •

I sneak the newspaper page and envelope back into
Mom's closet as soon as I get home from school. Principal
Newman said he assumes I will show it to my mother. I'm
having none of that. Mom might order David to our bedroom for the rest of his life, and I couldn't stand that for
long. David shows me where he got it, underneath three can-
isters holding home-made movies of Dad's motorcycle races.

"Stop sneaking into people's stuff, my stuff, Cheryl's stuff, and especially Mom's stuff," I say, and David nods like he means to never do it again. That's doubtful. He likes exploring, like he can't help himself. I guess he doesn't mean anything by it.

But before I return the page, I copy the telephone number on the inside cover of my social studies notebook.

David promises not to say anything about what happened at school even if Principal Newman calls. I'm a little worried about Cheryl, though, 'cause she's teeth-grinding mad at David for crying in front of his whole class. Cheryl's in the third grade so she didn't see it, and she didn't hear about any newspaper page. Word just got out that David cried in front of everybody in second-grade math. That news, of course, made it to Cheryl's ears faster than lightning.

"I could kill him," Cheryl says to Mom. Even as tired as Mom is when she gets home from work, Cheryl's ranting upsets her. Mom threatens to get the wooden spoon and use it for real, and Cheryl says, "Go ahead, see if I care. It won't change how I feel— I smell him! I swear I can!" And there's David, in the hall, peeking his head around the dining room entrance. He darts back and slams our bedroom door shut.

Mom orders Cheryl to her room for the rest of the night, no more TV. "Good!" Cheryl shoots back. Cheryl slides her saddle shoes across the dining room floor, skating, and the noise scratches like sandpaper.

"I don't know what to do," Mom says to me. "Maybe she needs to see a professional."

Mom sounds as though she's confessing she isn't able to be a mom, or a mom and a dad at the same time. That's what she has to be, I guess. I ask Mom to watch the rest of *Star Trek* with me, and then I'd be willing to watch *That Girl* with her, 'cause she knows I wouldn't ordinarily watch *That Girl*, not in a million years. So I'm thinking, please, just don't go to sleep early tonight, Mom, please! I'll watch *That Girl* with you.

Mom pats the couch next to her and drops her high heel work shoes on the floor. We finish watching some teenage boy named Charlie Evans take over the Enterprise and fly it just by thinking, and then *That Girl*. Ann Marie's not nearly as pretty as Laura Petrie, and Donald Hollinger doesn't dance or do anything, he just wears a tie all day and looks shocked at everything Ann Marie does.

Mom doesn't make it to the end. She lowers her head on mine until the news comes on, then wakes with a jolt, telling me to go to bed. Through the office and typewriter smells sticking to her suit, and the stinky feet smell from her high heel shoes, if I try hard enough, I can find a little of the way Mom used to smell when we used to watch TV together all the time.

•   •   •

Once I go to bed, I fall asleep right away, but I wake up in less than an hour. I kinda will it to happen. I planned it when I went to sleep, like setting an alarm clock in my head.

My eyes are used to the dark now, and I see David's got his covers pulled off again, lying on his stomach, his BVDs a little puffy like they blew up from a fart. There's that reel-to-reel recorder beside his bed, ready for him to set by me when his own head alarm goes off. Especially after what happened today, I wonder why he does it.

Sneaking from my bedroom, down the hall toward Cheryl's room, I hear Mom's little black and white TV going, but I know I'm not gonna wake her, not even if I drop a Kennedy half dollar on the floor. I open Mom's door a bit and see the light from the TV set on the stand reflecting off her face. With her eyes closed and mouth open a little, the TV's light and shadows flicker grayish shades and make her head appear as if it were floating through storm clouds. I close her door and wait there, thinking about the image— Mom, flying through TV clouds, asleep.

At Cheryl's room, I see a half-inch stripe of faint light along the space between the floor and the bottom of the door. Cheryl's saying something, but I can't hear what.

Standing there, I wait. I don't know what for. I used to go in
her room all the time. She's got photographs from magazines
taped all over her walls— The Beatles, Tommy Roe, Tommy
James, Donovan, Lovin' Spoonful, The Association, The
Beach Boys, Herman's Hermits— all these rock bands all
over her walls. I asked her maybe a year ago, "Where're the
Rolling Stones?"

"The Rolling Stones look like the bogeyman," she told
me. "All of them."

"Who's your favorite band?"

She looked at her walls. "I don't know. But I'm thinking
about taking Herman's Hermits down 'cause they're like
bogeymen, too, when you get a good look at them."

I asked her, "How do you sleep in here with all these pictures watching you?"

"I watch them, they don't watch me. They're only pictures. And they only *look* like bogeymen."

The way she said that, her stare and calm voice, made me
feel a little stupid for even asking, like she was past make-
believe and maybe I wasn't.

As I stand at Cheryl's door, she begins to talk like she's
humming. Her sounds make me feel kinda creepy. *Psst, psst,*
Cheryl's mumbling voice comes faintly through the door,
sharing secrets with ghosts. I lean my head forward and the
wood beneath my feet groans a little. Cheryl calls softly, but
louder than her ghost-talk— *Daddy?*

I straighten and look at the door, knowing the door's
being stared at from the inside. Frozen, the air around me
has been shot full of Novocaine, and I'm numb inside it,
waiting for something to happen, afraid to breathe. I'm
afraid as I stand here that I can't deal with my sister. She
doesn't believe in make-believe, but she talks to ghosts and
calls out for Dad.

The last memory of my father, his blood on Mom's pajamas, burns in my head. I doubt it will ever leave me. It's a
final nightmare to every good thought I have of him.

Three days before he died, Dad came home from Michael

Reese Hospital, the rest of his body cast taken off, learning to walk again using a metal walker. We had him home, and not like those months with him in his body cast, like a doll stuck in a box, lying on a cot in the living room as if our house were a hospital. Then that morning, Mom screaming like her mind was leaving her body, and I run, and there's Cheryl by Dad's head. He was belly down on his half of the bed, his face to the side toward Cheryl. Dad was still, and blood poured from his ears and mouth. David came in running behind me. I thought then how Mookie's dog got hit by a car the summer before, and the animal jerked his limbs like he might still be alive, and Missy Grossman said, *The dog's dead, he's just convulsing.* Dad started convulsing, and Mom stood up on the bed screaming, screaming, *Get David and Cheryl out of here, now!*

Cheryl stood so close to his face, a foot maybe, and she stayed there, saying nothing, doing nothing, just kinda leaning toward him, looking, her pupils so wide and black even in the morning sun pouring through the window. As I grabbed her hand I saw Dad's eyes were open, the top one a little more than the bottom one. That's what Cheryl had been watching, Dad's blue eyes not recognizing her anymore. She was cold and silent when I walked her out of Mom and Dad's bedroom, like she had stopped breathing. Her pupils closed to pinpoints, maybe to keep what she had seen from ever coming out of her head, and that she didn't want to see any more.

The sunburst clock's skinny second hand moved to the fat minute hand, eight a.m., exactly, May 31, 1966. And Mom said after the ambulance left, "His heart stopped, and he died."

Cheryl saw the same thing I did. We were not supposed to see such things. When we did, we were thrown into a whole different world. We're kids, but we can't be kids anymore. We saw too much, too soon. I guess it isn't strange at all hearing Cheryl call for Dad, even if she doesn't believe in make-believe. I've done it, 'cause I've hoped it wasn't make-believe.

My body feels like it can move again, but I don't want to go in Cheryl's room anymore. I have the same questions for her, but it probably isn't right for a twelve-year-old brother to be asking. Like Mom said, she needs a professional. We all probably do.

Before I walk away, I wait to hear if Cheryl says anything more, but she doesn't. The stripe of light under her door goes out and it's just black standing there outside her room. I walk down the hall, hearing TV voices whispering out Mom's bedroom, laughing whispers. This house is full of whispers. I whisper to myself, inside-my-own-head whispers, telling me things about death, and dead fathers, and the crazy Rosenbergs, and, finally, the loudest thought, Bup Miller's dominos, Dad's first domino.

My social studies notebook is piled on top of my school textbooks on the kitchen table. In the dark, light from the Ellerson Street lamp sneaks through tree leaves and curtains to land on the kitchen floor, moving pale light and shadows in front of me as I reach for the notebook. I raise it and hold it under my arm. Stopping at the kitchen telephone sitting black on the counter, its plastic dial rotor looking like an open eye, I unplug the wall cord and take the phone down to the basement landing with me, closing the kitchen door, the cord trailing behind.

The basement light switch at the top of the stairs is hard to find in the dark. As I hear the banging noises from the furnace, my insides start to flutter. Sometime when I was David's age, Dad finally convinced me that the furnace wasn't the gateway to hell, that gargoyles like the ones from *Johnny Quest* were not climbing the staircase from hell to our basement. It was just metal expanding and contracting to the heat and cold. The noises were not gargoyle footsteps.

Switching on the light makes these thoughts disappear. I'm embarrassed that I've even thought of that memory.

The basement is cold and has some water stains on the cement floor from when our sewage drain backed up last fall. There's a wood frame, wall studs, Dad called them, looking like a cage around the furnace and water meter and the rest of the basement. It was the beginning of a finished basement Dad started to build with Big Ben the spring before the accident, and there's a wire coming down one of the studs connecting to a phone socket. I slip the phone plug into the socket and sit down, feeling the cement's cold working in through my BVDs.

With my social studies notebook open on my lap, I find the telephone number Grandma Elaine wrote on the newspaper page, and dial. The rings sound heavy coming out of the ear piece and they make *ka-thunk* noises between each one.

"Good evening, I mean good morning, Atlanta police, can I help you?"

I don't know what to say so I say nothing and hang up.

On the top basement stair, there's David, sitting in his BVDs, his little boy belly sticking out like a toy drum. The kid's a snooping spy and he walks as quiet as the bugs he keeps saving. He's looking at me, smiling, like there's a light bulb in his head shining through his teeth. He asks me simple enough, "Are you trying to find out who made Dad die?"

"I guess I am," I say.

David keeps smiling, popping his opinion out like a small firecracker, "Good!"

October

There isn't anything meaner to a kid's day than having to get up early, I mean no later than seven, out the door by eight-thirty, paying attention in school for six hours, collecting homework assignments in every class and going home on a bus with Christian boys talking about playing football after school. I know I still have Hebrew school for two more hours, collecting homework assignments in a language that reads from right to left. I get confused between American school and Hebrew school just remembering which end of the book is the front cover. When am I supposed to study for my Eisenhower K-8 classes? When am I supposed to study my Hebrew school lessons? When can I play ball? Every three years, there are more months in a Jewish lunar calendar than the regular American calendar. Maybe that's the problem I'm having, fitting in doing my Jewish stuff *and* my American stuff in different calendars. There just isn't time for it all.

On the bus this morning, Bobby Kinder sits between David and me. "Three to a seat!" the bus driver shouts, which is all right if you're sitting with the littler kids. David's little and Bobby Kinder is a wimpy bigger kid, as wimpy as Mookie, and I'm to the small side of Mookie, according to Coach Slowick. So we fit, Bobby, David and me, three to a seat. David's whining about his first day of his first year of Hebrew school starting after American school today.

"You Christians are such lucks," David says. "You only have to go to church once every Sunday. From October to June now, I've got to go to Hebrew school three times a week!"

Bobby Kinder's wearing his white shirt and black pants. It was his uniform for Catholic school at St. Peter's, but his family couldn't afford both Kelly Kinder's first year at the University of Chicago and his school at St. Peter's. Now Bobby's going to Eisenhower K-8, sixth grade, so Kelly can afford to live in her college dormitory. Bobby wears that outfit every day, black and white like the TV shows they're not making anymore. Last month, I secretly dashed a blue ink Flair mark on his white shirt at his elbow to make sure he was changing shirts and not wearing the same clothes over and over. It took a week to see that little Flair mark again, a little faded. I imagine Bobby's got five white shirts and five black pants in his closet, refiling them at the end of the line after every school day. He's tidy— *Immaculate,* Bobby said once about himself, and he laughed at that and looked out for lightning bolts and wondered why I didn't do the same thing.

"I've got to go to catechism class as well as church," Bobby says.

"What's that?" I ask.

"Every Sunday, I sit in religious school for three more hours after church."

"Big deal, you're there anyway," David says, emphasizing how easy Bobby has it. "That certainly beats three times a week!"

"What's 'catechism' mean?" I ask.

"Yeah," David says. "Sounds like something you fall into and can't get out of."

"We learn about Jesus and stuff and the New Testament."

"What's the New Testament?" David says.

"It's the Bible. The second Bible. It came out right after

Jesus died for our sins. It replaces the old Bible."

"What sins did we do that Jesus had to die for?" I ask.

Bobby thinks for a moment, scratching his thick tangled hair. "I don't know. They call it original sin, like we all got it when we're born. I guess that's why I've got to keep going to catechism class."

"How's it original if we all got it?" David asks.

Bobby shrugs.

David says, "We just had Yum Kipper— that's like three hours long all by itself."

"Yom Kippur," I say, correcting David.

"What's that?" Bobby Kinder says.

I say, "It's like a contest to see how long we can sit in our chairs listening to Hebrew without passing out."

"Why do you go then?" Bobby asks.

I answer, "We have to or else if we die, we die with God writing down a whole page of our bad deeds without being forgiven."

"What kinda bad deeds get forgiven?" Bobby says.

"I don't know," I say. "Everyday things like lying or swearing or cheating on school tests. Regular stuff, I guess different from original stuff."

"We've got to do that every Sunday," Bobby says, looking at David. "I've got it just as hard as you do."

"I guess original sin is harder to get forgiven than regular stuff," I say.

David and Bobby nod their heads.

"Does Jesus have a last name?" David says.

Bobby says, "None I've ever heard of. Sometimes I'm told he's Jesus of Nazareth, but that's where he's from, like Jeremy of Skokie. But I don't think he's got a last name."

"Just like Donovan," I say.

"So is Jesus God's helper?" David asks, "like Robin is to Batman?"

"Not at all. He's God, too. He's God's son and He's God, that's what I'm taught."

"That's weird," David says. "A disguise? Why would God

have to do that?"

"I guess so he doesn't scare anybody," Bobby says. "So he can walk with us and be like us and be God all at the same time."

"Maybe it's like when Superman touches red kryptonite," David says. "He doesn't start dying like from green kryptonite, but he does weird things, like splitting into two Supermen. But when that happens, usually one of the Supermen is all mean and starts causing trouble, and the other one's all good but is too much of a pansy to do anything."

"Jesus is all good," Bobby insists, "and he isn't a pansy."

David starts talking like a teacher, all serious, with his mouth and eyebrows scrunched down. "God knows everything and sees everything, and is everywhere all the time, even when you're taking a bath, but that's no big deal 'cause it's God and He can see us with no clothes on anyway. He's got a right to be checking up on us all the time, even when we're doing business in the bathroom."

I laugh at David but he keeps wearing his I'm-serious look. "Where do you get that stuff?" I say.

"From Dahveed!" David says. And for proof he adds, "Dahveed's been going to synagogue since he was three!"

"Christ!" Bobby says slapping his forehead. "That's Jesus' last name. I can't believe I forgot."

"Maybe if you went to catechism three times a week, you'd remember better," David says.

"God can't know everything all the time," I say. "If God did, seems to me He would've known about the second Bible when He was making the first. Why would there be a need for God to make a second bible if He knows everything all the time?" That sounds pretty smart, I'm thinking. It's got David and Bobby looking like how people do when they're asked, *Where does outer space end?* And they answer and you say, *But what about on the other side of that?*

"Faith," Bobby Kinder says. "When you don't have an answer to a question, you have faith. That's what I know."

Saying *faith* seems to untwist Bobby Kinder's face, like he has the answer to things, and if he doesn't know something, then at least he knows for certain that there's an answer out there, and he'll be told about it some day in catechism class. I like hearing about being Christian from Bobby 'cause I didn't feel any answers from God at Yom Kippur service about why Dad had to die. I asked a lot of questions like that last Yom Kippur, and that's when God is supposed to be really paying attention. I got nothing. But I don't hear anything or feel anything from what Bobby says either. I don't feel *faith* on this school bus even though, as Dahveed has told David, God is supposed to be everywhere all the time.

Skyler Jenner thinks there is no God 'cause the Cubs couldn't even win sixty games this year. Grandpa Erwin thinks there is a God for the same reason. I think it's 'cause the Cubs just stink whether there is a God or not.

•   •   •

Arnold Grossman drives us to the first day of Hebrew school in his Buick Riviera, which I think looks better than any Cadillac. Mr. Grossman likes to try to shock us by talking to us about sex, so we get our sex education on the way to Hebrew school. Mom leaves out some stuff for me to read written by a lady named Ann Landers. She's got a regular column in the Chicago Sun-Times, advising people about life. I've never seen anything serious about sex in her column so I don't pay her much attention, except for maybe her picture. She's got a hair-do flip that nobody, not even Laura Petrie herself, can compete with. It's like the dive and rise on the roller coasters at Riverview, and so pointy, like a weapon. She's got a book called *Necking and Petting, by Ann Landers*, and it's full of figure drawings, colored in drab green, having sex, I think, but it's hard to tell with figure drawings. Mom leaves that stuff out for me to read, but I've got no use for it. They don't come even close to Mr. Grossman's magazines. Those give me a real Mr. Stiffy. Figure drawings colored in drab green don't give me no feeling at all.

Mr. Grossman must not know that we sneak into his room and look at his magazines or he wouldn't bother with the sex education talk on the way to the Skokie Jewish Congregation. In the years he's driven me, his talk has only shocked me twice. Once when Karl asked, "But what if you pee in the woman?"— and Mr. Grossman said that's kinda what's supposed to happen. That shocked me and bothered me for a while, and I still haven't been able to figure it out. The other time is during the drive today. I ask him about what *tuchas* means, and he laughs. I hear it all the time, whether someone is real religious or not. Even the Christian parents like to say it.

"It's a real good word," Mr. Grossman says. He then says *tuchas* slowly, growling spit at the *ch* like his mouth is full of chewed food. Then he rattles off, "It means tush, rear end, derriere. It's what you yell at your friends, and when a woman has a good one, hold on to it!"

"Why do you yell *tuchas* at Mrs. Grossman, real loud like you're mad?"

"It's because I love her, with *tuchas* passion! I love her madly, so I yell at her madly, *Get your tuchas over here!*— because I want to grab hold and never let go."

"I don't hear Mr. and Mrs. Jenner saying that to each other," I point out, figuring they've got the best *tuchas* passion on the block. "They just hold hands a lot."

"The Jenners, *ahch!*" Well, I certainly understand from Grandpa Erwin what Mr. Grossman means with *ahch*. "Those Jenners don't have passion. You think holding hands and kissing air around each other's face is passion? *Tuchas* is passion. It's a wonder those Jenners have any kids at all." Mr. Grossman winks at me. "Your father had passion. Your mother had passion. They had three knock-down drag-out shouting matches, and after each one your mother had a kid nine months later."

It's nice to hear people say good things about Dad, especially when they're saying it 'cause they mean it. Honestly, I

don't remember Mom and Dad having arguments, except
one about buying a movie projector, and a big one about
Dad's semi-truck rig, or in particular when Dad was home in
his body cast, and Missy Grossman kept coming over to
sweep up under him and his cot in the living room. Dad let
Mom know that bothered him.

Maybe I shouldn't think bad things about Missy
Grossman. She's got a good *tuchas*, one that Mr. Grossman
likes to grab on to. Mrs. Jenner's got a nice *tuchas* too, nicer,
I think, than any of the other moms on the block. But Mr.
Jenner doesn't seem to want to grab hold of it, at least he
never says so, and has never done it in front of anyone I
know. Maybe there's something more to having a good
tuchas than the good *tuchas* itself.

We don't get much of a sex education talk on the drive
over this time. David sits in the back seat with me, and even
Mr. Grossman knows enough to break a little kid in real
slow. Karl and Charlie Grossman go with, of course, 'cause
we're all members of the Skokie Jewish Congregation and
have to be there on the same day and time, even if we're all
in different classes. The Waxbergs go to a synagogue I can
never get straight 'cause it sounds like *Banana*. Banana
Moon-ah. I know that's not right, but it's close. That's where
the Waxbergs and Jenners go. There are others in Skokie, like
Temple Judeah, and they're all called conservative and
reformed Hebrew schools, which means they're not
Orthodox. At Orthodox Hebrew schools, Mookie told me
once, the kids can't speak English, only Hebrew, when class
starts, and the girls have to sit in back behind a veil. Mom's
having none of that. "The goal is to get bar mitzvahed," she
said, "and become a man. You don't become a man by learning how to put the women in the back."

So David and I go to reform Hebrew school three times
a week at the Skokie Jewish Congregation, where the girls sit
anywhere they want. A lot of Jewish girls don't have to go to
Hebrew school at all, that's just something certain families
don't believe they should do. I suppose Mom believes it's

impossible. It would be something to see Mom try to make Cheryl go to more school after American school. "That would cut into my after-school fun," Cheryl once said about Hebrew school, and that worked in ways David and I could never get away with 'cause we're Jewish boys in Skokie, so we have no choice about it.

"But think how she would ruin our little talks," Mr. Grossman said when I first complained about this unfair situation. "Besides, that's just the way it is."

David said it best— "Cheryl's such a luck."

Mom's making Cheryl go to the professional counselor at Eisenhower K-8, once a week, until something can be figured out about her bad behavior. "That cuts into my during-school fun," Cheryl moaned at first, but Mom is determined that Cheryl has to go see Dr. Bondurant. Cheryl meets with Dr. Bondurant during regular school for a half-hour or more, and never during lunch, recess, or gym class. David says that for beating him up and acting weird, Cheryl gets to miss math or science or social studies once a week. "If she's not the luckiest luck," he whined to me the night before his first day of Hebrew school, "I don't know who is."

In Hebrew school, in Mr. Trauby's class, I'm thinking about Mr. Grossman's magazines and *tuchas* passion, and all that, and Melinda Levinberg's sitting right next to me. I smell some sort of perfume on her.

"You just don't become a bar mitzvah and say you're Jewish— you need to deserve to be Jewish," Mr Trauby's saying, but it's just blah blah to me through all my sex thoughts, and Melinda sitting there with the air throbbing around her.

Melinda's kicking at me with the side of her foot. It makes me smile. She says my name real quiet, but then so does Mr. Trauby, only he's talking to me real loud.

"Mr. Rosenberg. Can you repeat anything I've just said?"

I swallow, feeling the stares of fifteen other kids, especially Melinda's. Then I remember. I say, "We need to deserve to be Jewish," and I can feel all those stares returning to Mr. Trauby.

"But why?" he adds. "What did I say about why that is so?" Those stares are on me again. I freeze and smile like I would at a joke.

"Mr. Rosenberg, we're not just Jewish because we're born that way. We also have to keep the Jewish faith alive and understood. We must keep it from becoming something else other than our belief in God and family and respect. Do you understand, Mr. Rosenberg? Do you understand about keeping your faith alive?"

Mr. Trauby's sitting at his desk, watching me with serious eyes through glass lenses almost as thick as Grandma Elaine's. He's wearing a brown suit, brown shirt, and a darker brown tie. His hair is dark, his skin is tanned-looking, his eyeglass frames are black, but he's got a smile like a car grille, and it's whiter than sunshine on snow. As I hesitate, Mr. Trauby's smile begins to fade and turn into a frown. I could fake an answer. A *yes* might do. But that word, that *faith*, I just have no feeling about it.

"It's six-thirty, Mr. Trauby," I say, and I make the class laugh. Melinda's smiling at me, but I also see Mr. Trauby's face showing overwhelming sadness at my answer as the kids pack up their books to leave for home. I've disappointed him, I can feel it watching him sit a little shorter behind his desk.

"I'm sorry," I say real soft, but I doubt he hears me.

I wait for David to meet me at the planned spot when his class is over, in the library, where Rabbi Abrahms serves us Tam Tam crackers and fruit punch ten minutes before class starts. I don't know where Rabbi Abrahms gets those Tam Tams, they're really good. I can eat a whole bunch more than I do, but we're allowed only three crackers and two Dixie cups of juice each. David stuffed his three crackers in his mouth at once and chewed until he made a pocket of mush bulging at his cheek. "I love taking little sips of the juice," he mumbled, "and then I let go of the cracker mush just a little bit at a time with the juice still in my mouth. Then I swallow and do it all over again." He demonstrated this for me, slow-

ly shrinking the mush bulge in his cheek as he took small sips
of fruit punch. "It works good with orange juice, too." For
this, I knew, Cheryl would pound him right in the synagogue.
It's safer for David that she doesn't go to Hebrew school.

"How much time we got?" David says darting into the
library.

"Maybe five or ten minutes. Mr. Grossman's always that
late picking us up."

"So where's the telephone?"

David's anxious, bouncing around as if he's got to go to
the bathroom. He denies it and tells me to hurry up already.
The telephone's always been in here somewhere, sitting on
one of the tables. But they had our books on the tables for
the first day of Hebrew school, so it's not there. We look
around the library. David goes to the podium where Rabbi
Abrahms serves us the Tam Tam crackers and fruit punch.

"Is it a yellow phone?" David says.

"I think so," I say walking to the podium. I take the
cracker box out of David's hand and remove the phone sitting on a shelf built halfway up the podium.

"If this operation's gonna work," I say, "we have to be
quick about it."

I place the yellow telephone on the podium and find the
phone socket along the wall behind it. David's got his hands
together like he's about to pray, and then he cracks his
knuckles, making pops as soft as soap bubbles bursting. I
remove the piece of paper from my pocket, study it a
moment, and dial. The ring starts *ka-thunking*.

A woman answers, "Good evening, Atlanta Police, can I
help you?"

"Yes," I say trying to make my voice sound deep. David
nods at me like I'm doing a good job. "I'm from the Skokie
Police Department. That's Skokie, Illinois. I need some information involving a truck driven by Mr. Alan Rosenberg." My
mouth goes dry saying Dad's name like he's not my dad. I
keep going. "It's from October 9, 1965. A real bad accident."

"Who is this?" the woman says.

"I'm from the Skokie Police ..."

"But what's your name?" The woman sounds like she's trying hard not to laugh.

"Detective ... detective ..."

"Oh, little boy! Why don't you make a name up?" The laughing comes out the receiver sounding no different from the chipmunk peeps squawking out a *Flintstones* telephone.

"What's wrong?" David says as I hang up.

I think to myself, *What's wrong?* The words bang around in my head. What's wrong is that I'm smaller than Mookie, I'm not Jeff Schuber, I'm way down the line on the Eisenhower K-8 seventh-grade piano keyboard. My voice is still a little boy's voice.

"She's not believing I'm a detective," I say.

"You just don't know how to lie good," David says. He whispers really quick, "And maybe we shouldn't be lying in Hebrew school anyway. We should do this in the basement at home."

"If Mom gets a big phone bill from Atlanta, she'll start figuring things out."

"We need a good liar," David says scrunching his face up in little-boy thought. His eyes light up. "Bup Miller!" he announces the way a magician says *ta-dum!* after a trick. "Bup Miller would be perfect!"

I sneer at David and tell him he's being ridiculous, it's a reaction I have whenever David gets any kinda idea. I have to admit, though, that nobody lies better than Bup Miller.

"Bup can convince them he's a detective. They'll talk to him."

"How will we get him to Hebrew school? This is the only telephone I know about that we can sneak these calls from."

"Doesn't Bup go to Hebrew school?"

"I don't think he does."

"Isn't he Jewish?"

"Yeah, but I think he just doesn't go."

"You can sneak him in, Jeremy. We can pretend he goes here. He's the best liar in the world, you know."

Bup Miller's the only one I've said anything real personal to about Dad. Nobody else has said anything about what I told Bup on my garage roof, so I guess he's kept his mouth shut about it. Maybe his dad is dying for real. If anyone could understand why we're calling the Atlanta police and can lie real good in a Hebrew school, it's Bup Miller.

I pat David on top of his head. Man, is he smiling at me.

"There you are," a man's voice says both angry and funny at the same time. Mr. Grossman uses his W.C. Fields voice, "Get your *tuchases* out to the car!"

"Tell us more about *tuchas* passion," David says, skipping out of the library.

I'm thinking maybe David and I are the lucks, not Cheryl, with the things we learn and do going to Hebrew school.

•   •   •

Bup Miller's house, sitting on the corner of Ellerson and Loblolly, looks like it doesn't belong on the block. It's shaped like the other houses, but shrunk down a bit, a smaller box of bricks. And the bricks are almost pink. Not pink enough to say, *Hey, Bup Miller lives in a pink house,* but close enough to wonder, *Is Bup Miller's house pink?* Anyone seeing Bup Miller's house for the first time, and all the times after, would look at it and wonder about that. It makes the Millers a bit odd even before you meet them.

Until four years ago, the Switzers had lived there with their three kids, and they'd come out to serve us lemonade all summer long for free. Mrs. Switzer, all blond without a black cartoon outline around her head like Mrs. Jenner's, had her hair up and wore shorts, T-shirts, and gym shoes like she was about to do some sports. She baby-sat for us when Mom had to work at the animal hospital three mornings a week, and she hugged David, Cheryl and me a lot, and sat us with her kids in her kitchen like we were all one big family. I can't remember Mr. Switzer too well, just that he was tall and had dark hair like Rob Petrie's, and that he was married to Mrs.

Switzer. He had some important job to go to and eventually made so much money that he said all excited to Mrs. Switzer one morning, "Corrine, we're moving to Northbrook!"

Northbrook, woo!— that's what I thought, even though I didn't have any idea where Northbrook was. But it sounded like water way up north, real exotic. Big Ben and Arnold Grossman both said *woo*, but in their own way, and seemed impressed about this Northbrook— "Lots of two-story houses with attached two-car garages," Big Ben said like he was describing heaven. Even Mr. Waxberg was impressed, like going to Northbrook might almost be as good as going to Israel to live. Nobody wanted the Switzers to leave, but who could blame them, living in that small, almost-pink house?

The Millers kinda snuck into the neighborhood, arriving late at night with a big truck, and then all moved in by morning. We only got to see them in bits and pieces at first. Mr. Miller was fat from the beginning, fatter by far than any other father on the block. He had the last remaining strands of his hair slicked back like he had taken sweat from his face and rubbed them up and over his forehead.

Skyler Jenner right away started telling us that Mr. Miller was a garbageman, that's why he stunk so much. We all thought Skyler Jenner would know 'cause the Millers' house was right next to the south side of his. "Real glad we don't have any doors on that side," Skyler Jenner said. I laughed with the other kids when Skyler Jenner said that, and I hadn't ever met Mr. Miller before then. But I took it to mean it was good to have a door facing my house. I did see Mr. Miller leave his house many mornings in dark pants, white shirt, and a tie. Didn't look like garbageman clothes to me. "He works for the Northbrook Garbage Company," Skyler Jenner said, still so sure about it. "He picks up the Switzers' garbage, and you have to wear a tie when you're a garbageman in Northbrook."

Mrs. Miller does look like a scarecrow, just like Bup had said on my garage roof, not much different from the one in the *Wizard of Oz*, which is the only scarecrow I've seen. Her hair is short, straight, and thick, and the color of straw. It's broom-bristly looking and comes down like a cone cap on her head. She's so wiry and skinny and about a foot taller than Mr. Miller. She has a large nose and Skyler Jenner told us why.

"'Cause air is free!"

He told me that one with his dad standing next to him, and I caught Mr. Jenner smiling out the corner of his pipe. "Did I say it right, Dad?" Skyler Jenner said. Mr. Jenner nodded and placed his hand on Skyler's shoulder. I learned then for certain that it was right to make fun of the Millers. They deserved it for not looking anything like the Switzers.

I realize as David and I ignore the Saturday morning cartoons and head out to Bup Miller's house that I'm gonna be asking Bup for help. *How dare you think you have the right to ask Bup Miller for help, help to find your father's killer, no less?*— it seems now that everything I've said and thought about the Millers over the last four years has come crawling back into my body, collecting in my throat to make me choke. My father was a truck driver, Big Ben messes with electricity, Mr. Waxberg manages a department store, Arnold Grossman's a crook. How much different is being a garbageman from any of that, if Mr. Miller really is a garbageman?

"What're you going to say to Bup?" David says as we pass the Jenners' house. The leaves on the Jenners' tree were the first to get yellow and fall. They spread over the ground, making a circle that reaches to my lawn and the Millers' lawn.

"I'm not sure," I say. I'm thinking I'd like to apologize for everything, but it'd sound like I'm only doing that to get a favor, which I know is exactly what I'm doing.

David and I turn down the Millers' sidewalk leading to their door. We kinda have to step off the walk to make our way around some bushes growing wide. There's a cement step up, one step, and a cement landing outside their door. The metal screen door is silver and a little off so it's not closing all the way. When I knock, it's like shaking a rattle. I hear the inner wood door being tugged at, and then it opens with a whoosh of air. I smell Cheerios in milk.

"Yes?"

That's all Mr. Miller says. I'm sure he wasn't expecting us, or anybody, and looks suspiciously at us, like we might do something mean 'cause he's a Miller and Halloween's real close. The kitchen is dark behind him and he's standing with the door only halfway open.

"Is Bup home?" David says. "We'd like to play with him today."

Mr. Miller's blinking kinda fast, like he's been blind and can see for the first time in his life. David repeats himself, "Really, can we play with Bup today?"

Mr. Miller opens the door to let us in. He's wearing a dark blue robe and gray slippers that drag on the kitchen floor as he steps back, his right arm stretched behind him. The kitchen doesn't look much different from when the Switzers owned it. But it's like entering a cave, I'm thinking, all dark inside. The light on the ceiling is off and the kitchen only has one window. Sunlight barely makes it through the curtains, and it feels smoky inside even though there's no smoke at all.

There's Bup, in blue jeans and long-sleeved white jersey, sitting at a white and green metal kitchen table. He's plowing Cheerios and milk in his mouth and uses a napkin to catch a drip before it falls from his lips. Mrs. Miller walks into the kitchen from the hall.

"We want to play with Bup today," I say like David did.

Bup starts grinning, squeezing a line of milk between his lips.

"Sit down, then," Mrs. Miller says. "Have some break-fast."

I already ate. David did, too. But we sit 'cause it seems like we should, and Mrs. Miller asks us what kinda cereal we want. I realize I'm only smelling Cheerios. If Mr. Miller stinks, he's not stinking today. He sits down with us, kinda heavy. His eyes look tired and he asks Mrs. Miller for oatmeal. That's sick-people food, I think, for when you're getting a cold or flu. Mr. Miller's eyes seem more than real tired. They're sad and sagging, showing me that Bup was telling the God's honest truth about his father's stomach cancer. Mr. Miller takes a pill with some water. Poor Bup, being told all these bad things about his dad, that he stinks real bad, and Bup seems to have grown to believe it when I smell nothing bad at all.

David and I eat our Cheerios in the kitchen we haven't been in for over four years.

•   •   •

"So why do they call you Bup?" David says.

Personally, I thought *Bup* was what his parents named him, and I never thought to ask. Bup's sitting on his bed, made up neat, with sharp square corners in the blue blanket tucked in at the foot. The white sheet folded over the top of the blanket at the head end is flat and crisp, as if it had been ironed right there on the mattress. I'm sitting on Bup's desk chair, turned to face him, and David's sitting on the worn carpet, pulling at a thread as he would a blade of grass in a lawn.

"My real name's Bartlett," Bup says looking down, kinda red-in-the-face. "It's the name my grandpa had, and I guess Mom and Dad felt obligated. Dad never liked it, so he shortened it to Bup."

I ask him, "How do you get *Bup* out of *Bartlett*?"

I swear every time I see Bup, every time he blinks, his face looks different somehow, like a *Twister* game wheel spinning to choose a new set of face parts, never landing on good-looking.

"*Bup*'s short for *Bupkis*," Bup says, raising his big head. "It stands for nothin'."

"I know what *Bupkis* means," David says. I laugh at David, and he insists that he really does know.

"*Bupkis* is nothin'," Bup says as if he's about to sing a song. "What do I got? I got *bupkis*. Nothin' in the bank?

Bupkis. No place to go? I'm going to *bupkis*. I see, hear, and speak nothin'? I know *bupkis*."

"That's a horrible name, Bup," David says.

"That's not what Mom and Dad say," Bup insists. "They say when they got nothin' going on, they still got me. I'm their *bupkis*. No matter how bad things get, I'm there. So I'm *Bupkis*. Their *Bupkis*. I don't think that's so bad."

"I guess you can look at it that way, Bup," I say.

"That's the way we look at it here," Bup says, folding his arms.

"I think your nickname should be Egg," David says to Bup.

"Why would you say that?"

"'Cause when you were nothing, you were an egg."

"Oh, I was never an egg."

I snap my fingers at David. "What're you talking about? Bup was never an egg."

"Was too. Remember what Mr. Grossman said? All of us were eggs in the beginning."

"Don't listen to Mr. Grossman."

"Why not? He's laid two eggs, and they became Karl and Charlie."

"I know I was never an egg," Bup says.

"Uh-huh, you were. You just didn't know it then 'cause eggs don't have any brains until they're . . ." David stutters a bit saying, "pollinated."

"Now what do you know about pollinated?" Bup says. "What does that mean?"

"I don't know. Mr. Grossman's gonna tell us next time he drives us to Hebrew school."

"Pollinated's for plants," I say. "Plants get pollinated and make more plants."

"Then it's the same thing with people," David says.

Bup frowns, scrunching his fleshy eyelids. "You've got to be kidding?" he says. David's nodding. Bup thumps his chest and declares, "I was never an egg and no plant ever pollinated me, that's for sure."

"Just to be safe, I wouldn't stand too close to flowers," David says. "That's how we get people."

"You know Mr. Grossman drives us to Hebrew school," I say to Bup. "If you want to come with, maybe he can explain it to you and not mess it up like David."

"I don't want to go to your Hebrew school."

"Aren't you Jewish?" David says surprised.

"I'm Jewish," Bup says. "How else would I get called *Bupkis*?"

"Then come with us to Hebrew school next Monday."

"Why should I?"

"'Cause you're Jewish," David insists. "That's why *I* have to go!"

Bup swings his feet up on his bed like he's making to lay down. But he sits there with his hands on his knees. His face scowls. "Why did you guys come over here? You've never been here to play with me before. Did you come over so you can call me an egg?"

"You're the best liar in town," David shoots back like he's making a compliment. Bup doesn't take it that way.

"You guys can go home right now!" Bup's voice growls angry and low. "I mean it. I'll have you arrested for trespassing if you don't."

I walk to his bed and sit down at his side. I stare right into his eyes and smile as wide as I can. "That was perfect, Bup. We need you for this."

"What the hell are you talking about, Rosenberg?" Bup is good. He's got that voice, that mean voice, when he wants to. His "hell" and his calling me by my last name like a tough guy convinces me.

"Bup, I don't think you're a liar. I believe your dad is sick. I believe you, Bup. I believe what we've done to you ever since you moved in was mean, and I'm sorry."

Bup puts his nose near mine. His cheeks are getting rosy and his head's so big, like his face is a movie screen and I'm in the front row. "Do you mean that, Jeremy? Why would you say that now?"

"We need you to do something for us, and I know it's not right after all this time, with everyone being mean, and then I come over only when it suits me. I'll say that right now. You can say it, too, 'cause that will be the truth." Bup's eyes don't leave mine, they're examining me, waiting for me to tell him something he hasn't known since he got to Loblolly Avenue. "It was your idea, Bup, your idea, when you were up on the garage roof with me, asking about who killed my dad. I want to know, Bup, and I need your help. I can trust you 'cause you haven't told anybody about what I said to you on the roof. I've got the telephone number to the Atlanta police, but I can't do it. I tried. They know I'm not a detective. I can't disguise my voice."

"We need a good liar, Bup," David says.

"Shut up, David," I hiss. "Let me finish." Bup's looking at his knees, shaking his big head side to side a bit. "Please, Bup. You got me thinking about this. If you call the Atlanta police and..."

"Lie real good?" Bup says.

I go back to the desk chair and sit. Sighing, I finish, "Yeah, Bup. Like David told you. We need you to lie. You're the best liar in town."

Bup swings his feet to the floor and stands. He walks toward me and lifts a glass desktop cover off a Tommy John autographed letter. It's got a White Sox logo and says, *To my good friend, Bup.* I recognize this letter. Skyler Jenner said it was fake when Bup tried to show it off, and everybody believed Skyler over Bup. Bup holds it so we can see its large letters. He's staring at it, reading it closely as if he's making to kiss it. Lowering it to his waist, he rips it in two and then in fours and over and over. The pieces fall to the floor, looking like ragged snowflakes.

"Tommy John!" David gasps.

Bup slumps a bit and says straight away, "Not real."

I ask, "Why, Bup? Why do you lie so much?"

"If I do this for you, what do I get back?"

"What do you want?"

Bup points his finger at David and then at me. "I want something real important." Bup's ears start turning red, and the red in his cheeks reaches back to meet them. "When my dad's real sick, I want someone besides Mom and me to care about it. And when he's dead, I want a funeral with lots of cars like your dad had so people will believe me. I don't want people thinking I'm lying about my dad dying. I don't want to be alone with Mom, no dad, and nobody showing up at the funeral."

"Your dad's dying, Bup?"

I tell David it's true.

"I'm sorry I called you an egg," David whisper-talks. "I don't understand what Mr. Grossman says most of the time anyway."

"Okay," I say. "I'll get people to show up."

Bup smiles at me and maybe, just a little, his face freezes in a way that's not so bad-looking. He says, "I know what you're doing, Jeremy. You're trying to find that first domino."

Bup kinda gets it right, but he hasn't thought about what happens to a family after a father dies. I could tell him. Maybe I should. But I think you can't really know until it happens to you. Even now, I'm not so certain of all the consequences.

"It's weird," Bup laughs, and David and I tell him the rest, about the newspaper page and the telephone number and the secret phone at the Hebrew school, and he likes the idea about being a detective. Detective Bartlett, he decides.

•   •   •

It's going to be at least fifteen minutes before I see the school counselor. Mom wants me to talk to her. She thinks I can help with Cheryl.

Dr. Bondurant's office shares a waiting room with the school nurse's office. Each side has its own plain burlap-feeling gray couch with a chrome frame, facing each other on opposite walls. It's kinda hard ignoring somebody else in here 'cause your feet almost have to touch the other guy's, it's that small.

Kids have been coming in and out of here all day 'cause it's Monday, and it's Halloween, and everyone seems to be eating too much candy corn. Eisenhower K-8 has a snake dance on Halloween, where each class gets up and marches down the hall in a line to the neighboring class to show off their Halloween costumes. They weave up and down the aisles between the desks and then out the door. Then that class gets up and follows the last kid to leave, and the whole school snakes around until everyone's been in every homeroom.

The kids in kindergarten love it, and up to the second or third grade. They'll paint their faces all sorts of colors, or put gunk on their teeth, and go as Martians or witches or fairies or Batman. But the excitement of dressing up for the school Halloween snake dance fades by fourth grade. Beyond fifth grade, nobody's wearing anything but what they usually wear to school. And all the eighth-graders point at each other and say the same joke, *Hey man! Nice costume. You really scared me!*

Usually a bunch of little kids in painted faces and colorful costumes have to go see the nurse 'cause they ate too much candy corn. That stuff must be made out of pure honey, and it makes you want to eat it even when it's already starting to make you dizzy. You want to stop, but you can't. After all, it's candy corn, and it has to be eaten until there isn't any left or you pass out. The smell of costume makeup on little faces just puts them over the top, and some puking begins.

Jill Beckman's a third grader. I've never met her before, but the story's gotten to me that she was already gagging from candy corn when she was in line to pay her thirty-five cents for the chicken, buttered bread, and mashed potatoes with gravy lunch the cafeteria was serving. She stepped up to Mrs. Walker in her white Glenda the Good Witch costume, all lacy and floating along in red ruby ballerina slippers. "Can

I help you?" Mrs. Walker said, and she smiled from her chair behind the cash register like she always does.

Jill began to hand over her money, but just then she jerked her body like a cat that's gotten sick from eating field grass. Mrs. Walker froze, didn't even try to dive out of the way. Out it came, maybe three cups of candy corn mixed in with pancakes from breakfast, all over Mrs. Walker. Half the kids in the cafeteria sitting at the long tables were facing that way and saw what happened, and they let the other half know they should turn around to see what Jill Beckman's done to Mrs. Walker. Then all the kids in Halloween costumes and makeup, with their poor tummies filled up on candy corn, started getting sick, too. A boy dressed as Pinocchio bent over and gagged out his mashed potatoes in a swirl like a soft-serve ice cream dispenser, but decorated with the bright orange and yellow of part-digested candy corn. And a Cinderella sitting next to him jumped up and ran to the bathroom with her hand over her mouth, with something gross leaking out between her fingers. Prince Charming and a Sneezy started getting white-faced, and three of the seven kids dressed as Batman coughed up Bat-puke with nothing to help them in their Bat-belts but play Bat-rope and plastic Bat-boomerangs.

The line of kids outside the nurse's office lasted until three p.m., and Principal Newman had to drive Mrs. Walker home. He came back, kinda woozy-looking himself, with a bunch of pink bottles and gave it to the school nurse.

Karl Grossman's in here looking pale sitting next to some little kid in a Peter Pan costume. The kid's face is as green as his tights and curl-tipped shoes. Karl's not wearing a costume, of course, being in the seventh grade and all. He's just sick.

"One too many oom-pahs," he explains, keeping a hand on his forehead.

Karl Grossman plays tuba in the seventh-grade band. I've never seen or heard him practice at home so he can't be any good.

"Mr. Waldrop kept yelling at me, 'Christ, Grossman, this is a Sousa march! We need more tuba!' I swear I was blowing as hard as I could, but that tuba's twice bigger than me! All I get to play are all these oom-pah notes, B-flats mostly, over and over— oom-pah, oom-pah, oom-pah, oom-pah— it takes so much air to poop out just one B-flat from a tuba let alone a whole Sousa march of them. Just once I'd like a song where the tuba's got the melody. All those marches are written by trumpet players, you know. So Waldrop's yelling, 'Grossman! More tuba!' I got light-headed B-flatting all over the place, and it just doesn't end. I start seeing swirls, and I start thinking about Kelly Kinder dancing crazy with your sister, and the next thing I know, I'm on the ground with the tuba beneath me and Mr. Waldrop shouting, 'Grossman! What have you done to the tuba? The tuba bell looks like closed lips!'"

Karl Grossman's laughing and holding his head. "Oh!" he says, "I'm still a little dizzy."

Peter Pan's looking sick-faced at Karl. "Hey," Karl says to him, "if you're gonna puke, do it somewhere else." Peter Pan leaves his chair and flies out of the waiting room. Karl moans, lowering his head, "Wish I could puke. I know I'd feel better afterwards." He raises his pale head and says, "You look all right. What're you doing here?"

There's no easy story to tell about seeing the school counselor. The counselor's door opens and a lady wearing tight dark curls and a suit outfit like Mom's steps out and calls my name. Dr. Bondurant smiles at me as I stand up. Other than her curly hair, she looks exactly like Sheriff Andy Taylor's new girlfriend, Helen Crump, and nobody I know likes Helen Crump as much as the other girlfriends he's had. Too prissy.

Karl's looking at me like I'm hiding something from him. "Are you going to Hebrew school today?" Karl says.

"I don't think I'll make it. Tell your dad to just take David."

"Come over when you can," Karl says, his stare following me into Dr. Bondurant's office. "There's something we're

doing for Halloween tonight." Dr. Bondurant steps back out
and glares down at Karl. "Nothing bad, just the usual stuff,"
he says to her. She smiles and puts her arm around my back
to lead me in. Before the door closes behind me, she says to
Karl, "I know who you are, Mr. Grossman. So be careful." I
catch a last look at Karl's eyes bugging out as the door shuts,
his mouth hanging open, like he can't wait to yabber to
everyone, *Jeremy's at the head-doc's office.*

Dr. Bondurant sits behind a wooden desk so large it
seems to shrink her. " Jeremy, you know Kelly Kinder." Kelly
Kinder stands from a brown leathery couch next to the office
door. She reaches a little down toward me and hugs me tight
around my back.

"I'm so sorry, Jeremy," she says.

Her breath reminds me of mint chewing gum, and when
she turns to sit back down in the pretty heart-shaped impres-
sion her *tuchas* left in the couch, my body tingles with the
fresh memory of her boobies pointing into my chest through
her dress. She's smiling at me, like I'm so important, her face
delicate and square, with tan skin smooth over her cheek-
bones. It's as if all other thoughts, baseball, football, it-kid
tag, and even Bup Miller and my plan to find Dad's first
domino have to move to the back of my brain so I can look
at and think about Kelly Kinder.

"Miss Kinder's been good enough to come in and tell me
about what Cheryl did at Skyler Jenner's birthday party." The
nameplate on the giant desk says she's Dr. Kathryn
Bondurant, just to remind everybody, I suppose. The wall
behind her has got three diplomas on it, also telling everybody her name, and a wooden book stand loaded with books
as thick as unabridged dictionaries. "Sit down, Jeremy," she
says pointing to a chair alongside her desk. I do as I'm told.
"Tell me, Jeremy. How have you been doing?"

"I'm okay, ma'am."

"I see from your first trimester report card that you're
getting B's and C's this year."

Dr. Bondurant lowers her chin and raises her stare, like

she's trying to dive into my brain for an explanation of how average I am. Don't like Kelly Kinder hearing about my average grades.

"Is there something going on, Jeremy?"

"Honestly, Dr. Bondurant, I'm okay. My grades are no different from any other year."

Dr. Bondurant reaches for a yellow file with my name on it. She turns the cover and sorts through some papers. I turn to the side to see Kelly Kinder. She smiles at me, then crosses her eyes, shrugging, and smiles even wider like she wants to laugh.

"Well, Jeremy, I guess that's true. Want to tell me why you're getting B's and C's?"

Dr. Bondurant asks that like it's the same thing as flunking. I can't figure out how this has anything to do with Cheryl. "How're Cheryl's grades?" I say. "Wouldn't that be more helpful?"

"I'm not allowed to tell you another student's grades, Jeremy. That's confidential."

"How come you're telling mine in front of Kelly Kinder?"

Dr. Bondurant's face flinches when I say that. "Do you want her to leave, Jeremy?"

"No, it's all right. I'm just asking how come the difference?"

"That's astute of you, Jeremy. You probably could get better grades if you tried harder." I doubt she's intending to answer my question. "Jeremy, when Cheryl went to the Jenner party, how was she acting?"

"Normal."

"Normal for who?"

"Just normal."

Dr. Bondurant picks up a pencil and makes a note in the file with my name on it, covering it with her hand so I can't see it. Seems like everything's kept a secret from me, even the secrets about me.

"Why don't you tell me what you saw that day."

"I wasn't paying too much attention until she put on that

record. She came out and started dancing, dancing really good, like I've never seen her do before." Dr. Bondurant watches me and wiggles her index finger for me to continue. "Kelly gets up and starts dancing, too. And I'm amazed 'cause I don't know how they learned to dance the same steps together. That's the biggest thing."

"Did Cheryl say anything to you? Anything at all?"

"She told me she wanted me to get her out of there, so I did."

"Why do you think she said that?— Jeremy, a shrug is not an answer. Try to answer."

"Skyler Jenner yelled at her, accused her of cheating in front of everybody, then Bup slugs Skyler Jenner, and Mrs. Jenner's all mad at us. It wasn't fair. Cheryl was just dancing really good, that's all she did. Why wouldn't she want to leave after all that? It felt good to leave."

"Why, Jeremy? Why did it feel good for you to leave?"

I cough and Dr. Bondurant makes another secret note, probably about me coughing. Every breath I take gets super-analyzed and inspected for secrets by Dr. Bondurant.

"Is there something about the Jenners you don't like?"

"I didn't like them yelling at Cheryl and ordering us out."

Dr. Bondurant turns to a small reel-to-reel recorder sitting behind her on one of her shelves and presses down on some buttons. *Wild Thing* starts playing, real quiet and tinny. I think I hear Kelly Kinder tapping her toes on the carpet.

"Is there something about this song, Jeremy? Anything at all?"

I listen to the words and the rhymes and I feel relieved. Dr. Bondurant has been knocking around my thoughts, getting warmer, like a hide-and-seek game in my head, and she's made a wrong turn to where she's polar cold.

"Yes, Dr. Bondurant," I say, "I think it's that song. Ever since Cheryl's heard it, she's been acting crazy. I've tried taking it away, but she gets another somehow."

Dr. Bondurant scribbles away in her secret Jeremy Rosenberg file 'cause every word I speak must mean something important, or the opposite of what I say. She *Mm's* every now and then until she puts her pencil down and smiles at me. She looks just like Helen Crump, for real, listening to *Wild Thing*.

"Listen, Jeremy. I think we've made some progress here." She raises my file and shows me her notes— *Day One. Jeremy Rosenberg's been bullshitting me.*

Kelly Kinder snorts a laugh that feels like spit in my ears. Dr. Bondurant might just as well have run my BVDs up the school flagpole. I don't think I'd feel any worse.

"Can I go use the bathroom?" I say.

Dr. Bondurant nods and corrects my grammar the same way teachers do, as if they can't help themselves, "Yes, you *may* use the bathroom."

I get up. I get up and leave Dr. Bondurant's office not even looking at Kelly Kinder. But I'm not stopping at any bathroom. I don't ask permission, I just do it. I keep going. I feel anger inside me. It starts in my stomach and moves up, making my skin red hot until it reaches my forehead. I don't need Dr. Bondurant to tell me what I'm thinking, to show off how smart she is. I don't need to hear her tell me I'm full of bullshit. I'm beginning to think that getting Bup Miller to help might be a mistake if Mom makes me come here again. If Dr. Bondurant keeps banging inside my head, it'll ruin everything.

The long hall is empty except for the janitor cleaning up torn pieces of Halloween costumes and decorations. The clock over the main entrance says three-fifty. Mr. Trauby's class starts in forty minutes, and I'm at least two miles away from home and three miles from Hebrew school. Outside, the sun's getting low for afternoon, it seems. Eighth-graders play fast-pitch against the side of the school. I walk through them and let them curse at me for interrupting their game. Mothers walk children in groups, some groups as large as twenty or more. They're marching from house to house, asking for tricks or treats, and watching their bags fill up with candy, and the mothers say, *Save it for home! Save some for your daddies!*

Loblolly Avenue meets Church Street at the foot of the Edens Expressway bridge, and I wait there. I look down Church Street and follow its rise over the expressway. Dad would gun the Hydra Glide's engine at the bridge's peak over the Edens, and then suddenly let go of the throttle. It felt a little like the drop of a roller coaster, like the bridge was letting me and Dad float over it. *It's a kiss-me-quick!* Dad always said at that moment, and he'd nuzzle his stubbly face against my neck and make tickly kissing noises below my ear. I don't think I've ever told anyone about that, even when Dad was alive.

To find my father's first domino, Bup wants to wait until there's a big bar mitzvah. He doesn't think the time between the end of Hebrew class and when Mr. Grossman comes will let him do his best. I found out about the Koning, Mussman, and Skelnick triple bar mitzvah.

"Perfect," Bup said.

That's not until November twelfth. It's hard for me to wait now.

"Hey, handsome! We thought you flushed yourself down the toilet!"

Kelly Kinder pulls her orange VW Beetle along the curb. "Dr. Bondurant's gone and called a plumber!" She's laughing at me, I'm thinking, but she waves me over. "Get in," she says. Even if I might be feeling embarrassed, I don't wait a split second. It's Kelly Kinder, after all.

Twelve-year-old boys shouldn't get too close to Kelly Kinder. Getting too close makes me ask myself too many questions, and wonder about things I'm probably not ready to wonder about. I'm trying hard not to look at her more illegal places, but it's hard 'cause even her face seems to be a little illegal, and her eyes, after all, are only a foot over her boobies. I concentrate on the inside of her Beetle. It's white, with millions of little holes poked evenly across the cloth curving over me completely round, as though I'm sitting inside an egg. There's a flower vase on the dash with a white and yellow daisy in it. She's got Barney Pip on the radio playing some talk song, *They're coming to take me away, ha ha!* The radio doesn't sound too good and keeps fading out. With the engine putt putting behind us, it just doesn't seem like the type of car Kelly Kinder would drive.

"I can understand why you left," she's saying. Her Beetle sputters a little, shaking us with a quick jerk, then catches like a slipped bicycle chain suddenly finding the gear teeth. Kelly Kinder starts apologizing, first for the VW, then for Dr. Bondurant. "I hope you don't think I actually wanted to be there. I don't know how Dr. Bondurant knew to call me in my dormitory room. She's a bloodhound, Jeremy. She said exactly, 'Your presence is absolutely needed for the well-being of the children.' How could I not go, Jeremy, when I hear things like that?"

Kelly Kinder's stare darts between me and Loblolly Avenue. She's got that look on her face, the one adults must give all kids who have dead fathers, and who have their well-being discussed with or without permission. I notice it practically everywhere. The adults on Loblolly Avenue seem to stare at me, a look that's a second longer than the ones they give the other kids on the block, with their eyebrows a bit raised and their cheeks and lips a little pouty. It's a small thing, I guess, but I can't help noticing. Now I seem to never miss finding that expression in every adult face I see. It's pity. Whether it comes from Kelly Kinder's wonderful face or Missy Grossman's sour face or Big Ben's Dean Martin face, to me it feels the same. They're pitying the dead-father boy. Without meaning to, they make it hard for me to think about something else.

For her own reasons, Kelly Kinder is anxious to explain herself to me. She doesn't have to 'cause I'm not angry at her. "I'm sorry," she repeats. "Dr. Bondurant is reading something into the Jenners and that birthday party. She thinks maybe it's their house or something. I mean, it was only a song, that's all." Her pity turns to pleading. "I had no idea anything's wrong with Cheryl, please believe me." Smiling and leaning toward me, her words carry the smell of mint and perfume. "I still have no idea."

"Cheryl hates David," I say, wondering if I'd be saying anything at all to her if she didn't look and smell so pretty. "It's not like brothers and sisters regularly hating each other."

Kelly Kinder's messing with the gears again, balancing her car between running and shutting off. She says, "David's like your father shrunk down to a little doll. It's not that hard to figure out." The Beetle rolls us past Ellerson Street and Kelly parks behind Big Ben's Cadillac. She's smiling like she knows something she figured out long ago. "You've never been a little girl, Jeremy. I know it's hard for you, but…" She reaches down to her purse stashed behind her seat. It's a white purse and hand-sized, not at all like Mom's purse or any other mom's purse. Dad called Mom's purse her life-support pack and claimed Mom might shrivel up to nothing if she went outside without its houseful of supplies. I guess Kelly Kinder doesn't need so much stuff yet to live outside a house. She pulls out an accordion-folding picture holder. "Look at the last one," she says.

I know which one it is immediately. It's Dad and Mom on the Hydra Glide, in their leathers, smiling and hugging. They're about to drive to Niagara Falls for their honeymoon.

"I asked your mother for a copy of this years ago. My family just moved in and I was being nosy. Your father told me about it, and I couldn't believe it— a mom and a dad riding away like that on a motorcycle, going on an adventure. No real plans, just going east and north until they see the Falls. Just the two of them holding each other the entire way. Even then, it sounded so romantic. My parents don't have any pictures like that. Their honeymoon was a drive to Milwaukee in a Buick. I decided long ago that I wasn't going to take that picture out of my old holder until I could replace it with a picture of a man, with me, on a motorcycle like that going to Niagara Falls, or anywhere, just like your mom and dad did."

Kelly puts the picture holder in her purse carefully, like it's as delicate as butterfly wings. She smiles and raises her hands to my cheeks. "You were never a little girl, Jeremy.

Your mom and dad," she says, then stops. Her eyes, sweeter than candy corn, aim somewhere over my head. It's as though she's dreaming about what she wants to tell me. She breathes in deep, lowering her hands to her lap. "How special your mom and dad were together. Like they were going to stay young together, forever, no matter how old they got. You know what I mean, Jeremy? Your brother, he's a child, but he owns your father's face. It's got to be hard on a little girl, Jeremy. Do you think you understand?"

Kelly Kinder's convinced herself it's simple to understand Cheryl. Maybe she's right, I don't know, but we can't wait for Cheryl to tear David's face off before she'll get along with him. Still, it's more than that. It's more than just Cheryl and David. Kelly Kinder didn't see what we saw. She hasn't lived in my house since it happened. She looks at the old photograph like she can't wait for her life to be like that. For Mom and us, we're trying to go on, knowing that it's a picture of a life we've lost forever.

That's the problem with people, even nice people, who are trying to understand what we're going through. They're on the outside looking in with their pity. They mean to help, but they don't really know. I can't trust their advice.

•   •   •

It's drizzling but Karl Grossman wants to go out for Halloween, says he's got something interesting planned and he isn't wearing a costume anyway. "I'll bring my dad's black umbrella and say I'm Mary Poppins." His laughter booms over the telephone. Karl laughs a lot like his dad, I can hear the spit in his throat and the W.C. Fields whine through the earpiece. I hang up and go to leave the kitchen. Mom's standing in the hallway, wearing the same work suit she had on just last Friday.

"What happened with Dr. Bondurant today?"

If I'd answer with a curse word, I might feel better, but I'm not sure whether I should curse about Dr. Bondurant or at Mom. So I bite my lip to keep the curse word down, and it burns in my stomach.

Mom repeats, "What happened?"

I can't look at her straight away, and I go past her in the hall with that curse word bubbling up my throat.

"I want you to answer." Her high heel steps follow me.

I say, "Going trick or treating with Karl," and I'm so mean about it.

"It's almost eight. Why're you going now?"

"Because," I say.

I open the front door closet, where the money envelopes magically slip in through the mail slot the first of every month, and I look for a black umbrella, a man's umbrella, but can only find the blue umbrella with frills along the rim, and a clear plastic Bubble Umbrella.

"Answer me," Mom says.

With the curse word crawling around in my mouth, I clench my jaws tight.

"Why did you run out?"

David walks up behind her in his Keds.

"It's Halloween, Mom," I say, and pretending it's a curse word, I shout in her face, "Boo!"

David hops in place, "Can I go trick or treating now, too? Can I?"

Looking away from me and David, Mom says, "Take your brother," and I'm wondering what's happened to me to make me feel so good when she turns and runs to her bedroom.

Grabbing the Bubble Umbrella, David skips out the front door. He opens his umbrella and it curls over him. On the pinners porch, inside his clear mushroom cap, David smiles at me, turning cross-eyed trying to watch a raindrop dripping down the plastic.

Down the pinners porch with David, we cross the street toward Karl Grossman's house. Karl's standing under his porch lamp and black umbrella. I can talk to goofy Karl Grossman about stupid things and Halloween pranks. I can't talk to Mom anymore 'cause all that's left to talk about are serious things, sad things. Whether it's about what it was like before, or how it's been since, or how it's going to be from now on, the talk wears me down.

More bad things are happening to the Rosenbergs, obvious things I'm sure of and invisible things I'm afraid of. Something invisible is pushing us along toward a quicksand pit, and we have no choice about it. Although I'm not sure who to blame, or that there's someone to blame at all, I find myself blaming Mom somehow, for being a widow— and I'm a widow's son.

I hope Bup Miller's right about first dominos 'cause I can't stand all these feelings. I want to find someone else to blame.

•　　•　　•

"I hear when you stop eating for more than a week, your stomach starts eating up your insides," Karl Grossman's saying.

For Halloween, the night's drizzling a thick mist that seems to evaporate off the ground, hovering around our feet in a cool fog, a crash-landed cloud. Goblins and ghosts and witches with black cats riding brooms watch us from every window and glass-panelled screen door, eyes carved in pumpkins with hot candles inside follow us as we walk. We see our own feet, and ourselves, and maybe ten feet ahead, before the darkness hides the sidewalk. Above us, tree branches without leaves reach down toward our faces with their broken-fingered pointing. Cars rushing by in the distance along Edens Expressway send their whoosh of wind to our ears, like bats flying, searching for boys walking without adults on Halloween night. My skin-tingling reduces me to a little boy, sends me back to memories of not too long ago when I believed in ghosts and ghost stories, and everything on *The Outer Limits* was true— *Do not attempt to adjust your television sets. We are in control...* and I'd lie awake all night

worrying about large cootie spiders and space alien inva-
sions.

I wish Karl would shut up, but he doesn't— *I hear your
stomach starts eating up your insides.*

Karl walks beneath his manly black umbrella. I follow
him under my own ring of blue ruffles. That pointy
Grossman chin of his sticks out below the shadow of the can-
vass as he turns to talk.

"There's a skeleton in the Yellen house. Dahveed
Waxberg said so, and he heard it from his mother— overheard it when Izzy Yellen cried about it to his mother in the
kitchen. Brian Yellen won't go to Vietnam so he's starving
himself, and his body's chewing itself up. That's what happens when you don't eat. Yum yum, a liver. Yum yum, a
heart. Yum yum…"

"Shut up, Karl," David says inside his Bubble Umbrella,
sounding like he's got a sock in his mouth.

Karl laughs, "Should've stayed home, little boy. Go
home, little boy." But David doesn't go home. We keep going
in the darkness toward the Yellen house. Boys have to see
something gory and sickening, like a body eating itself up,
'cause that's what boys have to do. "Like bugs to light," Karl
says. "We're going to see."

The Yellen house is a square box of bricks, like every
other house on Loblolly Avenue, but it has no Halloween
decorations. Even Mom's taped a few to our windows, and
she'll throw pennies from her purse into Halloween bags,
and the little kids will love it while the older kids will stick
their tongues out at our house when Mom closes the door.

A group of six little kids and Sklyer Jenner, all close to
Mrs. Jenner and her umbrella, comes toward us— little
clowns, cowboys with six-shooters, one with an arrow
through his head, and Skyler Jenner dressed as Dick Butkus
in full football uniform. Mrs. Jenner wears cat whiskers
painted on her face, and the flip of her hair's been hair-
sprayed into cat ears. She smiles as we pass but says nothing.
A little cowboy shouts back, "What kinda costumes are

those? Those aren't any kinda costumes!"

"We're Mary Poppins!" booms Karl.

"You can't *all* be Mary Poppins!" the cowboy with the arrow through his head says.

"Who says we can't?" David cries.

"Mary Poppins don't look like that! She's not a boy, she don't wear jeans, she don't have a Bubble Umbrella! She couldn't fly with a Bubble Umbrella!"

Karl yells back, stepping a bit toward the cowboy, "Mary Poppins can send *you* flying with a Bubble Umbrella!"

Mrs. Jenner scoots the cowboy and the other trick-or-treaters along, saying, "That's not Mary Poppins, children. Move along now," and they disappear in the black behind us, their little voices saying, *Taffy apples at the Kinders'! Snickers at the Waxbergs'! M & M's at the Lipshilts'!* —and Mrs. Jenner's voice answering, *One to a customer, but hurry along, we'll make popcorn balls.*

"Can't we go with them?" David says real whiny.

"We're not here for candy," Karl hisses. "Look at you. No candy bag for Halloween."

Karl points to the Yellen house, its brown-red face of bricks made black by the night. The front picture window watches us, like a Cyclops eye wide open. Shadows of people appear against the curtains, then shrink away.

"You scared to see the skeleton?" Karl challenges David.

David shakes his head inside his plastic cocoon, his knuckles squeezing the umbrella handle.

"I'll take you home," I say, "if you want."

Karl hoarse-whispers at me, "That's just an excuse for you to go home, too, Jeremy."

"Let's go on," David says. "I'm not scared."

"Are you sure?" Karl says stepping on the Yellens' lawn. "I thought I smelled something in your diapers."

"Shut up, Karl," David says, doing his best to sound tough.

We cut across the lawn and squeeze through lilac bushes growing tall against the corner of the house, finding our way to a bedroom window. Karl and I huddle down under the window, unlit and as black as a new chalkboard. We throw our umbrellas toward the bushes separating the Yellens' house from the Dapins' house. It's dark against the Yellen house, as dark as it ever could get, and I don't see David.

"Wait," his voice calls. I look to my right and hear David trying to get that Bubble Umbrella between the lilac bush and the house. One side is thumping through bare lilac branches, the other side scraping against brick.

"Close it," I say.

David keeps pushing until I hear a final thump, and he stumbles next to me. A panel of the umbrella's clear plastic is scratched and torn, and dead lilac bush leaves, like leeches, stick to it everywhere. He lowers the umbrella over his head and body, scratching the plastic against the brick behind us as he hunkers down.

"Shut up," Karl growls.

"What's so bad about Vietnam?" David says. "Aren't we winning?"

"We've been winning for years," Karl says. "I don't know what Brian Yellen's problem is."

"I'd like to go on a trip," David says. "Is Vietnam a good place to go?"

"I don't know," Karl says. "All I know is it's a free trip, and you get to win a war. Lots of people are going."

"They're shooting guns there," I say.

"So what? It takes twenty dead Viet Cong for every dead American. Haven't you been watching TV?"

"What's a Viet Cong?" David says.

"You don't know what a Viet Cong is?" Karl snorts. "I'd go to Vietnam. I wouldn't starve myself. I'd shoot 'em."

"You get beat up by tubas," I say.

"You go to the head-doc," Karl snaps back.

"Dr. Bondurant only wanted to know who left their brain on her desk. I showed her your name on the bottom, right beneath 'Made In Japan.'"

"Where's Vietnam?" David asks.

"On the other side of the world," Karl says. "By Africa."

"I thought the other side of the world was China," David says. "I thought when we dig holes, we dig to China. I've never heard anyone say, 'Dig to Africa.'"

I say to David, "It's definitely Karl's brain on Dr. Bondurant's desk. He can't think anymore."

"I think you should shut up," Karl says.

And David starts, "I think I hear…" then shuts up with a squeak as light flashes over our heads.

"Shut up! Shut up!" Karl orders.

"Nobody's talking but you telling us to shut up," I say.

David says, "Is there anyone in there?"

"Idiot," Karl says. "Somebody had to turn on the light."

"Now what?" I say.

Karl's eyes bulge as he turns to speak. "I'm here to see what Brian Yellen looks like after not eating forever. I'm gonna see." But Karl stays on the ground with us, breathing hard, his butt glued to the grass.

Skeletons don't cast shadows, I'm thinking, or if they did, the light would leak through the spaces between the bones and make a shadow like a xylophone. I hear children shouting *Trick or Treat!* from somewhere across the street, laughing, getting candy. Here I sit with my brother as he huddles inside his Bubble Umbrella, and Karl Grossman itches at the wet grass with his nervous fingers. We're cringing against the Yellen house, in the dark, with a streak of light above our heads, maybe carrying the shadow of Brian Yellen, or his skeleton, or maybe not.

"This is stupid," I say. I pop to my feet, and Karl's saying like a whisper that's too excited to be a whisper, "What're you doing? What're you doing?" David stands beside me, his head moving up along with his Bubble Umbrella. I'm his older brother, and he's doing what I'm doing. I'm not surprised it's Karl staying on the ground.

I hear shrieking, little boy shrieking. David's shrieking to wake himself, to get away from some monster chasing him in a nightmare. It's like an explosion of fright and fear, and wanting to get away, but it's hard 'cause the nightmare sticks to him and won't let go.

Karl crawls away along the side of the house toward the front. He hasn't seen, he doesn't see. He just wants to get away. I shove David and yell, "Go home!" His little body's gone stiff and he stumbles a bit to the side when I push. "Let's go! Now!"

David's shouting something, I can't tell what for sure, and he squeezes his Bubble Umbrella between the lilac bush and house and falls through.

I turn to the window for another look before I go. I just have to.

Like the sudden pop from a jack-in-the-box, Izzy Yellen's face pressing near the bedroom window electrifies my skin. She's only a foot away from me, watching the light land on my face. Her eyes look black, with tiny drips of black streaks spilling into the whites and running down from the corners. She mouths, *Go home, Jeremy— Go home*, and raises her arm to point the way out. Under her arm, I see Brian Yellen one more time, lying face up on his bed against the back wall. He's naked, and there's a chair by him and a plastic bucket, with towels and sponge on the floor. His hair is thick and wiry, like troll doll hair, piling up at the top of his pillow, his head half-buried, and eyes low in their sockets. His arms and legs seem lost in the bed sheets, showing here and there in the folds like sticks. He raises his hand to his forehead and it seems eerie, evil magic, to see how he moves his arm 'cause there's nothing there but bone covered in a thin layer of skin.

He's doing nothing but lying there with his hand at his forehead, staring up at the ceiling with those shrunken eyes. He breathes in deep, and his rib bones stretch under skin, skin so thin it's like lizard skin ready to be shed, and a skeleton, a real skeleton, is about to come out, empty of insides.

• • •

At home, everything seems normal. Normal for how we are now. The porch light is off. The TV in the living room is on with nobody watching. Books and papers and toys mess up the floor, and small bundles of dust collect under tables and beds and just about everywhere. Cheryl's in her bedroom, door closed, muttering things to herself or somebody. Only she knows. It's nine-thirty and Mom's asleep, I hear the TV in there going. Somebody needs to do the dishes 'cause they're filling the sink. I should do them, I guess, but I don't.

My bedroom is cluttered with comic books, magazines, and baseball cards. It's my habit to drop them on the floor beside my bed when I'm through with them, and let them pile up. David sits on his bed, his arms wrapped around his knees pulled to his chest. He's wet— his hair, his shirt, his jeans. He's tossed the Bubble Umbrella to the floor, still open and torn, looking like an empty half of an eggshell. David loosens and lets his legs stretch forward.

"That's what Dad looks like in the ground," he says.

He says it like he's answering a question on a test, his face serious and confident. He knows he's got it answered right. David goes to bed, falling to sleep without saying a word more.

November

After Halloween night, I thought I might dream about Brian Yellen, time and again, like a never-ending rerun, about his bones, alive but looking like death. But in the days since, instead, I dream about dominos falling, one into the next, knocking the line over, falling like pages in a book. I dream about miles and miles of dominos, standing straight but doomed to fall. Somewhere in the middle of the line, a domino falls into one that won't go down. It doesn't wobble or sway or lean, and holds against the pressure of the dominos that fell before it, as if it has grown thick roots into the ground, deeper than it is tall.

The dominos after it, all the way to the horizon, stay upright, standing as they did when the first domino took its fall. And that colorful bird with the one wing sits on the rooted domino. Its head turns toward the toppled line, then cocks about to look at the standing line. Stretching its legs, the bird begins to flap the wing and its body rises, as if the other wing were there to make it fly. The blue, yellow, and red feathers carry the bird over the standing pieces, slowly at first, then, in a rush of confidence, the bird soars, graceful as any bird has ever flown.

David's been getting up early, and this Saturday morning at six-thirty, he's already up and out of the room. Water's running in the kitchen. I roll over to look at the floor. There's no reel-to-reel recording my sleep, not since we saw Brian Yellen. I lay back on my pillow and think how much I wish the recorder were there.

It's strange how the money came again, fifteen fives, two ones, in an envelope telling us how much we're loved. After all I've done to anger the Yellens and the Jenners, it still keeps coming. I guess when a family is singled out to pity, it can pretty much get away with a lot of stuff.

David's acting different. He's been making instant coffee for Mom in the morning, and cooking scrambled eggs— they start out trying to be sunny-side upside downside, but they always finish scrambled. He's been cleaning, too, getting down on his hands and knees and washing the kitchen floor. He's got his own way about that, squirting Ivory soap on the floor and pouring two or three buckets of water across the tiles. It starts raining in the basement, but he mops away, using the sink to rinse off the dirty water from the mop, and then gets down on his hands and knees with our bath towels until the kitchen floor looks brand new. Then he wipes the drippings that fell to the basement using the same towels, and finishes by doing the wash, throwing those towels in with our clothes. I have to say, it works. My clothes feel a little crunchy, but clean, and he knows not to use any bleach.

I'm not saying he's perfect about it, or adult about it, 'cause I catch him playing *Star Trek* using the stove as the Enterprise. "Warp One!" he shouts, and he cranks the center burner. "More power, Scotty!"— and he cranks up the four other burners. They're blazing away, heating up the kitchen. "That's all she's got, Captain! There's no more power!" His voice changes and commands, "There's more power, Scotty, don't lie to me! I don't care how you do it!"— and David powers up the rotisserie and oven. He stands there wearing Mom's old apron over his jeans, staring at the stove top, smiling above the flames, his eyes shining at what Warp 9 looks like. He blinks, turns off the engines and goes back to scrubbing the kitchen floor. It's very odd.

Cheryl can't seem to figure him out either, and I thought she would pound him more, but instead she just watches him wash floors, cook food, do laundry, and make it rain in the basement. I guess she's like a cat that's always the most interested in the person trying hardest to ignore it. That's the person the cat wants to rub up against. David's too busy with his projects, he has no time for Cheryl, and now she's spying on him, quietly, not saying a word to criticize.

I have to get up. Today's the triple bar mitzvah, and my music alarm's gone off three times already. Every station keeps playing that *Winchester Cathedral* song. Honestly, I can't imagine anyone listening to that mush. It's an old-people song, with trombones and whistling and no guitars, sounding like a slow walk in the park, and that nostril-pinching voice *bo-bo-dee-oh-bo*-ing— it's a song for old people. But even Barney Pip plays *Winchester Cathedral* as many times as he can get away with, as if Grandpa Erwin can even stand listening to *radio shmadio.*

When I walk by Mom's room, I slow down, say, "Good morning," and feel like a crud for all the things I've been thinking. Mom doesn't say anything, just smiles over the newspaper she reads in bed, with a plate of finished breakfast on the floor next to her slippers, all served by David. She sips a cup of coffee and her glasses steam halfway up the lenses.

From the bathroom, Cheryl's laughter mixes with the sound of someone tinkling in the toilet. Mom shakes her head, smiling wider, and goes back to reading the paper.

I'm curious 'cause I know from Arnold Grossman that girls have to sit down when they pee and don't make loud tinkles. I have to see what's going on.

Cheryl's blocking the way to the bathroom, standing at the door, facing in. The door's wide open and Cheryl giggles and looks back in.

"It's just Jeremy," she says talking to David. "Keep going!"

David's standing on the bathroom scale. He's got it

placed at the toilet and he's peeing from it into the bowl.

"What're you doing?" I ask.

"Seeing," David says, holding his little dickie thing with two hands. His arc of pee looks graceful and golden. Golden Arches, I'm thinking, like the McDonald's on Dempster Street, except there's only one of them coming out of David.

"What're you seeing?"

David leans his head forward and speaks around Cheryl's shoulder like he's teaching me something. "I'm seeing how far the scale goes down when I pee." He turns his head back to the toilet. "I want to know what it weighs." He looks up at the small electric clock on the glass shelf over the toilet tank. "I'm seeing how long it takes, too." His arc begins to fade and dribble.

"Careful! Get it all in the bowl!" Cheryl says, then kinda sad, "Wish I could stand up and pee."

"A whole two pounds!" David says like he's just landed on the moon. He looks at the clock. "Sixty-five seconds!"

"Wow!" Cheryl says. "You gonna try, Jeremy?"

"Maybe Jeremy can figure out a way to do this doing number two business," David says, tucking his dickie thing in his pants. "He'll have to be a good shot."

Cheryl laughs the kinda laugh that could make her puke if she doesn't settle down. David's done his scientific tinkle experiment and the result is better than anything Dr. Bondurant can do. David cups water in his hands at the bathroom sink, loading up for another try. He bubbles out to Cheryl that he'll figure something so she can play. I stand on the scale, listening to Cheryl's laughter while I watch my golden arc, the second hand on the electric clock go past forty-five seconds, and the scale go down one-and-a-half pounds.

•   •   •

Mom's taking Cheryl to Dr. Bondurant for a special meeting this Saturday morning. I guess they're thinking it's necessary 'cause everyone's getting together at Dr. Bondurant's other office at the Old Orchard Professional Building. I don't think any of it's necessary. As long as David keeps cleaning the way he does and peeing off our bathroom scale, Cheryl's never going to torture him again. David's found a cure by accident, and I hope all this professional help doesn't ruin it.

In our bedroom, David and I get ready for the triple bar mitzvah. David's dress pants rise a bit high over his ankles and he has to tug a little to get the waist button to slip through the slit. His dress clothes will be all right as long as he doesn't eat anything or breathe too hard. He wears his dark brown penny loafers, which don't go too well with his black pants, and he's fancied his loafers up by putting in new, shiny pennies. They look like eyeballs squinting up at me suspicious-like, and make me nervous about this whole plan.

"Clip-on tie or real tie?" I ask, standing at our closet.

David darts his stare between the black real tie and the silver clip-on tie that twinkles in light. He taps my hand holding the real one, and I begin to tie it around my own neck. David watches my hands, studying how I'm making the Windsor knot. I peer down my chest and find I've made the fat end come down way too short. I tug at the top, loosen it off my neck, and start again.

"Can you teach me how to do that?" David says. His face is one big curiosity watching my hands flip the tie's ends around. "I'll have to learn it one day, you know, if I'm gonna be a businessman."

"When did you decide to be a businessman?"

"When I picked the real tie."

The collar on David's white shirt rubs tight around his neck, his skin puffing over the edge. He looks like he's gonna burst out of his clothes or choke before he does. It's hard to breathe watching that shirt collar grip his neck. I reach to his top button and undo it.

"There," I say. "You're not a businessman yet so you don't need to button it all the way up." David tilts his head, a little suspicious, so I undo my top button and tell him,

"This is the way Dad taught me to do it."

"When did he teach you?" David says.

I lift David's tie over my head and drop the loop over David's. "I don't know. Two years ago maybe."

"Why didn't he teach me?"

"You were too little then," I say. "He was teaching you how to ride a bicycle, you know, important stuff like that."

I push the knot higher up near the top of his shirt, and tug and adjust the collar and tie until things sit just right. The tie's fat end comes down a little too long, to his zipper. David smiles at me and I tell him it's perfect. I guess David's thinking the same thing I am, that Dad's dying means we'll never know things he might have taught us, more important things than riding bicycles and tying ties. Maybe David expects me to teach him some of Dad's secrets, but I can only teach him what fathers teach their twelve-year-old sons. After that, I'm guessing, and hoping I'm right.

David's face is so much like Dad's. Wearing a sport coat and real tie only makes it more obvious.

"Do you still want to do this?" David asks real serious. I push his hair up over his forehead so he doesn't go to the bar mitzvah looking like a Beatle. Cantor Morton hates that.

"Don't *you* want to do this?" I say.

"I know Dad's dead now," he says the way a businessman might talk, real flat and professional. "I guess I thought he'd always come back. Don't laugh at me, okay?"

"I'm not gonna laugh."

He breathes in deep and begins.

"Dad wasn't supposed to come home after the accident, remember when Mom told us that?— but he came home anyway. And when he wore that cement all over his body, the doctors said he might never walk again. But the cement came off piece by piece, and he walked, Jeremy, right through our front door with that walker. And then Dad promised us, he promised he was gonna be the same, without the walker, and he'd do the Hydra Glide rides the same as before. Remember Dad promised that, Jeremy? I remember."

David's eyes pour into mine, and I have to turn away. He can't stop telling me.

"I thought everything was gonna be the same again, and we'd go for rides on the Hydra Glide, and everybody would want to be like us and go for rides, just like before. Even after the funeral, I thought he'd come home. Dad always came home, Jeremy, no matter what. Now I know what he looks like, like Brian Yellen, only worse, and in the ground. You can't breathe in the ground. Dad hasn't breathed for five months. He's not coming home, Jeremy. He's not."

I feel myself wanting to cry and it's embarrassing 'cause David doesn't look like he's gonna start.

"I want to do this," David says. "I want to 'cause I want Mummy back. She's so sad, Jeremy, but she's not under the ground like Dad. Maybe if we find out who made Dad die, she won't be so sad."

David doesn't know what to do 'cause his arms hang at his sides, and he leans back a little, but I have to hug him. Finally, somebody in this family has said what I'm feeling. I want my father back so much, my insides get that hollow feeling again just wishing and wishing and knowing it's not going to happen.

David's smiling, maybe for a hundred reasons, I don't know. He's a bug-saver, a spy, a whiner, a pest. He's my little brother. But for the first time ever, I see that his little boy dress clothes can hardly hold him.

• • •

November lets you know summer is over. It's true that school starts in September, and it gets cooler in October, but even then we get some nice warm days, and we're fooled into thinking it may stay that way. November lets you know we're in for it. It tells you 'cause the sky seems lower to the ground. The clouds, if they were any lower, could be touched by tree-tops. The clouds rush across the sky, chased by something evil. Bitter cold isn't far behind. And it rains. Not like spring rains that are powerful, warm, and quick. November sneaks over us like a gray blanket and stays that way, covering us up, not letting us see the sun or blue sky or stars or the moon unless it wants us to, and then only for a peek. The rain falls like mist, so slow, taking its sweet time 'cause November's thirty days long.

David and I huddle together as we walk hunched over to keep our faces out of the wind. Our sport coats stick out below the bottoms of our army brown cloth jackets, making us look like we're layered up in mismatched clothes. It's what we got. We walk our way to Bup Miller's house and he lets us in.

"Did you watch Gemini 12 splash down last Tuesday?" he says. Bup's wearing black pants that fit him too big, and he's wearing a light blue tie and white shirt under a comfortable-looking gray sweater that has leather patches at the elbows. He can hardly keep from jumping out of his dress shoes talking about Gemini 12.

Bup sits at the kitchen table and waves us over to do the same. "Dad's getting ready to drive us," he says. He whispers, "He thinks we're invited. I've got ten dollars to give the Koning bar mitzvah boy, and I've got no idea who he is!" Bup sees David and me looking at each other kinda worried, like Bup's cheating his dying dad out of ten dollars. "Don't worry," Bup says. "I'm not really going to give it to him."

"Bup," I say, "we're going to do this right. We're just going in, and you're going to sneak to the phone and make the call. Then we're calling your dad to drive us home."

"Don't we get bar mitzvah cookies?"

"We're not really their guests, Bup."

"Taking a cookie's going to cost less than a call to Atlanta," Bup says.

"Taking a cookie doesn't help us much," David says.

Bup shoots us a half smile. His upper lip rises like he's got Elvis Presley's mouth, but it doesn't fit him right. He ought to give it back to Elvis before he ruins it.

Mrs. Miller walks into the kitchen and kisses Bup on the

cheek. "Oh, Bup," she says, "you're so kissable, don't deny it." Bup's turning red. "Your father will be ready in a minute." Mrs. Miller's teeth are big and white, almost horsey, but her smile is friendly, like she enjoys seeing David and me sitting in her kitchen with Bup. "Do you boys want something to eat?"

"We had scrambled eggs already," David says, and brags, "I made them."

"Oh, you did?" Mrs. Miller says nodding her head. "But maybe you'd like a Space Food Stick?"

"I'd like one," Bup says.

"For a kiss," Mrs. Miller says.

Bup groans as she kisses him on the cheek. Mrs. Miller gets three Space Food Sticks from a box in a cabinet and hands one to Bup. She gives me and David one, too, and before I know it, she's kissing me on the forehead. David smiles as she leans to kiss him on the forehead, too. It doesn't feel different from a kiss from any other mom on the block, and the moms like to kiss us kids a lot, except for Mrs. Grossman 'cause we never let her get close enough. Mrs. Miller still looks like a scarecrow, an ugly one, but her kiss is a mother's kiss. It probably means a lot to Bup to get kisses from her, and it probably means a lot to Bup that she gives them to us, too, and we don't seem to mind.

•   •   •

Space Food Sticks are nothing but cheap Tootsie Rolls. They don't have nearly enough chocolate in them, just enough to keep you from throwing them away. The one I ate made me dizzy, and the driving in the rain with the wipers beating doesn't help any.

Mr. Miller kinda drives like Mom, with the driver's seat pulled all the way up. He's such a big man and hunches over the steering wheel, even in his big Chrysler, looking like he might honk the horn with his belly. From the back seat, sitting behind Bup, I see Mr. Miller's black overcoat bunching over his shoulders, and the back of his head has got a fleshy fold in the back where his neck ought to be. Then the rest of his head is as round and bald as a balloon, and his cheeks push forward from his face real puffy. The whole thing reminds me of Kelly Kinder's VW Beetle sitting on top of Mr. Miller's shoulders, except Mr. Miller isn't orange. I thought really sick people started losing weight. Mr. Miller isn't losing weight at all, at least not in his head.

"It's nice of you to go to the bar mitzvah together," Mr. Miller says, clearing his throat. Bup winks his eyes over the headrest like a spy.

I'm getting queasier. It's not just 'cause of the Space Food Sticks, but also 'cause of the guilt I feel lying to Mr. Miller and knowing we're going to a bar mitzvah to do more lies. We're showing up pretending to be invited in front of hundreds of people just to use a free telephone. Like Bup said, that phone's probably not free to somebody, but we're gonna lie to the police about who we are, and then sneak out so nobody can ever find out it was us using the phone to call Atlanta. The worst thing is we're doing this all in a synagogue!— and God's watching, I'm sure of it. I never know if God's watching when I'm doing something good, but when I'm doing something full of lies, I feel certain God's watching, and not smiling about it either.

"Theodore Koning's a classmate of mine from fifth-grade math," Bup says.

I don't even think Theodore Koning goes to Eisenhower

K-8. He's a Devonshire boy, which is in Skokie but it's the rich section, with bigger houses and shady trees everywhere. The kids there go to Devonshire school and say what a wimpy school Eisenhower K-8 is. Bup's just practicing his lying, I guess, and he's really good.

"How's Theodore Koning in fifth-grade math and getting bar mitzvahed?" David says. "That makes him eleven. Don't you have to be thirteen to get bar mitzvahed?"

Bup says, "He's really in seventh, but he's smart and tutors us fifth-graders."

"What's that?" David says.

"Just helping the teacher. Theodore Koning's real smart and likes to be teacher's pet. He's such a show-off. Nobody likes him."

"Why are we going to his bar mitzvah, then?" David says.

I push my fist into David's side. "You know why, David."

"Oh, right," David says, and fake-coughs. "'Cause we're invited, right?"

"Right," Bup says. "You've got to go when you're invited. Even when you don't like somebody, you've got to go."

"I never saw that invitation," Mr. Miller says.

I belch up a nauseous taste of the Space Food Stick, thinking Mr. Miller's figured something out for sure. He holds his head straight, watching through the wipers.

Bup keeps humming along, saying, "We got them in school. His parents are cheapskates. They didn't want to spend money on stamps. But you got to go just to be nice, I guess."

"Um hm," Mr. Miller says. "You've got to be nice."

Bup's good, really good, and I guess it's good he's practicing and showing us how good he is before we get there. I'm just nervous about whether he'll keep going on saying lies until he says one he can't explain. I can't think anything bad about Bup 'cause he's just doing what I asked him to do. I'm every bit the liar he is even if he's doing it for me. Bup finally stops talking, and I focus my eyes on the back of his head to keep from feeling worse and throwing up.

•   •   •

The Skokie Jewish Congregation smells like a library
absolutely everywhere, even in the bathrooms. It's a deep,
serious smell that makes you feel guilty for not reading the
books. There aren't nearly as many books here as there are at
American school, but the books are so much older, and that's
why every one of them lets out an old-book smell that takes
at least a thousand American school books to match.

David asks me what the sign at the entrance means, *29th
of Heshvan, 5727*. I tell him that's the date and he's arguing
that it's not.

"It's November 12, 1966. By 5727, the astronauts are
sure to be flying in the Enterprise."

"That's the Jewish date, not the American date."

David wants to know what changed to cause people to
start all over with a new calendar 1,966 years ago. I shrug
'cause I don't know why. "It's too bad the Jewish calendar
didn't stay the regular calendar forever," he says, " 'cause it
would be 5727 for real and we could all be flying in the
Enterprise by now."

I tell him he's just not understanding, but he insists we
could've been spending all that time working on spaceships
instead of fighting over something silly like whose calendar
to follow.

It's 9:15 and the triple bar mitzvah is scheduled to start
in fifteen minutes. The Skokie Jewish Congregation's lobby is
stuffed with adults dressed up fancy and kids forced to dress
up fancy. People line up from the outside stairs to the building's entrance, packed into the lobby, and pressed to the
sanctuary's closed double doors. Parents tell their children
where to stand and not to slouch. The boys constantly pull at
their ties. Some boys forget they're wearing clip-ons and pull
them to the floor. Mothers lick their hands and slick spit into
their boys' hair to change Beatle bangs back into Elvis pom-

padours. The girls walk around as much as they can with the little room they have, in tight circles around their parents. They're watching their fancy dress shoes, making them click along the lobby's tiled floor to see how adult they can sound, like their mothers' high heels. Seems the girls are as tall as their mothers and certainly taller than most of the boys.

The sanctuary doors open out and the congregation stands at attention. The three bar mitzvah boys, in dark suits and choking black ties, begin to announce *Shabbat shalom!* kinda nasally, and they stumble over the words, starting, then stopping, and spying at each other 'cause they each want someone else to speak first. Rabbi Abrahms stands behind them raising his arms high to invite the congregation in. I can't tell one bar mitzvah boy from the next.

"They look scared," Bup says.

"That'll be you soon, Jeremy," David says.

I say, "I know," and we watch the frightened faces on the bar mitzvah boys get swept into the sanctuary by the entering congregation.

The Skokie Jewish Congregation is in the middle of building a huge addition in the back that's supposed to be the new sanctuary. The bricks are all in place, but the inside isn't done. Until then, services are held in the old sanctuary, a room that looks like the Eisenhower K-8 cafeteria, with its gray floor tiles, cinder block walls painted yellow, and florescent light fixtures that come down from a ceiling high enough to cover a second story. It's got a stage in front that's kinda big. That's where the Rabbi and Cantor and bar mitzvah boys will lead the service. There must be over three hundred folding chairs set up in row after row, and they're filling with parents and children wearing clothes they'd never wear except to a bar mitzvah, wedding, or funeral.

Bup, David, and I stand at the outside edge of the sanctuary doors letting people pass. Bup doesn't seem to know what to do with himself and he's gotten real quiet. I hope being in here doesn't change his mind about lying, or that being in a synagogue doesn't weaken his powers to lie like green kryptonite weakens Superman.

A part appears toward the back of the entering congregation, spreading forward, making room for Cantor Morton to enter the sanctuary without any interference with his grand, broad steps. He's wearing a black robe that swoops along the floor, flowing back capelike as if Cantor Morton is guided into the sanctuary by God's wind. Bup's eyes fly around in their sockets. He's probably never seen anyone like Cantor Morton before.

"*Jee*-sus," Bup says.

I tell Bup he probably shouldn't say that in here. I know he means it just as an expression, but I guess it might get him kicked out. Cantor Morton, without stopping, glares at Bup for a second before passing through the double doors. Bup doesn't know, he couldn't, that Cantor Morton hears everything.

"Jesus was Jewish," David says, "so it's okay, Bup. I bet Jesus even had to get bar mitzvahed when he turned thirteen."

"Jesus wasn't Jewish," Bup says.

"Yeah he was. That's what I learned here."

"That's just nonsense," Bup insists to David. "Why don't you make the telephone call if you can say stuff like that."

"It's not a lie. It's what they taught me." David looks at me like I should be agreeing out loud with him.

"I don't know about that, Bup," I say.

Bup says, "I'm not buying it."

"That was Cantor Morton in the black robe," I tell Bup.

"What's a cantor?"

"I thought you were Jewish, Bup," I say.

"Yeah, but I've never gone to a synagogue before. Dad says it's a bunch of hooey."

"What's a 'hooey?'" David says.

"I don't know exactly," Bup says. "When I was little, I thought it was some guy Dad didn't like. But now I think it can be anything Dad doesn't agree with. Dad doesn't think there's a God, that it's all hooey."

"I hope he doesn't say that out loud," David says. "God

might hear."

"Not if there isn't one."

"That's just stupid, Bup," David says.

"It's not stupid. It's hooey, like Dad says. You guys go to Hebrew school, I don't. Your Dad gets killed and mine's dying. What difference does it make for any of us?"

"God didn't kill Dad," David says pretty loud. Some ladies wearing lacy black hats turn back to stare at us.

"Quiet down, both of you," I say.

"I didn't say God killed your dad. But if there really is a God, why did he let it happen? Do you need a secret password or something?"

I'm not mad at Bup for saying these things. I go to Hebrew school and believe in being Jewish. Bobby Kinder went to Catholic school and believes in being Catholic. Bup stays at home and believes it's all hooey. I'm taught that Noah and Abraham and Moses did talk to God, and there is only one God, not a bunch of them like the Indians believe. And the Christian families have Jesus, who David insists was Jewish so I'm not sure what's going on with them. But Bup is right. It's hard for me to see how any of this made a difference for the Rosenbergs and the Millers.

The back of the congregation reaches the sanctuary entrance and I keep David and Bup at the sanctuary doors with me. I figure we can't sneak out of the sanctuary once we're in 'cause somebody might think something's up if three boys get up and walk out of a triple bar mitzvah together and don't come back. David's bound to knock something over on his way out. Bup might get lost in a trance during the service and forget to leave at all. I make them wait for everyone to go in the sanctuary, then head for the drinking fountain by the bathrooms down the hall. Mr. Trauby steps out from the sanctuary and looks ahead.

I whisper, "Get down," and we hunker low behind the drinking fountain. The fountain doesn't do much good hiding us 'cause Mr. Trauby could still see our three pairs of legs below it pretty easy if he decides to look our way down the hall, and we'd look real suspicious to him if he did. I hear the sanctuary's door handles being pulled and soon a solid clunk closes the congregation in the sanctuary. Raising my head over the fountain, we are alone.

"Ready to start?" Bup says. He's smiling like he can't wait. My head and stomach spin, and I hear my heart beating fast in my ears. I hope Bup remembers what he has to do.

"Follow me," I say.

We hurry past the closed sanctuary doors. Our dress shoes tap along the tiled floor, giving us away to anyone who might be listening. With a rush, congregation voices from the sanctuary rise up like every key on a piano's being struck at once— *Oh, my God, the soul with which thou didst endow me is pure!*

"God's watching! God's watching!" David says. "They're calling for God! He'll be here!"

We hurry down the stairs, away from the congregation busy calling for God. Bup's giving David a hard time, taunting, "I'm God! *Boo!*"

David flinches and Bup lets out a little laugh and says it again.

Everything's so easy for Bup, not believing in God, 'cause he doesn't have to try to figure things out. It's like not having to take a math test 'cause you've decided there's no such thing as math. I'm wishing I could be like Bup and believe there's no God 'cause I don't think God likes people lying long-distance over a Hebrew school's telephone.

The stairs take us down and around to the basement, toward the classrooms and the library with the Tam Tam crackers and fruit juice and the telephone. The ceiling's pretty low here and the hall is narrow. We rush along, listening to ourselves step and breathe. The walls have floor-to-ceiling pictures and print beside them telling what the pictures are showing— God creating the Earth and the heavens, and day and night, and Adam and Eve standing behind a large row of bushes.

Bup stops to look at one with a large pointing finger coming down through thick clouds surrounded by lightning and a man below with a long beard. The man wears white robes and his big round eyes stare in fear at the finger. Bup runs his hand around in circles over the clouds and lightning, then along the long arm and hand coming down.

"Is this supposed to be God?"

Bup's puffy face blanks into a glob of clay. He steps to the large print beside the picture and reads out loud, *God Talks to Abraham:*

Take now thy son, thine only son, whom thou lovest, even Isaac, and get thee into the land of Moriah and offer him there for a burnt-offering upon one of the mountains which I will tell thee of… And they came to the place which God had told him of, and Abraham built the altar there, and laid the wood in order, and bound Isaac his son, and laid him on the altar, upon the wood. And Abraham stretched forth his hand, and took the knife to slay his son… And the angel of the Lord called unto him out of heaven, and said… 'Lay not thy hand upon the lad, neither do thou anything unto him, for now I know that thou art a God-fearing man, seeing thou hast not withheld thy son, thine only son, from Me.'

Bup leans close to poor Abraham's fearful eyes. "That's a mean trick to pull on somebody," Bup says.

"It's not that simple," I say.

"Yes, it is. God's playing tricks on people. How do you explain that?"

David stands at the picture and says, "It's like a test. Abraham passed the test. I believe in God even though Dad died. I passed the test, too."

Bup wiggles his head about like he's making figure eight's in the air with his nose. "That's crazy," Bup says. "God could tell us he's around. Seems to me all those clouds and lightning bolts and God talking with that big finger of his would be enough to convince Abraham or anybody. If God did that at my house, I'd believe pretty quick. He doesn't have to kill my dad."

David kicks the toe of his shoe into the floor. "God didn't kill my dad," he says so soft I can barely hear him. "Somebody in Atlanta killed Dad."

"God didn't stop it and he could've. It's the same goddamn thing."

Bup's smiling his crooked smile. He's challenged God, sworn at him in our synagogue, and no clouds or lightning bolts or pointing fingers from the ceiling appear to scold him.

"Let's go," I say.

I tug at Bup's elbow-patched sweater sleeve. The sleeve stretches like a piece of rubber and Bup finally begins to give. Bup keeps hesitating at the pictures showing scenes from the Bible and words from the Ten Commandments painted gold in Hebrew and English on the wall. *Thou shalt not kill!* he snorts under his breath. I pull him along the hall, feeling his hesitations. He keeps wanting to stop and I keep pulling, as if he's a bad dog wanting to pee on all the trees.

Cupping my hands by my eyes, I peek through the sliver of glass beside the library door. The library is empty, lit by gray November light leaking through a basement window well. I blink and see my eyes staring back at me half-reflected in the glass. My eyes are ghost eyes in the glass, and I have to concentrate through them to see inside the room.

The walls are lined top to bottom with books as thick as dictionaries, and pamphlets cover the table and podium where Rabbi Abrahms serves us the before-school Tam Tam crackers and fruit juice punch. Near one corner, there's an old desk cluttered with papers and books, and a plastic chair pushed back behind it at an angle. The yellow telephone sits in the middle of the desk, facing the chair as if it's been waiting for us. My hand reaches for the doorknob and turns. David and Bup huddle behind me, leaning forward at my back. There's a little pop from the door jamb and air rushes out of the room into our faces. The heavy smell of ancient books blows up my nose.

"Keep the lights off," I say. "Our eyes will get used to it."

Bup pushes through ahead of me and walks directly to the desk. David closes the door behind us and it clicks shut. There aren't any other chairs in the room except the plastic one Bup's pulling up to the desk. It's colorless in here, like being inside a black and white TV show with the brightness knob turned far back to dim.

"Do you have the information?" Bup says. I have to look at Bup square in the face to make sure it's him. His voice is deep and adult-sounding.

"Is that the voice you're using, Bup?" I say.

"Detective Bartlett," Bup says. "Who's Bup?" In this room, Bup's lips seem to move like they're in a movie that's got the sound a half-second behind the picture.

"That's good, Bup," I say. The paper in my pocket is folded over four times and I hand it to Bup. He unfolds it slowly and it sounds like oil sizzling in a frying pan. "The phone number's on the top. The date of the accident, the highway, my father's full name and birthday are below it. Find out everything you can, Bup. Try to see what they got."

"Detective Bartlett, son." Bup lowers his big head to the paper and begins.

The telephone dial winds up then clicks along like fingertips being rapped on a desk. Bup leans back in the chair and its metal legs make an official sounding office squeak on the tiled floor. He's got the telephone receiver pinched between the side of his head and shoulder, his arms folded so the elbow patches stick out thick and muscled-looking. David and I lean over the desk toward Bup.

"Hello. Good morning, Atlanta police. Who am I talking to?— Sergeant Fenmore? Good morning, Sergeant Fenmore. I'm Detective Bartlett of the Skokie Police. That's Skokie, Illinois, right by Chicago— No, it's to the north of Chicago— Yes, correct— I'm doing a follow-up investigation of a crash involving one of our residents on I-20 in your fair city last..."

Bup rustles the piece of paper I gave him by the telephone mouthpiece.

"Let me check the reports your department's already mailed to me. That's it, last October. October 9, 1965— Your traffic patrol division? Lieutenant Reese? Oh, yes, that's the one. Connect me right away. I'll hold. Thank you and have a great day, Sergeant Fenmore— Oh, you're welcome."

Bup's confident. His body stays still in his chair as he tells lies in our synagogue to policemen. Sticking a pen behind an ear, squaring his chin, he's Detective Bartlett, and he's expecting answers. David urges, "Find out who did it, Detective Bartlett."

"Yes, who am I speaking to?" Bup says.

My insides freeze up listening to Bup in control. His lips move in shapes far different from the words I hear, like he forms the word *dog* with his mouth and out comes *cat*.

"Lieutenant Reese?— Yes, how are you today?— Oh, yes, I can understand, but I guess crime keeps us all in business— Yes, it's a sad truth. Listen, I want to thank your department for sending that report to my office— Skokie Police Department in Illinois— That's right near Chicago— It was a multi-vehicle accident report involving, let me see here again— Alan H. Rosenberg, that's middle name, Harris. It's a D-O-B of five, five, thirty— Uh-huh, Uh-huh— Sure, I'll hold— Do you need my badge number?— That's fine, I'll hold."

"Bup!" I say, and I place my hand over my mouth realizing what a squawk I just made. Bup lowers the phone and glares at me to let me know I'm interfering with Detective Bartlett's investigation. "Why'd you offer a badge number, Bup? He can check that!"

"Bartlett," he says a little peeved, like "Bup" is some insect swirling around his head. "I offered it up before he could ask me for it. Now he's not going to ask me for it at all, and he's not going to check me out. The trick about lying," Bup says like adding up one plus one, "is sounding like you've already told the truth." Bup looks directly at David.

"It's the first commandment in the hooey religion."

"This is horrible," David says. "Find out, find out."

"I'm going to find out, my boy."

"Stop doing that," I say.

"Stop doing what?"

"Acting like a big shot, like we're your boys. Just do it right, Bup. Don't blow it. Don't say something you can't get out of."

"Detective Bartlett, son."

Bup raises the receiver to his mouth, looking like his face is made of Silly Putty, his eyebrows and eyes, his nose, cheeks, and chin, all melting into the phone, reaching into Atlanta.

"Yes, I'm still here— I wish I could read the police report number. It's chicken scribbles— Yes, yes, that's it— That's the one I got, but I've only got the one page— No, no, I don't have the second and third page— I just need the name of the guy— Yes, the family's been asking questions. I think they're hiring some lawyer to sue— No name?"

Bup looks up at me, placing his hand over the mouth-piece, and says, "No name, son."

"Find out what they got, just do that."

"Listen, Lieutenant Reese. You mean to tell me there's a big pile-up on one of your highways and you've got no one to blame a year later?" Bup's voice deepens and scolds into the mouthpiece like he's making to bite it off. "The truck driver died, Lieutenant. I've got a dead man on my hands here and a family that's got money, you know what I mean? Lots of money. I need to get answers before we both get Perry Mason on our butts."

David shrieks, "Bup! Don't say 'Perry Mason' !" — and slaps his hands to his mouth.

Bup whisper-shouts, "Quiet, son. It's a crime to impede an investigation."

We've lost Bup. We've got Detective Bartlett and I can't control him. His voice is booming into the telephone, like God's into the desert ordering Abraham to slay his son.

"We're in big trouble," David says all worried. "Perry Mason's just a rerun now."

"What investigation did you guys do?— Why'd you stop?— What do you mean you don't know why, doesn't the report say?— It just ends?— I know it's not your investigation, but what do you have on the report?"

Bup takes the pen from behind his ear and begins to write.

"Partial plate, uh-huh. Paint color matches. Three possible trucks, two tow-trucks— Do you have car repair records?— Why not? Why not?" Bup throws the pen in the air and slaps his fist on the desk as if Atlanta can see what he's doing. It sounds like he's got Lieutenant Reese crying. Detective Bartlett booms on, "You've got a partial plate and three possible trucks? Seems to me that would be enough, man, but then I'm just a detective— Don't apologize— Stop apologizing— I need answers— Stop— Just get me who's in charge, son, and we can forget I know your name."

Bup twirls the paper around and shows me: *One tow truck, one pick-up, both red, brought in for repairs at Lou's, October 17, 1965. One tow truck, totaled at Stumper Bumper's Repair, October 16, 1965. Partial plate found at scene, 371… no names.*

Bup's right, I'm thinking. How come they couldn't get a name with all that? How come the newspaper page didn't say anything about the plate number? Bup's forehead crinkles up and he brings his voice down so low like he's the great-grandpa of all detectives.

"Yes, I'm Detective Bartlett from— Yes—" and Bup sputters to a stop.

A voice deeper and louder than Detective Bartlett's barks out the earpiece.

Go to hell, Bartlett— you and Rosenberg's lawyer can go to hell!

Bup's eyes widen at the explosion of cursing coming from the phone. It blows Detective Bartlett off Bup's face. The crinkles and folds in his skin vanish, and he's just Bup again, plump-cheeked and pale. Bup drops the receiver on the desk and the earpiece lets us have it. We're frozen by the words. The hatred is new to me, and I'm sure to David and Bup. In the synagogue's library, the phone connects us to another place we've never known before.

To hell with you, Bartlett. I've got the goddamn coloreds running around trashing downtown Atlanta, Bartlett, and you want me to bother with a dead Jew? That's one less Jew to help the coloreds. I'm not bothering, Bartlett! Goddamn! Goddamn! There aren't any more reports for you, Bartlett! I don't give a goddamn! Rosenberg's just a dead Jew!

We jolt up in our dress shoes as the line pounds shut and disconnects.

The echo of these words will remain in my mind forever, I believe, a secret about the world I never wanted to hear. We're boys, that's all, and we've brought hateful words to the Skokie Jewish Congregation library, and the air inside has become thick and smelly and hard to breathe. We let the words in without knowing. How could we have known? I have no idea what to do with these words. They tell me I'm hated by people I've never met, and they hate Bup, David, and my father. They don't care about my dead father. They're glad I have a dead father.

"I've got a good start," Bup squeaks, no longer Detective Bartlett.

David begins to cry and calls out Dad's name. "What did they do to him, Jeremy? What really killed him?" His eyes fill with tears and his face begs me to do something, but there's nothing to do. David grabs the telephone receiver and slaps the earpiece into his palm as if he's pounding a baseball into a new mitt. Even in the November light, his face grows red. He takes the receiver and slams it on the desk. The noise claps sharp in my ears, and the books lining the walls snap back like gunfire. Again he slams it, again and again.

David screams— *How do you like it? How do you like it?*— and he pounds the phone so hard it seems to thump inside my chest.

Rushing into the library, Mr. Trauby grabs at David's arm, but David slips one swing of his arm free, and the receiver hits the desk again. With a crack, the earpiece splits and a circle of yellow plastic rolls away across the desktop. David grits his teeth and shakes his fist above the broken receiver, its wires and earpiece guts dangling out.

How do you like it? How do you like it?

Mr. Trauby holds David, only half-containing David's struggle to fight something he can't see. My Hebrew teacher's prayer shawl, his *tallit,* slips off his shoulders and floats to the floor. The receiver lands beside the *tallit* and throws out pieces, broken and disconnected. Mr. Trauby looks so sad at his prayer shawl on the floor with the broken plastic and metal. But I'm not going to move to pick up anything. I'm just going to watch it, and try not to think for a moment about what really happened to my father.

•   •   •

Mr. Trauby's office is one big apology. Sorry for being so small, sorry this is all we got for you, sorry about this little desk and chair, sorry about not having a window, sorry about the light switch being in the Rabbi's big office next door. The light goes on and Mr. Trauby returns. He has to squeeze through us, and the space between the wall and the edge of his desk, to get to his desk chair. He brushes by me, and I feel the warmth of his body and the smell of sweat in his wool suit jacket.

David and I sit in a straight-back wooden chair in front of Mr. Trauby's desk, sharing it, each of our butts hanging part way over opposite sides. Bup's standing and taking small nervous steps beside us. He finally sits in a pink plastic chair shaped like a soup ladle. A crack in the back creaks as Bup settles in.

Mr. Trauby sits at his small desk, resting one hand on his *tallit,* which he has kissed and folded on top of a purse-sized pouch. Maybe something bad happened to it when it touched the ground. A broken telephone is just that, but Mr. Trauby cuddles his *tallit* like a pet that's been trained to help him talk directly to God. I'm hoping it's not broken, or dead. I wouldn't want to be responsible for killing Mr. Trauby's *tallit*.

The chair holds Mr. Trauby high against his desk, and he hunches low to rest his elbows on the desktop, reading again and again the paper with Bup's notes. His eyes beam into the paper, and I follow his stare as it moves across each word, then returns to start over. His fingers loosen and the page slips across the desk to one side. Cupping his hands, Mr. Trauby stares at me through his black-framed glasses, steadily, not once glancing at David or Bup.

Then Mr. Trauby says something I think is kinda odd, not 'cause his words are complicated, they aren't. They just mess up my thoughts even more than before.

"You know, Jeremy, you certainly don't *look* Jewish."

I feel like Mr. Trauby's accused me of some sort of crime in this synagogue. "I look like my father," I say. I jab David with my elbow. "David does, too, even more than I do. I can't speak for Bup."

Bup shifts about in his chair. It's not so easy being Jewish and saying you don't believe in it, or God, to a Hebrew school teacher. David doesn't help Bup any.

"Bup's hoo-ish, or hooey-ish," David says like reading a fact from a dictionary. Bup can't help but droop his big face. It's hard to figure out what Bup's face is gonna look like at any time of the day, let alone say it looks like a particular religion. Mr. Trauby goes on about my face.

"I know you're Jewish, Jeremy, but if it weren't for your last name, I'd guess you for a *Goyim*."

Mr. Trauby's talk reminds me of a story Mom's told us more than once, about being reluctant to marry Dad when he first asked her. *I don't like your last name, Al. It sounds funny to me, like roses on icebergs, or a rose iceberg.* But she married Dad, obviously, in spite of his last name, or 'cause her last name had been Finkelwitz up to then and figured at least

Rosenberg wasn't any worse.

"Do you know what it means to some people to say, 'That person looks Jewish?'" Mr. Trauby seems to be serious, so I tell him as seriously as I can that I really don't know.

"I want to get home to eat," David sniffs. "Hurry up and give him an answer."

"But I don't have one."

"Let's see," Mr. Trauby begins, breathing in like some kid trying to belch the alphabet in one breath. "'That person looks Jewish' means— Short kinky hair, a big nose— a huge nose with a bump like a curled knuckle right in the middle— and dark brown beady eyes, weak chin, and dark skin like a tan in the winter. And the things 'That Jewish person' has under his shoes and hair— *Oy!* There's hooved feet and pointy horns under Jewish shoes and hair! And the money, oh, the money 'That Jewish person' has!— he owns banks, his parents own banks, his grandparents and great-grandparents own banks, and he plans to take over the world with all his money in his banks! Why, the first words 'That Jewish person' spoke as a babe was, 'Where's my money?'— and his *Bubbie* and *Zadie* stopped counting their stash of gold bars long enough to snap their fingers and create a bank on Main Street, with gold deposits for their little Jew."

Mr. Trauby points to the center of his large nose, at a bump the shape of a curled knuckle. He then runs his hand over the top of his forehead, pretending he's pushing strands of long hair off his eyes. There's no need for that 'cause his hair's as short and thick as brush-bristles, and it pokes up on its own and probably would go on poking up even if someone dumped a bucket of water on his head. I follow his hand to the small black *kipah* centered on the crown of his head. His skin is brown, like a tan in the winter. Mr. Trauby then points to his chin, a weak chin that fades from his lower lip.

"I'm Jewish!" he says, holding his palms up. "I don't have to say so, do I? I'm a walking road sign for what Jewish is supposed to look like. But I don't have rich parents, I don't have any gold, and my savings account passbook couldn't buy a piggy bank. But look at you, Jeremy. Everything about you says you're a Christian. You have a nose as straight as a popsicle stick, you have Beatle hair, you have blue eyes, you have skin that probably gets tan only when you've been outside too long in the summer." He winks at me through his glasses, and smiles, whispering like someone might overhear who shouldn't. "You look like a Christian, Mr. Rosenberg. As long as you don't use your real last name, you can sneak into churches for our side and see what's going on."

Mr. Trauby talks as if religions were sports teams or something, competing for the world championship of God's attention.

"Be assured," he says, "when that last policeman heard your father's name, he figured your father had that big bumpy nose, kinky hair, brown beady eyes, weak chin, dark skin, and probably the hooves and horns and the banks and money and the desire to control the world, even knowing he drove a truck for a living. You go to Atlanta and introduce yourself to that man, tell him you're a Rosenberg, and he'll see you— he'll see that you look exactly like me."

Mr. Trauby looks at my face, examining me, probably looking for my reaction, a shudder or groan, to the thought of looking like him. "Do you now believe you know what that Atlanta policeman was thinking?"

It seems right to apologize, and I do, quietly, but loud enough in this small office. It must sound silly to Mr. Trauby to hear me say I'm sorry. It doesn't fit his question, like I might not understand what he's been saying. He's talking again— *You need to learn why that policeman hates you, Mr. Rosenberg. You need to gain strength in knowledge*— he's trying to be helpful about the Atlanta policeman and my father.

I know my thoughts when I go to Grandmaland, how a lot of times I stare at the Grandmalanders in their dark clothes, pulling their odd shopping carts before Sabbath arrives, seeing something about their faces that makes them different from the good people on TV, feeling glad not to be *them.* Maybe I do know what the Atlanta policeman is thinking, at least some of it, a small part of it, and it's hard for me to look at Mr. Trauby without feeling ashamed.

Mr. Trauby stands and pats his stomach. "Are you boys hungry for an early lunch? My wife's got my favorite leftovers ready." David makes his *yes* fly out before I can even think about it. "Let's get your coats. We'll walk to my apartment. I only live a block from here."

I think we're all interested in seeing what the inside of a Hebrew schoolteacher's apartment looks like. Mr. Trauby gathers his *tallit* and slips it inside the blue pouch along with the paper with the telephone number and Detective Bartlett's notes. David skips out the small office, shouting to Bup, "You'll see about God!"

As we walk by the sanctuary doors, a bar mitzvah boy sings in Hebrew. His voice stumbles, and his fight to sing either all high or all low is made loud by a microphone and speakers. Standing by the lobby exit to snap, zip, and button ourselves into our coats, we hear Rabbi Abrahms ask the boy to now read the passage in English. The boy's words vibrate, his voice cracking under the attack of puberty and snickering children in the congregation:

> *From Haftorah Toledoth, Malachai Chapter Two,*
> *Verses One through Three—And now, this command-*
> *ment is for you, O ye priests. If ye will not hearken,*
> *and if ye will not lay it to heart, to give glory unto*
> *My name, saith the Lord of hosts, then will I send*
> *the curse upon you, and I will curse your blessings;*
> *yea, I curse them, because ye do not lay it to heart.*
> *Behold I will rebuke the seed for your hurt, and will*
> *spread dung upon your faces, even the dung of your*
> *sacrifices; and ye shall be taken away unto it.*

To these words, Mr. Trauby begins rocking and bending his knees. David, a brown fuzzy puff in his cloth coat, hops behind Bup, warning, "Listen, listen, I told 'ya! The curse is upon you!" Bup doesn't appear to be bothered any, but I guess fear of being wrong about God and being hooeyish can hide pretty easily in his fleshy face.

It's suddenly a heavy feeling being Jewish, like there's no fun in it, only danger. I'm taught to believe in God, *or else!* —like some unbeatable bully on a playground demanding attention and lunch money. What kinda God is that? And if I do believe in God, if I'm Jewish, other people will want to bully me anyway, and God won't keep it from happening. Maybe God will show up eventually, but only when it's too late, my father long dead and buried.

Outside, I look for lightning bolts and wait for the curse to fall upon me 'cause of the things I've been thinking. It doesn't happen. We gather beneath Mr. Trauby's umbrella. Though his umbrella hovers low over our heads as we walk to his apartment, the cold wind and drizzle find our faces and sting us like tiny pellets, and we draw tighter to Mr. Trauby's side.

•   •   •

Mr. Trauby's apartment is the upper floor of a two-floor building. A living room and dining room area form one square. It has one bedroom, one bath, and a kitchen barely large enough to hold a small, round table. Though everything looks put away, the apartment feels messy, as if all the books, papers, and record albums are expecting to be used at any moment, and Mr. Trauby's wife is obviously black, even after I blink hard at her to make sure I'm not mistaken.

Mr. Trauby's wife is only the second black person I've ever met. Missy Grossman has a young black lady, Ruby, come over once every other week to clean house. I don't know why 'cause Missy Grossman cleans all the time and ropes things off afterwards with her vault-closing mean look. She cleans up right before Ruby comes, then follows Ruby around watching her clean the already clean house, and then cleans up something after Ruby leaves, maybe a thought of future dirt. Ruby's so polite and quiet even though she should be bopping Missy Grossman on the head for tailing her around like a spy. I can't say honestly that I have *met* Ruby, I've just seen her, been in the same room with her a couple times, and know who she is. I could never get over the fact of Ruby's deep brown face.

For the last several years at Eisenhower K-8, my teachers have said, *Don't hate black people, don't hate Indians, don't hate Christians (if you're Jewish), don't hate Jews (for the two or three Christians in class)*. We all nod our approval and agreement and go on to multiplication tables. We never stop to wonder why we don't have any black people or Indians in our classroom sitting and nodding along with us.

Bup, David, and I watch Mr. Trauby kiss his black wife— they kiss like they can't help themselves, as Arnold Grossman has explained, a real passionate *tuchas* kinda kiss. We watch them like we'd watch the sun at midday, drifting our stares away from the action so we know it's there going on in our side vision, but not direct 'cause it's too bright, too powerful. I'm thinking of her dark skin. I'd be lying to myself if I tried to think of something else about her. I know if Mr. Trauby came down Loblolly Avenue with his black wife, all the houses would be whispering, *Who's that schvartze?* I wouldn't 'cause I've been taught not to, but I would think it and try to fight thinking it. I'm feeling afraid to talk, like I know I'm going to say the wrong thing about being married to a black lady.

Mr. Trauby tells us she's from Jamaica, but her name can be found in any town in America— Mary, simply Mary, not shortened from anything more exotic. She says hello to us in an accent that's British, but nicer somehow, "A Jamaican accent," Mr. Trauby explains. She steps down the line of boys, hearing our names, kissing us quickly on our foreheads. Her kiss stays cool on my skin, and it tickles, but I force myself to ignore it. Wiping it away would be unfriendly, even if I'm thinking she could've left some of Mr. Trauby's spit behind along with hers.

"Bup?" she says. "Your name's Bup?"

Bup looks shocked at how beautiful she is, his face-fat pushed aside to show his goofy, tilted smile. She is beautiful. Her face is heart-shaped, with cheeks that rise to her wide dark eyes, and narrows quickly toward her chin, and her chin has a small dent in it, same as Karl Grossman's, only it's pretty sitting on her chin. She's at least a half-foot taller than me, and she's got curves showing through her gray slacks and dark blue shirt that are at least as good as Kelly Kinder's. Her hair is black, combed back straight and as thick as a three-layer cake. She wears a colorful scarf wound up like a towel meant to snap at a kid's butt in a locker room. It goes over her head like a crown and tucks beneath her ears, and makes a bow in the back.

"Bup," she says again in her Jamaican voice. "How unusual."

Even Bup seems surprised to hear his name pronounced as if it could be in a poem. She steps to Bup, extending her hand. Bup's looking at her palm, his eyes moving about in tiny jerks at her palm's much whiter skin, as white as our skin.

Bup says concerned, "Does the brown wear off?"

Mary doesn't say anything right away. She reaches for Bup's hand and shows him his own palm, and then his hand's back side. She repeats her gentle twisting and says, "See? — darker, lighter; darker, lighter. It's the same with you as with me. We're no different, Mr. Bup. I just start out with a deep tan, the kind you try to get all summer long." Bup starts inspecting his hand, wide-eyed, as if seeing it for the first time. "It doesn't hurt me if you ask such questions, Mr. Bup, especially if you just don't know and you want to learn about me. I asked Gregory when I first met him if it was a tradition for Jewish parents to break their little children's noses to make that bump. My mum taught me that when I was a little girl. Gregory told me my mum was all wrong and that he broke his nose all by himself when he fell out of a tree." She inspects our faces. "Looks like none of your noses has fallen from trees yet."

"Bup fell from a tree once," I say.

Bup says, "But I didn't land on my nose."

"Who's Gregory?" David says.

"That's my husband. I suppose you think 'Mr. Trauby' is his first name, too?" She's watching me, smiling. "Would you like to ask me a question, Jeremy?"

"I don't have one," I say, stuffing my hands in my coat pockets.

"Sure you do," she says. "C'mon. It won't hurt and I won't bite." Mr. Trauby stands behind her, rubbing her shoulders. He shows me, without meaning to, exactly what Jewish is supposed to look like. So I ask the question I've been thinking about since meeting Mary Trauby.

"Are you Jewish?"

"Are you saying you don't know?"

"I guess I don't know."

"Are you thinking I could be Jewish?"

"I don't know anything anymore," I say. "Anything's possible."

"I think I'm not going to answer you, Jeremy. I want you to keep your lovely thought, that anything is possible."

Mary takes our coats and finds room for them in a stuffed closet. She puts on music from an album with a longhaired man pictured on it, but it's like nothing I've ever heard before. "It's Tchaikovsky," she says. "*Capriccio Italien.* Do you boys listen to classical music? No? I bet all you listen to is pop music. I sometimes listen to that. But do you wonder why pop songs are less than three minutes long? Maybe they don't have a lot to say. Pop music can make your body move. Classical music makes your imagination move."

We sit at the round table in the small kitchen off the living-room-dining-room square, our faces close together as we push our five chairs in. Mary's serving us reheated chicken soup, and brings out a batch of perfectly round-looking matzo balls. Mary plops three— and they do go *plop*—in each of our bowls, like she was expecting extra company. Mr. Trauby thanks her and she runs back to the stove much the way Grandma Elaine does, but Mary soon sits with a bowl for herself.

"Listen to this part of the music," she says. "I see in my mind a circus coming to town, with elephants and giraffes, and horses dressed up to pull royal coaches."

Once during second grade at Eisenhower K-8, I rushed to the bathroom to do business, and there was Principal Newman at a stand-up toilet, seeming to be in a rush himself. The little toilet looked the size of a bucket on the floor with Principal Newman towered over it. He turned and laughed at my jaw-dropping face. *Teachers too, Jeremy*, he said. My joints feel filled with gunk trying to eat in front of Mr. Trauby and his wife. *Teachers too,* I repeat to myself. Teachers get married and *tuchas* passion kiss and do bathroom business and eat chicken soup. To me, it's not comfortable watching teachers do these things, it's not natural. My soup spoon weighs a ton, and I can barely eat at all.

Bup finishes his first bowl just as Mary announces that the music reminds her of riding fast horses. Bup takes his second bowl. The soup is good, full of spice and rich chicken taste. And it's wonderful how the apartment doesn't smell like it's wearing a layer of it, 'cause Mary Trauby says she knows enough to slow-cook it on the back porch. Grandma Elaine must make chicken soup all wrong. Salt and tap water don't have to be the only ingredients. I'd love to see Grandma Elaine come over to Mary Trauby's apartment so a black Jamaican lady can teach her how to make tasty chicken soup and *k'naidelakh*.

"Can I have yours?" David says, scooping his spoon under one of my three matzo balls. It rises from my bowl in David's spoon toward my face, and I snort a laugh at the bald-headed baby *k'naidel* creature. David frowns at my snort so near the matzo ball and whines, "Oh, now I can't eat it," and it splashes back into my soup bowl.

"No *k'naidelakh*, Jeremy?" Mary says. Mr. Trauby's drawing his large spoon out of his mouth and squeezes his lips together to keep the juices from leaking out.

"No *k'naidelakh?*" he asks.

K'naidelakh—that's Grandma Elaine's word, and hearing it spoken out loud makes me relax a bit and stare so hungry at them, poking up like islands in my soup bowl. I cut a wedge of *k'naidel* using the side of my spoon and slip it into my mouth. I chew it, my first successfully chewed *k'naidel* since the famous eighteen I ate as a nine-year-old.

Bup bites into one he holds in his hand like an apple. "Good *k'naidelakh,*" Bup says, and with that I snort *k'naidel* out my nose, fit-laughing like an idiot, just like the last time I tried. It sends Mr. Trauby into his own laughing fit. "Mm, good *k'naidelakh,*" I say, and Mr. Trauby starts laughing so hard I think he's got *k'naidel* bits coming up his nose, just like me.

Capriccio Italien rushes to an end, a swaying march of soldiers in red and gold uniforms, according to Mary Trauby. The soldiers carry gallant, glittering flags, and ride head-held-high horses. The horses are trimmed in gold tassels and raise their flowing tails to drop *k'naidelakh* horse poops to the earth. That's what Mary says she has in her *Capriccio Italien* vision now, thanks to me and Mr. Trauby. Kissing Mr. Trauby, then me, on our heads, she says, "I shall remember you forever, Jeremy, every time I play this music."

I think I might remember Mary Trauby forever no matter how old I get, no matter how many black people I get to know in my life. She's a good listener, and I know what her face looks like, not just its color. I'm not stupid enough to forget that many people have their minds made up about her, like that Atlanta policeman, with thoughts that are both mean and untrue. I might have thought such things if I had never eaten chicken soup with Mary Trauby in her tiny kitchen with my brother and Bup.

Mary offers to drive us home and Mr. Trauby keeps the piece of paper with the Atlanta information written on it. Mr. Trauby says he's friends with a black pastor ACLU-member lawyer all wrapped up in one person who lives in Atlanta. He might be able to help. As we leave, he says, "You should talk to your mother."

I don't know what a black pastor ACLU-member lawyer is. Mary Trauby says as she drives that it's everything that Atlanta policeman is probably afraid of.

"Good," David says from the back seat.

Bup drops his big head on David's shoulder and manages to fill the air in Mary Trauby's car, burping chicken soup in his sleep most of the drive to Loblolly Avenue. David grunts trying to get Bup's head back up. It's a hopeless fight for him. Bup's head is too much weight. David wants to know if I think Bup's become Jewish now.

"I don't know," I say.

Mary Trauby tsks at me and reminds me of my own thought, "Anything's possible, Jeremy."

"He's Jewish now," David decides, shrinking beneath Bup's head. "I saw him eat five *k'naidels*. I think he is."

•   •   •

I guess I expected immediate action once Mr. Trauby said his black pastor ACLU-member lawyer friend might help. All those titles made him sound like a superhero. But I heard nothing up to Thanksgiving Day. In Hebrew school, Mr. Trauby didn't act any different toward me, and I didn't try any harder in class beyond what I felt was necessary to pass. I did answer his question, though, "What does it mean to be Jewish?" I answered, "It can be tough sometimes." Mr. Trauby smiled a little and said, "Jeremy Rosenberg's been thinking about it. Good!"

I didn't talk to Bup except once at Eisenhower K-8. The teachers have us walk in two straight rows down the hall as we make our way to the cafeteria. Bup's class was coming back from there. I waved at Bup 'cause even if he's as dense as his five *k'naidelakh*, he did a really good job as Detective Bartlett. He's going to Hollywood one day or he's going to be shot dead, or both, I decided after his performance. So I waved and nodded and smiled at him.

As our lines slid by, he whispered to me, "Dad's in the hospital for tests only. He'll be home today. Come over after Thanksgiving dinner."

Bup reached for my arm, his fingertips grasping my wrist. Our teachers scolded us to move along, and I whipped my arm down, breaking his grip, saying, "No— I just can't come over," surprising both me and Bup with my fight to be left alone. Something about his voice, sounding like I was his last chance to have a friend, that we would be linked forever as dead-father boys if I became his friend. His fingertips felt bony and sharp, and he glared at his hand I broke away from with a smart look in his eyes that I had never seen before. Without looking at me, he walked away in his line of fifth-graders. He seemed thinner, much thinner than just a week ago, his knit slacks flapping as large as tents around his legs.

I've done a bad thing to Bup.

We've got Grandma Elaine and Grandpa Erwin over, and Ida Lipshilts and Big Ben. They all thought the same thing, *Can't leave Grace Rosenberg alone on her first Thanksgiving after ... well, you know.* None of them says it for real, but it seems pretty obvious watching them trying to change the subject every time Mom wants to talk about Dad.

Grandma Elaine is pretty useless as a turkey cook. It looks like a chicken, just larger, but preparing it for dinner is far beyond her abilities in the kitchen. Mrs. Lipshilts bastes the turkey with a long brush, her cigarette dangling, being careful to flick her ashes into an empty glass on the counter before they get too long and fall.

"How much longer?" Big Ben says.

"Three more hours," Mrs. Lipshilts says back.

"Hours shmowers," Grandpa Erwin says. "Should've made a chicken, we'd be eating by now."

We sit around the TV watching football game after football game, and Grandpa Erwin *Ahchs!* the whole day long. He *Ahchs!* at things both teams do wrong, all the time, so it's impossible to figure out which team he's rooting for.

When we start eating the Thanksgiving turkey, Cheryl

watches me every chance she can get. Between bites of food and sips of soft drinks, she stares, even during them. When I set my stare at hers she doesn't look away, so I have to look away, and keep eating, pretending I haven't noticed what she's doing. And she stares at David when she's not staring at me, the same strange way. She doesn't talk, she doesn't smile or frown. She's in neutral, a blank piece of coloring paper waiting for someone to draw an expression.

This Thanksgiving Day numbs me, all cloudy but refusing to rain, and the dinner goes by with talk that doesn't seem to matter much. When company leaves, they hug us one by one, harder than usual, even Grandpa Erwin. He hugs me hard and says he loves me in my ear. He's never done that before, but it only reminds me of the pity on the adults' faces.

Mrs. Lipshilts and Grandma Elaine have pretty much cleaned up after dinner so our house is cleaner than it was before the day started. So it's a bit odd watching Mom decide to do some more cleaning.

Mom starts taking piles of Dad's stuff out of her bedroom and sets them up in bundles on the dining room table. I watch her do this all late evening long without offering to help. I'm not being lazy. I just think that if I do anything to interfere with what she's doing, even to help, that something might go pop, and she'll cry or scream. As it is, she keeps marching like a robot, her face still and firm. By bedtime, the dining room table, where we had our first Thanksgiving dinner without Dad, is completely covered with his stuff— his shirts, his slacks, his motorcycle racing films, and his personal things like shaving razors, combs, and aftershave. It's all either going into the garbage or going to Good Will.

Mom has papers in piles and sorts through them to see what to keep. Most go into the garbage, even the yellow folded envelope Grandma Elaine made me take. Mom tears that to pieces, flexing the muscles in her chin as she makes it too ripped up to even think about taping back together. When she's through, she sits at the dining room table and just kinda dazes at it all. When she finally speaks to me, her voice is so unexpected it makes me flinch.

"Jeremy, I need your help with the mattress."

I don't know what she means, I just follow her into her bedroom. She tells me to lift the foot end while she lifts from the head end. The mattress sags in the middle and we drag it across the floor to get it moving.

"Where're we going?" I say.

"I'm throwing it out."

I don't ask why 'cause I know, or at least I know why I'd throw it out if I were her. She may have other reasons, but I doubt it. I have to look away from the uneven circle, the deep red-brown stain near one corner at the head end. Mom can't look at it either. We do our best to ignore it, tugging and pulling the mattress until we get it out of the house and dumped by the garbage cans.

"Thank you, Jeremy," she says, and she walks back to our house just as robotic as she was taking Dad's stuff out to the dining room table.

Cheryl's voice mouse-squeaks behind the garage, letting me know she's there, but hiding. She steps out and the light from the kitchen window shows her face full of anger, as if her blank stares at dinner had been holding back her emotions.

"What have you and David done?" she says. And her mouth clenches, and her jaw muscles work, like they want to grind me up. Her eyes narrow and cast spells at me. If she really could cast spells, I'm hexed.

"We've done nothing," I say, beginning to walk to the house. Cheryl darts around me.

"You have, don't deny it!"

Cheryl shows me a regular white envelope all crumpled up at the corner in her fist. She shoves it in my chest and demands I read the letter inside out loud. I have to focus it in the light from the kitchen window, but I can make it out. It's addressed to me, but I've never seen it. I pull out the paper.

We have the name of the person who might have been responsible for your father's accident. Talk to me after Hebrew school next time.
Mary and Gregory Trauby.

I shout at Cheryl, "Why are you taking my mail? You're as bad as David!" The light goes out in the kitchen and I can barely see her.

"I didn't mean to kill Dad!" she cries. "Leave me alone!"

I try to grab her, but her body's as tense as wires strung tight together. Whipping about, running through shadows, Cheryl looks like she's breaking into puzzle pieces as she runs to our house.

Nighttime has a way of making me think strange thoughts, especially when I'm alone and outside, and my sister's just confessed to killing our dad, although not meaning to. Maybe she's in the house confessing to Mom. Maybe Cheryl's going to hide her guilt, inside her brain, and she'll show it in her brooding, or let it pop out to attack David.

I sit on the wet grass and feel the moisture work its way through my jeans and BVDs to my skin. The old mattress is as good a thing to lean against as any. It's garbage, with all my father's other things piled up along the alley. The letter I had hoped for floats away from me, blowing down the alley with a bunch of dead leaves, landing, resting, then rising inches off the ground, to go wherever the wind will take it.

YEAR'S END

December darkness seems to never end, and the sun rises enough to scratch over bare treetops before sneaking away to warm up other places. Some people hate all that nighttime, or are afraid of it, I think, 'cause it gives them more time to dream. Dreaming takes control, and dreams are either too honest or are such a mystery that they can drive you crazy.

David has this dream he tells me about, one with a tall old building made of bricks full of office people he doesn't know. The building is brown and ugly with its small windows covered in metal bars. He says it gives him an *oppressive* feeling, saying it smartly and telling me he knows exactly what *oppressive* means. David insists he dreams a smell along with it, that the building smells of wet newspapers, as if he were breathing the air in the Chicago subway tunnels. There's a small circle of light glowing at the base of the building on the alley side, coming from a strange place. It's there and it's growing up the side of the building bit by bit. While it grows, the brick building weakens. David says he can feel it weakening. But the people working there don't seem to notice. The light grows to such a size and the building begins to rattle so bad that everyone inside finally gets a little worried. Then voices, familiar voices, start telling everybody to leave, leave in a hurry 'cause the building's about to collapse. So the office people run down the stairs and out the doors. Suddenly the whole building starts glowing like it's caught in a fire. It sways and the cement between the bricks begins to crack and give way. It topples like a chopped tree, David tells me, but from the rooftop, the heroes who warned everybody to leave appear and jump to safety just before the building falls over. *And do you know who they are?* he rumbles at me. David waits and gasps to show how amazing the ending to his dream is— *It's the Three Stooges*, he says, *the good ones, with Curly. Woo, woo, woo— we gotta jump, Larry and Moe!*

When the bricks crash, and the dust settles, hundreds and hundreds of brick ranch houses, neat and clean on their mowed lawns, rise up to line brand new streets that curve like the letter *S*.

Moe, Larry— look! And the dream ends.

David throws himself back under his covers to try to make the dream come again. If he can get all the words and action memorized, he insists, he can make the best movie ever.

All I have is my dream about the one-winged bird. Sometimes I'll go to sleep trying to make a dream happen, usually one with Kelly Kinder or Melinda Levinberg or, with the feeling of guilt beating at my bedroom door, Mary Trauby. Forcing these dreams seems only to keep me awake. But when I do finally fall asleep they slip away from me and I dream, most likely, about that stupid bird flying so perfect with the one wing.

When I can't go to sleep at all I play a game with my mind. I try my best to think about how long ago I can remember, to the first memory I have in my whole life. Going backwards in time at first is easy 'cause I can use school to measure things. I can think of teachers and the other students I've been growing up with, and playground games, field trips, and some of the harder homework. But the easiest way for me to date and time my past is by using Jeff Schuber.

Jeff Schuber shaves every day now in seventh grade. He shaved twice a week in sixth, once a week in fifth, had a peach-fuzz moustache and muttonchops in fourth, gave out his first whiff of adult-smelling B-O in third, first became the tallest of us all in second, and was like the rest of us pipsqueaks in first. I can think of things, test grades, playground fights, ball games, anything, and match it up with Jeff Schuber's amazing puberty and figure out the year and time of year when something happened. But when I get to kindergarten Jeff Schuber's of no use, and before then, it gets impossible to remember my own life. It tunes in and tunes out like someone's playing a joke with the television set's plug. I wonder why I can't remember back to the first day of my life, the moment when I slid out with my eyes wide open.

Arnold Grossman says when babies are born they slide out *the passageway*, squeezed as tight as a big constipated poop the size of a bowling ball forced through the eye of a sewing needle. He insists we do remember that, the pleasure and the pain, *subconsciously*, and says 'cause of that pleasure baby boys spend the rest of their lives trying to get back in *the passageway* while baby girls, 'cause of that pain, spend the rest of their lives trying to keep boys out.

I know what the passageway is, and Kelly Kinder, Melinda Levinberg, and Mary Trauby all have their own, and they're so pretty standing there with their passageways. That's probably why I *subconsciously* want to dream about them the way I do.

When I was four Mom and Dad came home to the apartment in the Old Neighborhood with Cheryl soon after she'd arrived fresh out of Mom's passageway. Grandpa Erwin and Grandma Elaine jumped off our couch, actually having a moment when their old feet were off the ground at the same time, leaving me alone on the couch with my coloring books.

Isn't she … Doesn't she … Look at those … And then the word "cute" followed in slow motion. Everyone said "cute" drawn out like stretching gum from the mouth, as if it were the longest word ever made up in the history of the world—*Doesn't she have the kah-youuuu-tist this or that!* Cheryl was absolutely the best, from her kitten-sized wrinkly feet, the *kah-youuuu-tist* feet ever, to her crunched-up wrinkly face.

"She looks like President Eisenhower!" Grandpa Erwin said, running his hand over Cheryl's bald head, the cutest President Eisenhower, of course, ever.

Babies really do all kinda look like President Eisenhower. I still don't understand how that can be cute to the point that adults say "cute" as if it were a whole encyclopedia long. But there Cheryl was, held tight to my mother's chest, then to my father's, then to my grandparents'. Neighbors stopped by just to hold Cheryl like she was a lucky charm people had to rub themselves with. I sat untouched and watched all the adults go silly over Cheryl.

Kelly Kinder is right about something. There was a special feeling between Dad and Cheryl. It's not like he ignored me or didn't spend enough time with me. But to Dad, Cheryl was something new. She was his baby *daughter*.

Dad had a brother, but we never see him or hear from him, not even when Dad died. Dad didn't have a sister, and Grandma Rosenberg cursed and looked, to me, like a man. At the gas stations he managed, Dad was used to his men friends, his men workers, men truckers, and men bikers. Mom had to learn to ride that Hydra Glide — to do manly things — or else she wasn't going to get to be with Dad much. Dad certainly wasn't about to grow flowers or vegetables in a garden, so Mom wore her own leathers and rode that Hydra Glide with him, to Niagara Falls and back, and rode it with him until Dad couldn't ride it any longer.

Mom dressed Cheryl the way all the other neighbors dressed baby daughters, in pink, with flowers and ruffles. Dad looked at Cheryl and wondered out loud, "What am I supposed to do with this piece of glass?" He held her so close. She fascinated him, and their stares locked together like a handshake that doesn't know when or how to end. Even when David was born not more than a year later, Dad still got mystified, gooey-eyed, whenever he saw Cheryl. David was another boy, after all. Dad knew how to deal with his boys, his little men.

When Cheryl first learned to talk it was "Daddy" that came out of her mouth. It made Dad run to her, and she'd grab his hand or his leg and hold on as if to say, *He's mine!* If Dad was away managing his gas stations and called home, Cheryl would say, "Daddy, doll! Daddy, candy! Daddy, home!" It seemed as though Dad did get home sooner than expected, from Mom's reaction, loaded with dolls and candy.

One of my last memories of the Old Neighborhood apartment, Dad sat down with me on the couch. Mom took Cheryl out in a stroller, alone, I think, to give Dad a rest. He held David, wrapped mummy-tight in a blanket, in his arms, rocking him, cooing at him with motorcycle engine noises— *v'room v'room*— the sort of thing his little men wanted to hear.

"I just don't know how to raise Cheryl."

Dad's voice sounded as though his thought had leaked out by accident, not meaning for anyone, especially me, to hear it. Dad leaned his face close to mine. With an embarrassed smile, and the smell of work on him, his motor engine smells, Dad said, "I love you, Jeremy, and I love your brother. I just don't know about little girls." He spoke so quiet to me. "I'm sorry," he said, and he reached to hold my hand. I lost my anger at Cheryl right then, or at least my jealousy of her over Dad's time. Dad was teaching me, showing me how to be a man, to smell like a dirty old motor engine, to hold his sons, to admit weakness, to say *I love you*, all at the same time.

•   •   •

When we moved to Skokie and began the motorcycle rides, the neighbors at first didn't know what to think hearing a Harley-Davidson Hydra Glide's Panhead engine gunning at eight on a Saturday morning. Huffing out his house in his robe, Big Ben walked to our curb with his Sun-Times newspaper rolled up in his hand and a splotch of egg yolk at one corner of his lips. I thought Big Ben was about to whack Dad on his helmet with the newspaper.

Dad said, "Hop on, Big Ben!" and slid forward to give Big Ben some room.

Dad looked ahead, adjusted his helmet, and revved. Big Ben tried to say something but gave up with a grunt. Handing me his newspaper, Big Ben hopped on, or tripped on, trying to swing his legs around his bulky robe.

"Tuck that robe in, Big Ben," Dad roared over the Panhead engine.

They were off, Big Ben's robe flapping a good five feet behind him like Superman's cape in flight.

They must've rode down Loblolly Avenue four or five times, and Big Ben waved forward, reaching so Dad could see, saying, "Keep going, Al! Whee!" Neighbors started coming out of their houses up and down Loblolly Avenue and crowded around me at the curb. Everybody. If it could make Big Ben smile and say "whee," they wanted to try it.

The neighbors tried to make out where that motorcycle grumble was coming from. Suddenly, the Hydra Glide appeared going down Ellerson Street and Dad accelerated through his right turn onto Loblolly Avenue, leaping the Hydra Glide forward then curving it to a quick stop at the curb in front of the house, our house, the Rosenberg house, the house *everyone* gathered at to marvel at my father.

Big Ben tangled his legs in his robe when he tried to get off and would've fallen if there weren't so many people there to catch him. And the crowd inched forward, collecting around Dad, each neighbor asking the same question— *Can I go next?* But within the crowd, a tiny voice rose over them that made Dad snap to attention.

"Me, Daddy!"

Cheryl stepped forward wearing her first pair of saddle shoes, a white and pink dress, and a white hair ribbon.

Everybody started in with that *kah-youuuu-t!* business except Missy Grossman who warned in her grumpy way, "I don't think that's a good idea for a little girl."

"Quiet, woman. You'll get your turn," Arnold Grossman said.

"Me, Daddy!"

Mom brought Cheryl to the curb and raised her to Dad. He put his arms at her sides and brought her to his chest, so delicate, like he was making to sniff a rose. The neighbors went *kah-youuuu-t!* again at the curb. Even Missy Grossman couldn't help herself. Dad took off his helmet and placed it over Cheryl's head. She spun her face to look at us, swirling inside the big helmet so that it stayed facing forward while she turned her head to the side.

"Go, Daddy!"

"Be careful," Missy Grossman warned.

Dad kissed the top of the helmet and it wobbled a bit on Cheryl's tiny head. With Dad's left hand working the tank-shifter, the Hydra Glide jerked a few inches forward, then started to move down Loblolly Avenue, the engine bubbling and purring like I had never heard it do before. It had Daddy's Little Girl on it, and she was in charge.

•   •   •

When I was eight, Dad first came home with an interstate semi truck, entering our lives like a battleship in a bathtub. He squeezed it down the alley, its huge red cab and gray rig pulling in behind our backyard. It was impossible to see all of it at once with the garage, the Jenners' bushes, and our swingset blocking some of it, shrunk by it, making it look larger than it really was. It let out gasps when it stopped, like a giant sighing, and Dad popped out of the red cab and hopped to the ground.

Like the Hydra Glide, the truck got lots of attention from the neighbors, an attention that was not so friendly. Everyone inspected it, stepping close, and they seemed to shrink as they neared its cab and rig clogging up the alley. Maybe it was Dad's leather coat and his *Hogan's Heroes* hat, or his smile, but Dad didn't seem any smaller standing by the truck. He drove it into our little alley and turned it off. It had obeyed him. Seeing him leave the cab, so confident and in control, I thought that Dad had grown larger.

Cheryl came running out of the house to pet the truck. Her head barely made it to the bottom of the rig and her tiny hand rubbed a strip of chrome at its base. She ran to Dad's legs and latched on.

"You must be Santa Claus!" she said almost out of breath. "Show me what's inside!"

Calling Dad Santa Claus wasn't such a stupid thing for Cheryl to say, even for a little Jewish girl in Skokie. Dad seemed perfect to Cheryl. He did to all of us, except maybe to Mom, who was having her own reaction to the truck blocking our backyard. Santa Claus was perfect, never angry, always laughing. Santa Claus had powers as if he might be magical, or he might be Dad. So when Dad showed up pulling something as big as a house that could hold more things than Santa Claus' puny sack, it wasn't really wrong for Cheryl, being only four then, to imagine Dad might be Santa Claus. Little Jewish boys and girls on Loblolly Avenue knew who Santa Claus was. Even in houses that didn't have fireplaces, Santa Claus managed to pop out of furnaces somehow without getting hurt. We didn't know it as a Christian thing then. It was a December thing.

Arnold Grossman ruined it for me my first year of Hebrew School. "Santa Claus," Arnold Grossman explained as he drove Karl and me, "wasn't real. He was simply a creation of Jewish merchants to keep the *Goyim* shopping during what otherwise would be a slow sales season."

There was nothing in that big truck for Cheryl to see. Dad opened the back doors, lifting levers and raising metal bars like it was a super-secret vault of some kind.

"It's empty!" Cheryl said, hopping in place. "Like a cave!"

Dad sat her on the end of the hollow rig. "It's not empty," he hushed in her ear. "It's got air in it. Air from Wisconsin!"

"Real Wisconsin air?"

"Let's go breathe it," Dad said, stepping into the rig.

Cheryl's saddle shoes pitter-pattered inside the rig, her

pony steps rushing to one end, pausing, then galloping off to the other end. She tried to be everywhere at once, to breathe all the real Wisconsin air Dad had brought back for her.

"None left," she announced as Dad carried her off, and she stuck her tongue out at me and David.

That night was the loudest I ever heard Mom talk to Dad. My bedroom closet, stuffed with David's and my clothes and things, did little to block Mom's voice.

"Where did you get that thing?" Mom said. "Why didn't you tell me? What about managing the gas stations? What about the long trips? What about your family?" Before Dad said anything back, Cheryl's voice cut in from the hallway.

"No yelling at Dad!" and she rapped her knuckles twice on their door.

Dad opened the bedroom door and cooed to Cheryl, "Mom's just helping me solve some problems, honey. Now go back to bed." It got quiet then, like the house was holding its breath to see what was going to happen next.

Dad said, "I'll make more money managing the gas stations part time and driving the truck— it's only a three-year lease on the truck." And he said what I overheard him say a lot late at night through my closet stuffed with David's and my things. "You know I hate working for other people."

"I've always known that about you," Mom said— and then some kissing.

David slept through it, a round lump of tiny boy under blankets. What would he think, at age three, if he had heard Mom say— *Don't let your independence take you away from this family?* Maybe he would never remember it, or it might be the first thing in his life he remembers about Dad.

The next morning I found Mom sitting in a chair turned to face the kitchen window. I sat in a chair beside her, also turned to face the window. With the truck gone, we saw the sun hovering orange-yellow over the Levin house.

"How long ago did he leave?" I asked as regular as asking for breakfast.

Mom didn't look at me. She made wet sniff noises in her

nose, and I didn't want to see for sure if she was crying. "Before the sun rose," she said. "About an hour before the sun rose."

I think I was always suspicious of that truck after that. I'm not saying I predicted anything. It was only a bad feeling I got sitting there with Mom.

•   •   •

Cheryl's hair, like Cheryl herself, did what it wanted to do. She started out bald but her hair grew out in circling loops, heading in all directions at once, each strand curling one way, then doubling back on itself like a slithering snake. How lucky, Mom said, that Cheryl had such naturally curly hair. How Mom spent money on perms and hair spray and curlers to get that Laura Petrie flip, that one major curl in the back. And there Cheryl came, born with it— God-given Laura Petrie hair flips from beginning to end.

Then the Beatles came along and ruined everything.

When the Beatles first appeared on *Ed Sullivan*, David and I filled the bathroom sink with water and plunged our heads in. We swirled our heads about and came up with a towel to pat our hair flat. Our aim— to rid ourselves of our little Elvis pompadours that curled like a pig's tail at the tip and get them to fall, flat-banged, to our eyes, like John, George, Paul, and Ringo.

Our pompadour curly-cue tips had been Elvis-trained for so long, like a spring wound up in one direction and never allowed to loosen, that we had to flatten and flatten and re-dunk and finally take some VO5 hair cream to force them to curl under, to unwind the other way.

Ed Sullivan said the Beatles were coming back on near the end of the *Really big shoe* and we wanted to sit in front of the TV set and wiggle our heads about and make our fall-en pompadour bangs flop around.

Cheryl sat down with us with her hair dripping small puddles to the wooden floor. She had dunked herself, too, but the tough curls on her head sagged only a bit and held water like a million tiny spoons.

When the Beatles started playing *I Want to Hold Your Hand*, David and I be-bopped our heads about. David's Elvis curly-cue sprung back to its old shape without the rest of the pompadour. He looked like a bug with one antenna. Cheryl started head-shaking, launching water spray onto the television screen and into our faces.

"I'm the better Beatle," she said. She laughed at us and started playing with my Elvis curly-cue, saying *boing, boing.* Her own curls rose by the thousands, growing taller and tighter, as if to say, *How dare you try to flatten us!*

From the looks of things, Cheryl's hair makes her head bigger and gives her more brains. She used her brainy hair to trap Dad at bedtime, begging him to comb it for her before she went to sleep. And he'd do it, only to get the teeth of the comb lost in the mess, burying itself deeper with every struggle to get the comb out. She trapped our father that way, and he stayed with her, carefully pulling her hair away from the comb until she finally let him go. By then, David and I were long asleep most times, and he'd be gone in his truck before sunrise.

"We should cut her hair off," David said, and he tried to snip a big chunky sponge of it one early morning, but she caught him.

"What happened?" I said.

David rubbed his left eye, sore from a smack. Sniffing away the end of a cry, he put his little round-tipped scissors back in his desk drawer.

"I swear I was as quiet as dust," he said. "I don't think she ever falls all the way to sleep. She's scary, Jeremy. Really scary."

Cheryl always knew she had control over Dad, and it bothered her if he ever broke away from her spell.

"Jeremy," Dad said the day before he left for Atlanta. "I want you to help me with something."

Cheryl and David sat with me halfway down the base-

---

ment stairs, watching Dad and Big Ben put up wall studs around the edge of the basement. They finished making the last section to cage in the furnace and raised it in place.

"I can do that, Daddy," Cheryl said, and she started to get up 'cause Dad would, of course, do as she says.

"No," Dad said. "This is for Jeremy."

"You luck," David said.

Cheryl plopped her little butt down on the step below mine, her curls lagging behind as if falling in slow motion. She seemed knocked out, beaten. She turned to me as I got up and I heard her tsk and tongue-click, "It's not fair."

"Over here, Jeremy," Dad said. "Take the drill and drive the bolt into the wood."

Dad handed the drill to me like men shaking hands and its weight started pulling loose from my grip. "Both hands," Dad said. "Now place it over the bolt, like that, and lean down on top of it." I centered my shoulders, Dad directing me with his hands across my back. "I want you to squeeze the trigger when I say so. Are you ready?" There I was with my father and Big Ben, leaning the point of the drill bit straight into the crossed grooves on top of the bolt.

"I'm ready," I said.

"You sound nervous," Cheryl said.

"I'm not."

"Then squeeze," Dad said. "Lay into it and squeeze all the way."

If I pushed down harder I'd do a handstand on the point of the bit. I squeezed the trigger all the way and saw sparks jump about inside the drill. With a bump, the drill bit popped out of the cross grooves and skipped over the wood to the cement floor. The bit slipped on the cement and dragged me along until I belly flopped, my elbows slapping their funny bones with a sting that sent me curling up and rolling about like a spaz.

"I can do it!" Cheryl said.

Big Ben bent over and wiped some chipped cement pieces away from the gouge I made in the basement floor.

"Looks like you're going to have to finish this basement now, Al," Big Ben said.

"Don't worry about it, Jeremy," Dad said. He sat me up and rubbed my arms. "David," he called, "come here and help Big Ben keep this thing steady."

David skipped down the steps, jumping over the bottom one, and rushed to Dad's side. Big Ben held the far end wall stud with his hands, and Dad had David at the other end, directing him to stand on the bottom piece and wrap his arms around the stud.

"Hold it there," Dad said. He placed the drill bit in the crossed grooves and took my hands to the handle of the drill. We pressed our weight down together. With his finger over mine, we squeezed that trigger in, and the drill growled under the strength of the Rosenberg men. I felt the bolt drop beneath us, through the wood, into the cement floor.

"Good," Big Ben shouted. "Now over where I've marked."

As Dad took me by the hand to drill the next bolt, Cheryl's saddle shoes stomped up the last step to the landing.

"This is for men!" David shouted at her.

I agreed with that, out loud, and felt the warmth of Dad's body and smelled his motor engine smell as he showed me how to do the work that dads do. My heart beat hard with the thought that I could be like Dad. I know we got Cheryl mad. Big deal, 'cause she was always hogging him. That's what I thought, and there's nothing wrong with that.

•   •   •

Grandma Elaine, more than Grandpa Erwin, loved to do this thing called graveyard hopping. It's not what either of them called it, and they certainly didn't hop, but I figure it's what it must've looked like to strangers happening by.

"Grandma Elaine wants us to visit the Waldheim relatives," Mom or Dad would say, and we three kids, in a rare moment of agreement, would let out a group groan, our death wail, to mark the killing of our Sunday fun. Waldheim, after all, was a cemetery, and why anyone would want to ruin their day visiting dead relatives, I thought, graveyard hopping, escaped my understanding of what to do on a Sunday afternoon.

"You're going," Dad said to us all.

Our father, the manager of gas stations, the driver of trucks to far-away places, the father of three kids, got ready to go graveyard hopping for Grandma Elaine and Grandpa Erwin on his day off. There was no way a puny, Mad Magazine-reading kid like me could come up with an excuse. Not the way David could.

"I can't stand up!" David said under his bedcovers one graveyard hopping Sunday morning.

"What do you mean you can't stand up?" Dad said.

"It hurts bad to unbend my middle." David squinted through teary eyes. "Really, Dad. I can't."

Cheryl said, "I'll stay home and take care of him."

"That may be a good idea, honey," Dad said, petting Cheryl's spaghetti hair. "We don't want him accidentally getting up to play pinners."

"But I'm not faking!"

"Seems to me this happened your first day of kindergarten," Dad said. Dad walked to David's bed and ripped back the layers of cover and bed sheets. Still only in his BVDs, David lay on his backside to his waist, but there his legs bent up, folded cross-legged, as if he had been sitting on the bed, froze up, and fell over.

"My, my," Dad said. "Just like before."

"This is *worse* than before," David said. He pointed to his feet. They tucked up over his thighs, and his legs were twisted pretzels, ready to snap if anybody tried to undo them. Dad pressed down on David's knees, sticking out sharper than grasshopper joints, and David's body rose as stiff as the backside of the letter *L*.

"This is amazing!" Dad said. "It's a good thing your mother works with doctors."

"They're animal doctors," David said. "They don't know nothing about this thing."

"What thing?"

"The stuck body thing."

"Let's give Mom a chance with this anyway," Dad said, and he let go of David's knees. David fell back and his stuck legs rose again.

"He wiggled his toes!" Cheryl said.

"Did not! —everything's stuck!"

"What's going on?" Mom said, putting on an earring as she appeared behind Cheryl. Mom dressed in her black, graveyard hopping outfit— those Laura Petrie stirrup pants Dad liked and a black, halfway button-up sweater that looked light and puffy, like cotton candy. Dad watched Mom's body first before he looked at her eyes— his stare was easy to follow, from Mom's legs to her waist to her booby area back down to her hips. Dad's stare moved no different from my stare when Charlie Grossman showed me those foldout naked ladies in his father's magazines. It was embarrassing to think Dad had Mom pictured like that in my own bedroom.

"Al," she said, scolding, but laughing a little at the same time, and *then* Dad looked at Mom's butterfly wing eyeglasses. Those glasses were so ugly, like they were meant to hide everything beautiful about Mom's face. Maybe Mom wore them to calm Dad down.

"Stuck again, Mummy," David complained.

"He's faking," Cheryl said. "I'll stay home and watch him and tickle his feet if I have to."

"Oh, I don't think that's necessary," Mom said.

"I told you Mom would know," Dad said.

"I'm not one of your animal hospital animals, Mummy. I'm a people. I don't think anything you know will work on me."

"Oh, I'm not going to *do* anything," Mom said. "Not at first. First, we're just going to have to wait and see, like the snakes."

"But I'm not a snake."

"I know that, but you've got what some of our snakes get— My-tushy's-stuck-a-tosis."

David said, "I don't think snakes have tushies."

"Sure they do," Mom said. "They're just tiny so you can't see them, but they're there all right. And when they get my-tushy's-stuck-a-tosis, well, they look just like you, like they're forever stuck in a chair."

I suspected David had planned that Mom would come over and hug him and coo over him and tell him to get better and stay in bed while the rest of us went graveyard hopping. She did that the other time he had my-tushy's-stuck-a-tosis. Of course when Cheryl and I came home from school, David had recovered enough to teach Grandpa Erwin how to play pinners. We were all impressed with the name of David's disease, it was very long, but it was a made-up name, I knew, for whatever was going on in David's head.

"Here's the thing," Mom said to Dad. "This is the second time David's had this. When the second time happens, there's only one thing to do. We have to wait. Either he's going to get over it in the next five minutes, or it's forever. If he does unstick, then it's just nervous muscles and not my-tushy's-stuck-a-tosis. If he doesn't unstick"— Mom sighed as deep as she possibly could— "we're going to have to give him a shot to put his tushy to sleep like we do to the snakes."

"But I'm not a snake!"

"Let's go," Mom said, spinning Cheryl toward the bedroom door.

"Where do you stick the needle?" Cheryl said.

"Uh, boy!" Mom said. She turned to me to start the countdown. "Let me know in five minutes what I need to do with your brother."

Left in our room, facing graveyard hopping or a shot in the tushy, David didn't wait much of the five minutes before his feet began to slide. His toes wiggled along the mattress, legs stretching, pushing blankets toward the foot of his bed, and he blinked at the ceiling.

"C'mon," I said. "Nobody likes graveyard hopping except Grandma Elaine. Better that than having my-tushy's-stuck-a-tosis for real."

"I've got nervous muscles," David said. "Really, I do."

We all had nervous muscles going to Waldheim Cemetery. It wasn't a death thing, beyond our murdered Sunday fun, 'cause we didn't worry about death. It wasn't real and it wasn't something that could ever happen to us. We hadn't thought even a second about it, not until we had the sight of it forced on us in our own home. Before then we thought only that if someone wanted to make a monster movie, Waldheim Cemetery was the place to do it.

As Dad drove us to Waldheim, houses like ours soon disappeared— like driving to Grandmaland, the buildings packed together and piled on top of each other. Trees four or more times the height of Loblolly Avenue's honey locusts towered to the top of Harlem Avenue's buildings, often over the top, but the circle of green around them shrunk as we drove. Cement seemed to creep out from everywhere as we continued our way, "Into the city," Dad said.

"It's not Chicago," Mom said.

"It's got enough cement to be Chicago."

I agreed with Dad. I wondered how those poor trees got their drinks of water. Soon there were no trees, just cement— the street itself and the cracked, uneven sidewalks along storefronts only ten feet from the curb. Even on a blue-sky summer day we saw the gray cement, and it felt like we were going to a cemetery.

After Dad turned west on Roosevelt Road, a patch of green appeared above the south half of the horizon. These were the trees of Waldheim Cemetery, rising into a forest as we drove. I wondered why living people surrounded themselves with cement and gave a forest to the dead people. It seemed kinda backwards 'cause it's not as though dead people can go hiking or climb trees or anything like that.

"You know what Hannah Waxberg told me?" Cheryl said like she was reciting a reading-time school story. "She said that big trees suck things up in the ground, not just water, but…" Cheryl paused to ghost-hush her voice "…*every-thing.*"

"Like what?" David said.

"Like the *people.*"

"Stop it," David said. He was a nervous muscle.

"Then the trees become the people except they're really mad 'cause their feet are stuck in the ground and they can't move. They just throw things at you like twigs and branches and leaves."

"That's not true," David said sounding worried that it probably *was* true. "It's not true, Jeremy. Cheryl's just a liar, right?"

Getting teased a lot was David's punishment for being born after Mom and Dad had already had me and Cheryl. "Just the same," I said, "I wouldn't go standing beneath any of the bigger trees."

David was shocked. He called out for Mom and Dad in our Chevy Bel-Air as if they were a mile away.

"Of course they're gonna say it's not true," Cheryl whispered only loud enough for the back seat. "That's what Mom and Dad are supposed to say about tree monsters."

David was born only a year after Cheryl and was almost as tall. But even so, with Cheryl's brainy hair circling her head, high over David, and his face looking like he was always about to ask a stupid question, there was just no comparison. She beat him up with words. The thought of cemetery trees made his eyes dance the rest of the way to Waldheim.

Even with all our whining about graveyard hopping, Dad always managed to get us to Waldheim early. Grandpa Erwin drove up in his Buick with the holes along the hood. He wore his gray slacks and white, button-down shirt like he always did sitting in his chair watching *Family Classics* with us. Grandma Elaine stood from the passenger side, her dandelion-gone-to-seed hair glowing as bright as a summer sun, and she smiled her puff-cheeked smile that was wrinkled a bit, like aging grapes. She wore some flowered-up skirt that blew around her ankles, and a scarf that had its own flower show going on tied beneath her chin. She always dressed that way for graveyard hopping.

Every time it was the same. Grandma Elaine walked toward us, her long skirt and flowered blouse flapping in the breeze, carrying a picnic basket in each hand. She filled the baskets, overflowing, with little green-leafed plants and gardening tools.

"We're planting cucumbers today," Grandma Elaine said, or, "We're planting lima beans, or beets, or peas." Whatever we were going to plant, she said so right away carrying those picnic baskets full of food sprouts and gardening tools.

"Your mother's a bit odd," Dad often said to Mom before Grandma Elaine got too close.

Holding the baskets, Grandma Elaine stretched her arms out, like she wanted to hug us all at once. She sniffed the forest air. "This way," she said, and we followed her, giving her weary looks when we knew she wasn't looking at us.

"Do the roots of cucumbers reach down to the bodies?" David said.

Nobody answered him, ever, not even Cheryl.

Ashes to ashes, dust to dust, Rabbi Abrahms had said at Cousin Dora's funeral. We never graveyard hopped in the fall to see Grandma Elaine harvest the food over the dead relatives' bodies, the plants growing strong in the ashes and dust. Spooky, I thought of Grandma Elaine's food plants. Every other family planted flower plants or small bushes, or had something called "perpetual care" keep a neat mound of crabgrass over the graves.

"This makes me tired," Dad liked to whisper to Mom, "like watching you shop for shoes, it's the same feeling."

David warned him, "Don't lay down on the ground!" David grabbed Dad's hand. "The tree monsters might suck you up."

We hopped to Cousin Dora's grave first. We always did, as if we had to get her out of the way. She was Grandma's mother's sister's daughter, and she had done something bad in 1947. We stood in a half circle around the gravestone and planted three food plants. Grandpa Erwin *Ahched* pretty loud when he got up wearing grass stains on the knees of his pants. Grandma Elaine wasn't about to kneel in her flowered dress so she just gave Grandpa Erwin instructions. I think that's what he was *Ahching* about— *Ahch! Why did you wear that damn dress if we were planting?*

Grandma Elaine placed a remembrance pebble on the gravestone and started talking to it about not going to a wedding it certainly could have gone to in 1947, and that it should have gone to. "What's wrong with you?" she said. "He's your brother!"

"She was sick," Mom said.

It was the same old story told every time we went to Waldheim Cemetery and watched Grandma Elaine put a remembrance pebble on Cousin Dora's gravestone. "You weren't *that* sick," Grandma Elaine said, "not sick enough to miss your own brother's wedding!"

The gravestone said *1889-1961, Rest In Peace,* but Grandma Elaine carried on, ignoring that instruction.

We marched along the path to Cousin Shlomo's grave. Shlomo was the brother of Cousin Dora, and Grandma Elaine muttered on about that 1947 wedding as we followed her like baby ducks. We walked between tall gravestones and cranky-looking trees. The tree trunks were knobby and as thick as rocket ships. The gravestones near them tilted here and there, hardly any one of them standing straight as fat tree roots plunged into the earth and swelled the ground. Cheryl's voice peeped to David, "They're sucking up the people!" — and David tried to hop the rest of the way to keep from standing on the ground in one place for too long in case, you know, the people trees went after him. We were graveyard hopping.

Dad asked the question out loud that I was thinking— "Why would any parent name a newborn baby boy 'Shlomo?'"

I have a kid in Hebrew school class whose Hebrew name is Shlomo and he sits behind another kid named Pinchas, who sits behind another kid named Yakov, who sits behind a kid named Moshe— so by the time Mr. Trauby gets his classroom roll call to Shlomo, we're all pretty much laughing anyway. Shlomo stands for Steve 'cause his regular name outside Hebrew class is Steve. We tease him and call him slow-moe and do Three Stooges impersonations around him in slow motion.

Grandma Elaine placed a small remembrance pebble on Cousin Shlomo's gravestone. Beneath the Hebrew words, a Star of David, and *1893-1960*, the words *Shlomo Rabinowicz* carved deep into the red granite. We have our regular names back when our Hebrew school class ends. Cousin Shlomo stays Shlomo forever at Waldheim Cemetery.

"Dora didn't mean it," Grandma Elaine said to the pebble on Shlomo's gravestone. "She was sick. I saw her." Grandma Elaine talked on, trying to convince Shlomo as if it still mattered to him. The rest of us planted food plants on his grave.

Mom and Dad didn't say much the whole time. They kept themselves busy trying to keep David, Cheryl, and me from saying something that might sound mean to Grandma Elaine and Grandpa Erwin. Grandpa Erwin did as he was told, planting, walking, carrying baskets. Sometimes he gave a suggestion as to where another set of relatives might be. But Grandma Elaine always pointed directly away from where Grandpa Erwin suggested we should go.

"No, I'm sure it's over this way," she said, and we went with her.

"Of course you're right," Grandpa Erwin said. He wasn't good at helping Grandma Elaine with directions at Waldheim Cemetery. She already knew she was right.

Mom once explained to me that it was our job to go graveyard hopping. She liked the words "graveyard hopping," and I told her to watch David so she could see what I meant. Dad started saying "graveyard hopping," proud of me for coming up with something so perfect to describe what we do. Sometimes Dad said *boing, boing* under his breath when Grandma Elaine hopped us along, to Uncle Art and Aunt Adelle and second cousin this and second cousin that. Mom slapped him in the shoulder when he did that and grumbled at him to be quiet, but I saw Mom's lips curl up, then force themselves down, like a tug of war between smiling and looking serious. Mom and Dad didn't want to be at Waldheim either. I figured that out. It really was something of a job, I think, to keep Grandma Elaine happy, that's all.

• • •

This whole Sunday morning's been bad. Mom drove me to the Professional Building at the Old Orchard Shopping Center and she asked me to talk completely and truthfully to Dr. Bondurant about everything I know. Mom's got her graveyard hopping clothes on, the black stirrup pants and puffy black sweater. I feel her eyes on the back of my head as I leave her in Dr. Bondurant's waiting room. Dr. Bondurant's office smells like alcohol, the kind doctors rub on arms before they announce that the shot won't hurt a bit, and, of course, it does hurt really bad.

Dr. Bondurant's office has a space for a receptionist, with a desk, chair, and telephone, a note pad, a picture of kittens in a cat-shaped picture frame, and another of a woman and a man holding hands at a wedding. The receptionist isn't here, being Sunday, I guess.

Sitting behind her desk, Dr. Bondurant looks prissier in her thick gray suit and coat than Sheriff Andy Taylor's girlfriend, Helen Crump, could ever look. She locks her white-knuckled fingers together, working and grinding them on her desk blotter as if squeezing my brain in her imagination for some information. She tells me she knows that Cheryl thinks she's killed Dad, but Cheryl's not saying anything more. I watch Dr. Bondurant's tiny gold earring to avoid her stare, and make my sight go fuzzy by not blinking as soon as I should.

"Tell me about Waldheim Cemetery," Dr. Bondurant asks, at first trying to be nice.

"No."

She gets angry and squeezes her fingers hard.

"Tell me."

•   •   •

The last time we went graveyard hopping, the summer before Dad's truck accident, Cheryl shouted "1872!" at a gray gravestone, as if she had claimed a prize for finding the longest buried person. Cheryl's hair rolled itself up into poodle curls, looking brainy and busy calculating something important.

"Been down there a long time!" she said.

David's eyes bugged out at the ground in front of the gravestone, and he whined that he wanted to see someone come out of the ground and win a breath-holding contest. Cheryl laughed the kinda laugh that made David's face sag quicker than a popped balloon. He knew he had said something stupid, but didn't know what it was. Cheryl had her advantage of knowing everything, and it was dangerous to be David, around her, knowing just about nothing.

"Over this way," Grandma Elaine said, "and two rows to the south."

We followed, as we always did, to the last set of graves we visited when we went graveyard hopping. David held Dad's hand, scampering his short legs forward to keep up.

"For cry'n' out loud!" Grandpa Erwin shouted. "Quit stepping on the people!"

David squeaked, "I didn't step on nobody!" and squeezed Dad's hand harder.

David wanted to be carried, he begged for it. Mom grabbed David's other hand, and Mom and Dad lifted him, swinging him over the ground, letting his feet touch down for a second, then swinging him forward again.

"Careful where you let me down!" he said in the air, then down he went, and up again— "Careful! Careful!"

Grandma Elaine stopped to stand in front of a small gravestone set between two waist-high gravestones, each in the shape of a scroll. She lowered her baskets, almost empty of strawberry plants, and stepped forward.

"She's standing on somebody," David whispered to Mom.

"No, David. Aunt Rose is very small."

Our graveyard hopping trips to Waldheim Cemetery always ended with Aunt Rose, and Bubbie and Zadie, but I never knew how to find them, not like Grandma Elaine could. She always stood there stiff as a statue and the rest of us kinda stepped back. It felt natural to do that, to give Grandma Elaine some room. The last time, the time before Dad's accident, was no different. After putting her baskets of strawberry plants beside her feet, she said the same thing she always said, as if we had never been graveyard hopping before.

"This is my sister, your Great Aunt Rose."

Grandma Elaine's voice floated in the air as solemn as Rabbi Abrahm's *Mourner's Kaddish* on Sabbath evenings. Slowly, she brought her hands to the small gravestone. Grandma Elaine's skin, rough and spotted, blended with it as she petted it across its face. She said something in Yiddish, it sounded like a lot of spitting to me. Then she read the words carved there as her fingers followed along— *Into this world, February 11, 1901. Dearly departed, July 17, 1907.* Grandma Elaine stepped back, leaving a jagged remembrance pebble wobbling on the gravestone.

"Give her a strawberry plant, Erwin," Grandma Elaine said.

We watched Grandpa Erwin, with Grandma Elaine standing behind him pointing out instructions, go to his knees and balls of his feet, squatting a foot from Aunt Rose's gravestone. He began to dig into the ground toward whatever was down there. David refused to blink.

"She was only six!" Cheryl said, protesting that such a thing was possible.

"A lot of people died young back then," Grandma Elaine said. "There was nothing we could do."

The puffs of Grandma Elaine's cheeks smashed between her smile and her tightened scarf. Grandpa Erwin wasn't smiling, and he let us know his back hurt him with all his grunting and *Ahching* as he stood up and shook his pants.

"My sister would be older than me," Grandma Elaine said, as if people older than Grandma Elaine could not be possible. She stretched her arms toward the tall gravestones beside poor Aunt Rose. "These are Bubbie and Zadie."

I've never known any other names for them, and their gravestones were carved entirely in Hebrew. Bubbie and Zadie were Adam and Eve as far as Grandma Elaine was concerned, she refused to talk about anything before them, except this one time, this one last time before Dad's accident.

"Bubbie and Zadie took all six of us over on the boat." Grandma Elaine said *the boat* as though there could be only one boat, that there was in fact only one boat, ever, and Grandma Elaine was on it with Bubbie and Zadie, and with her brothers and sisters, including Aunt Rose. She spoke about her trip on the boat like she was teaching a history lesson, a time so important for all of us that it was natural for me to think she was talking about *The Mayflower*. I knew Grandma Elaine wasn't *that* old, not for *The Mayflower's* first trip, but there was no reason why *The Mayflower* didn't make more than one important trip. Bubbie and Zadie sounded important enough for *The Mayflower*.

"Where're their parents?" Cheryl said to Grandma Elaine.

While Mom shushed Cheryl, Grandma Elaine said, "We never had the money to get Grandma and Grandpa here."

"From where?" Cheryl said. "Where are they?"

"That's enough, honey," Mom said.

Grandma Elaine was about to say something. But she hesitated and pinched her lips together. In a moment, she blew air out her mouth, like she was glad not to say what she was thinking.

Cheryl pulled away from Mom, a little mad, her hair curling tighter in the humid air. She stepped behind Dad and shoved David away from Aunt Rose's grave.

Grandma Elaine clapped her hands and said, "Let's plant the rest of the strawberries!"

While Dad gave us the little shovels, Grandpa Erwin grunted and groaned and *Ahched* to his knees again, setting out the small strawberry plants for us to stick in the ground.

"This is wonderful!" Grandma Elaine said.

"Are we gonna eat the strawberries next year?" Cheryl asked Dad.

Dad's President Kennedy hair was neat except for a bit of it poking out over his left ear where he had scratched away a mosquito. Dad was thinking about something, and I felt chilled to think that *he* might believe in people trees and people strawberries.

"That would be interesting," Dad said.

"They might suck them up," David said, laying his little hand shovel down over Zadie. "Like the trees do. I'm not eating no strawberries!"

"I don't like this, not one bit," Cheryl muttered, digging toward Aunt Rose. "This place makes me think strange things, even in the daytime." She dropped her shovel and leaned toward Aunt Rose's gravestone. "What's this? What's this?" she said. Her little hand pulled back a bronze plate shaped like a stop sign, uncovering the black and white picture I had seen before, of Aunt Rose.

There were pictures of Bubbie and Zadie, too, I could remember them without having to open the bronze covers on their gravestones. Bubbie wore a dark dress and she was fat. She looked twice as big as Zadie looked in his picture, like she could've squashed him if she wanted to just by rolling over. I supposed she wouldn't, though, 'cause she had a friendly grin on her face that made her look like she wouldn't squash bugs, and certainly not Zadie. Zadie wore a hat in his picture in a way that hid the top part of his face beneath a shadow. But you could see all his teeth, and they were straight and as full as a smile in a toothpaste commercial, and they glowed right through the musty old black and white photograph.

"That's you!" David said, leaning over Cheryl's shoulder, pointing at the picture of Aunt Rose. He tried to touch the rounded glass covering the picture, but Cheryl pushed him back hard.

"Get away!" she said. She jumped to her feet, her voice commanding, "Stop digging! Stop digging!" She began to cry. Mom tried to comfort Cheryl, wrapping her little body in her arms, cooing, "What's wrong, honey?"

It wasn't as if Cheryl hadn't seen that picture before. But she never paid much attention to it until David pointed it out the summer before Dad's truck accident— "They look the same!"

Cheryl's shout hit my ears hard enough to make my head vibrate. The leaves on the trees waved overhead, rattling and rustling, like they were talking to each other. We stood beneath them, surrounded on all sides by thick trunks and the gravestones the tree roots pressed against.

"Don't let me die!" Cheryl cried into Mom's shoulder.

"Why, honey," Grandma Elaine said so calm and unafraid, "let me show you where I'll be buried one day."

Cheryl ran from Mom's arms. She had no idea where to go. Only Grandma Elaine knew the way out. Dad chased her and caught her by her elbow near a stone bench alongside a dirt path.

Dad said, "Nobody's going to die, honey."

Grandpa Erwin told me to close Aunt Rose's picture. I watched the shadow cast by the octagon cover as it fell over the old photograph, and Aunt Rose's sad eyes, her curly hair, her face, Cheryl's face, looked back as if she was sorry to see the world leave her.

Though she was so young, Cheryl understood about death. She understood it as well as a little girl could, the summer before our father died.

•   •   •

Thinking backwards in time feels dangerous, especially when I'm trying to figure out how things got the way they are today. I think of my dream, that one-winged bird flying away from the fallen dominos.

Now I understand the danger of thinking back 'cause I didn't plan on any of this. I had no idea trying to find someone to blame for killing Dad would one day make Cheryl say she was the one who did it. Looking into the past, trying to figure things out, has only made things worse. And looking back in time is all Dr. Bondurant keeps asking me to do. She curses at me, asking me one last time like a threat, to tell her about Waldheim Cemetery. Then she turns to blink at all her diplomas and apologizes.

"Tell me why you think Cheryl's said she killed her father," Dr. Bondurant says in a softer voice.

"*Our* father," I say, and I give her back her own curse word.

In a few weeks, I'll be thirteen, not yet a bar mitzvah boy, not a graduate of anything, not like Dr. Bondurant, who advertises on her office walls that she's graduated from everywhere. But she hasn't figured anything out. It was Bup, David, and me, and Mary and Mr. Trauby and their black pastor ACLU-member lawyer friend that got Cheryl to say anything interesting or important. And it took David peeing off a bathroom scale into our toilet to prove that Cheryl still knew how to laugh.

Dr. Bondurant's done nothing and her voice bothers me. It's high-pitched and whiny like a tattletale's voice— if three of her spoke at once, she'd sound like one of those carnival bagpipe players warming up.

My memories are my own, and they may not be accurate. If I talk about them, Dr. Bondurant will just turn around and tell Mom, exactly the way she told my grades to Kelly Kinder.

Dr. Bondurant will do more than tell Cheryl, she'll *confront* Cheryl with my memories of her.

What does that mean, Cheryl? What does Jeremy mean by that?

I can see it, and it would be no different from putting a mouse in a closet with a stray cat and expecting something good to come out of it. Cheryl would come home and I'd be the mouse.

Dr. Bondurant gets more disappointed and frustrated with me every time she asks the same questions about Waldheim Cemetery and why Cheryl says she killed Dad, and I say I don't know. We go on like that until my "I don't knows" turn into grunts.

"You can go, Jeremy," Dr. Bondurant says finally giving up. As I leave, she scolds me, "Keeping secrets is not doing anybody any good, Mr. Rosenberg."

"What did you two talk about for so long?" Mom says, putting down a *Reader's Digest* in the waiting room. Mom's watching me for some sort of reaction and I try to keep my face as blank-looking as possible. Her smile fades away.

"I don't want to come here again, and I don't want to see Dr. Bondurant at school either."

I expect Mom to ask me to repeat myself, the low-voiced, hands-on-hips way parents sometimes do right before they crack you one. Instead she takes my hand and squeezes. We walk together toward the elevator, down the narrow hall, the biting smell of doctor alcohol rising and fading as we walk by office doors.

"It's not like I can afford it," Mom says. Her hand, although around mine, feels small and weak. I am the one guiding us out of the Professional Building.

Dad said when I came home with my fourth-grade report card, "You made your bed, now sleep in it."

I knew he was trying to encourage me to study harder, that it was my own fault that a brilliant boy like me never got an *A* in school. I guess I wanted him to think that my best effort could only get *B*'s and *C*'s, and that I had studied all school year long. So I stopped making my bed and stupidly explained to Mom that it's what Dad told me to do. I know they must've wondered about my intelligence.

I figure Cheryl hasn't said anything about Mr. and Mrs. Trauby's letter except to me. Dr. Bondurant would've asked me about it twenty times if she had. I've kept my memories, my odd dreams, and the stuff about Atlanta away from Mom and Dr. Bondurant. Now Dad's words, *You've made your bed*, weigh down on me.

•   •   •

I avoid Bup Miller, aware of the movements of the fifth-graders at Eisenhower K-8. The fifth-grade boys' gym period is two hours after the seventh-graders', and lunch for them is shared with the fourth and sixth-graders, a half-hour before the seventh and eighth-graders have lunch. Bup and I pass in the halls once in a while, but the teachers keep their classes in two-by-two rows, barking out every five to ten seconds, *Straight ahead, straight ahead. In your rows, in your rows.* I could nod or smile or pass a quick note, but I don't. When Bup passes by me, I feel his stare, and I can only imagine what he's thinking about the promises I made to him.

Bup calls sometimes, especially during Hanukkah, asking me to come over. "I thought you don't believe in being Jewish," I say. "I bet you don't even have a menorah."

"I made one out of tinfoil," Bup says, "and we've got plenty of candles. They're different sizes and colors, but we have enough."

"Mom wants our family to be alone for this, Bup."

Bup's breathing through the phone. He probably knows I'm lying but he's not going to say so. I worry he might want to ask me over for New Year's Eve, and my mind busies itself trying out excuses. With a click from the earpiece, soft, like Bup might've popped a saliva bubble in his mouth, the dial tone comes back and I hang up.

Maybe Bup's going to light some Hanukkah candles, his

candles of all sorts, sizes, and colors, scrunched in the folds
of a sheet of tinfoil. His mother and dying father will stand
around those candles, silent, 'cause they don't know the
Hebrew blessings. They don't believe in any of it and certainly not in the miracle of Hanukkah, not when they can't
get a miracle of their own.

In my house we've forgotten all about holidays. It would
be nice just to stand around the candles and watch them melt
colored wax down the menorah. Bup's homemade menorah
will make his parents stand with him, even if only to stare at
the odd candles and tinfoil. They, at least, believe in standing
close to each other.

I know what Bup wants to talk about. I know what he
wants to do. I'm not stopping or giving up on our search for
Dad's first domino, and I know I promised him things in
return while he becomes Loblolly Avenue's next dead-father
boy. I just feel I need a little break from thinking about it,
and so I need to stay away from Bup for a while.

Mr. Trauby hasn't said a word about Atlanta or his letter.
He continues to remind me how close my bar mitzvah cere-
mony is and how far behind I am in my Hebrew school studies. He catches me in the hall and says, "Whenever you're
ready for the information, Mr. Rosenberg," and he smiles like
he did when he took Bup, David and me to his apartment.

"After New Year's Day, Mr. Trauby," and he nods at me
then goes back to his look of disappointment, a teacher's
look upon a student who should be doing better.

I don't know why I picked New Year's Day. Seems to me
that New Year's Day is a starting line of some sort, and people start promising how they'll be different from how they've
been behaving all year. And they get there, line up, and the
gun goes off. They run a few feet and start tripping or slowing down or just throw their arms up in the air and give up
completely. Other than being in a new year, after a week of
trying to change, or thinking of trying, they don't change a bit.

Cheryl hasn't talked much to any of us all December. She
comes home from school and locks herself in her room. I

don't hear her playing her record player or her radio. There's been no trouble in school. She ignores David and me in the halls and does her homework in the library. She moves to another library table whenever I try to sit near her.

Mom seems pretty regular about coming home after six-thirty most nights, making macaroni and cheese or serving us cold cereal before going to her room and closing the door. Her TV's on, it's on in the morning no matter how early I get up, even if there's nothing on except static hissing or a blaring test pattern. We haven't been to Grandma Elaine's and Grandpa Erwin's for Friday dinner in a while, and we eat what Mom makes for us in our own bedrooms.

It's too embarrassing to have friends over, even if David is keeping the house pretty cleaned up. Cleaning is some sort of guessing game or experiment with him, pouring the buckets of soapy water on the kitchen floor, making it rain in the basement, washing windows with Ivory soap, sweeping over the bare wood floors, trying to make our house look the way it used to look.

David knows enough now to stay out of Cheryl's bedroom, and Mom's bedroom, although for different reasons. With Cheryl's, it's out of plain fear that he stays away, like winding up a new jack-in-the-box with a nightmare inside, David tells me. He doesn't want to find out. And with Mom's, it's too sad seeing Mom's box spring with sheets and a cover, unmade, like it's supposed to fake being a mattress. She'll buy a new mattress when she can, which might be tomorrow, or another tomorrow, or never.

David stays away from my side of our bedroom out of some sort of respect, I think. It's easy to see the border separating David's neatly swept half of the wood floor from my messy side. David says it's 'cause I'm lazy that I leave my superhero comics all over the floor. It's not like I read them much anymore. I imagine some have been lying there, pushed around by David's broom, since last spring. David calls me Mess-Man and says that not even Superman could break through or even see through my amazing mess-making superpowers.

When Dad was home in his body cast, Missy Grossman told Mom, "The guests are coming constantly to see him. You've got to keep your house clean!"

Mom obeyed her, cleaning up clean rooms and wiping down areas nobody had the right to see, like the insides of closets or the tops of window frames. Missy Grossman came over to help out every other hour in the day and she inspected the housework, checking up on Mom to see if things met *her* expectations.

For the first time ever, Dad sounded like he was going to cry in front of me, telling me to get Mom. I yelled for her 'cause I didn't want to leave Dad's side.

"I could've done that!" Dad said.

Mom hollered through the floor, "You know I'm in the basement cleaning up!"

Whether she meant it that way, her voice sounded as if she didn't have time for a husband in a body cast sprawled out on a cot in the living room.

"I'm sorry, Jeremy," Dad said. He started crying, not hard, more like he was embarrassed— and I heard him, and I smelled him, going in his cot, doing his business like he was a helpless baby. "I'm sorry," he kept saying.

As I helped roll him in his body cast to one side to clean him, I started to cry, 'cause he was my father, and neither one of us felt that a boy should see his father that way. I told him I wouldn't tell anybody about it and that I'd probably forget about it as soon as I could. His face, though, I could tell— he didn't want to look at me the rest of the day.

I don't ask my friends over anymore 'cause odd things have moved into this block of bricks since Dad died. It's as obvious as walking around with a limp. People will notice things right away and whisper to each other, *Poor Rosenbergs*. I'll see it in their faces as they look around and fake that they haven't noticed anything wrong.

I play *Monopoly* with David, or *Aggravation,* or *Stratego,* and we stay holed up in our bedroom until it's time to go to bed.

"It's been pretty numb in this house," David says. "I'm sure you'll find Dad's first domino."

David removes my *Stratego* bomb piece with his miner piece. He's one move away from capturing my flag. He raises his chin and smiles at me, showing me he's confident that I know what I'm doing.

January 1967

Never stopped to think about it much before, but it seems almost every kid on Loblolly Avenue was born in January. We don't do much for my birthday, or Cheryl's, or David's— go to the Grossman's birthday party for Karl and Charlie, and everyone sings happy birthday to the Rosenbergs and gives us presents, too.

"The whole lot of you are bad for tax purposes," Arnold Grossman says out loud at the party. Under his breath, he says like W.C. Fields, "I guess it's our fault for all our spring-time *schtupping.*"

Everybody hears him. Mrs. Grossman blinks real hard and smiles one of those smiles that means Mr. Grossman is in big trouble, just as soon as we all leave.

The main thing about birthdays this year is that a bunch of us in Hebrew school are turning thirteen, the age we get bar mitzvahed. "It's like the draft," Karl Grossman says. "Now the Rabbi and the Cantor are going to pick us, one by one, and take us off to war."

"We're like fruit," Mookie says back. "We've ripened. And we're ready to be picked all right, picked to become men and read from the Torah."

It's easy for Mookie Waxberg to think that way. Being Jewish for the Waxbergs is how baseball is for the rest of us, a hobby you like and want to do all the time. Ruth Waxberg bakes for Rabbi Abrahms, who comes over once or twice during the week with thick books, and the Waxbergs sit with him at their dining room table, reading the books together, talking and laughing. Through their thin living room curtains, anybody who cares to see can watch them have a good time being Jewish. They often walk to Friday evening Sabbath services, and then again Saturday afternoons, smiling about it the whole time. Even during the school week Mookie sometimes can't play with me 'cause he has to go to *shul* or sit *Shiva* with some congregation family.

"Certainly *you* understand the importance of sitting *Shiva*," Mookie says. I nod, of course, and feel stupid just the same. Hebrew is as easy as English to Mookie Waxberg, and for Mookie Waxberg, getting bar mitzvahed, reading from the Torah in front of two hundred people with the Rabbi and Cantor looking on, will be as easy as reading comic books.

But Mookie is one Loblolly kid whose birthday's not in January, it's in July, and his bar mitzvah isn't until August. Karl Grossman goes first.

"January seventh is the first bar mitzvah date possible for him," Mookie explains to me, "and the Rabbi and Cantor want to get it over with." Since the Rabbi eats Ruth Waxberg's food on a regular basis, he must've told them about the synagogue's plans to get rid of Karl Grossman as soon as possible.

As dumb as Karl Grossman is in American school, he's somehow worse in Hebrew school. Hebrew school is about the same as looking into a kaleidoscope to Karl Grossman. Jewish history and Hebrew words spin around his eyes. He sits in class, he tells me, laughing away, pointing and making jokes— "Hebrew letters look like intestines!—Where did Noah flush the toilet water to?— Why didn't Moses just ask President Johnson to bomb the Viet-Pharaohs? — he'd've done it, you know."

Skokie Jewish Congregation students scheduled to get bar mitzvahed over a school year period are separated into

ones and twos as their bar mitzvah dates approach, the ones
becoming Rabbi Abrahm's bar mitzvah training students, the
twos becoming Cantor Morton's students. Karl Grossman's
failure to learn anything forced the Skokie Jewish
Congregation to form its first remedial bar mitzvah training
program, both the Cantor and the Rabbi trying to get something Hebrew to stay in Karl's thick head. Bar mitzvah training for nincompoops, Mookie calls it.

Mookie sits next to me during Karl's bar mitzvah and
says watching Karl is, "Like watching the Cantor repeatedly
pull the talk string out the back end of a dumb-dumb doll."
Cantor Morton stands at Karl's side, pressing his hand hard
on Karl's shoulder as Karl blinks and blank-eyes at the
Torah. Doesn't bother Karl a bit. He smiles at the Torah's
Hebrew, at the intestines, and moves his lips over his big
teeth while Cantor Morton recites the Torah's words two or
three at a time. Like a canary, Karl repeats them, changes
them somewhat, to Hebrew curse words judging by the pain
in the Rabbi's face.

"At least that's over," Karl says, sitting down after his
Torah reading. He says it regular, like he's talking on the telephone with a friend and not in a synagogue on his bar mitzvah day, with family, friends, the usual serious worshippers
and a really good microphone on a stand by the Torah.

Mookie hisses, "It's an insult, a blasphemy, and I don't
say 'blasphemy' very often."

Even Bobby Kinder, sitting on the other side of Mookie,
understands how bad Karl has done. Bobby whispers back,
"It's like watching everybody trying to ignore somebody
blow'n' a thunder-fart during church on Sunday."

With almost six years of school unable to teach Karl anything about Jewish history, or how to count to three in
Hebrew, Karl gets bar mitzvahed anyway. But Karl
Grossman's bar mitzvah party is the most spectacular event
on the bar mitzvah party circuit that anyone can remember,
and we all eat the food and treats the waiters and waitresses
bring out as fast as running water. After forgetting to say the

prayer over the bread before eating, Karl raises his head from a chunk of roast beef and winks at me. For a moment, there's something intelligent about him, a hidden genius, as if he's teaching me— *See, it's over. It's not so hard.* And he tells me during the Hokey Pokey, twirling his *kipah* around his index finger, "Bosses won't ask how good you did on your bar mitzvah."

I fear my bar mitzvah. I'm not as serious about it as Mookie, and I'm not smart enough or brave enough to fake my way through it like Karl had done.

● ● ●

Cantor Morton has an interesting way of sleeping. He holds a book, his copy of *The Soncino Edition Of The Pentateuch And Haftorahs*, and lowers his chin to his chest. He isn't fat in the least. He's almost too thin. But a jellylike blob at the front of his neck pushes forward when his chin-lowering gets past the halfway point to his chest. There, his chin rests. His thinness makes the pillow-lump on his neck look ghastly.

"It creeps me out," Melinda Levinberg says, sitting to my left. Watching her long, chocolatey hair makes me think of Pocahontas. Her face is sweetly perfect, even when she grabs her neck and gags, "He makes me feel like I've got to choke."

All the bar mitzvah and bat mitzvah students soon grab their necks. We're checking to see if it's natural to have that thing, or if *we* have something like it pushing out from our necks. I feel the point of my Adam's apple press against my palm. It moves when I swallow.

"See how gross?" Melinda says. "I hate it when he falls asleep like that."

Twenty of us sit in the old sanctuary, on cold folding chairs, fidgeting our fingers and feet. We face the stage, in two rows of ten, as Rabbi Abrahms speaks to us from a podium at the center of the stage. Cantor Morton sits in a high-back leather chair beside Rabbi Abrahms. Of course we never know for certain whether Cantor Morton really is asleep. He might be reading his *Pentateuch*, pointing his face and eyes at the pages on his lap. Although his head sags down, Cantor Morton's back is frozen upright, and he can sit as stiff as a board for hours, maybe days, eight days in a row, like a Hanukkah miracle. I've heard stories about him, that he once tried to be an opera singer but got rejected. Hebrew school graduates say he takes his rejection out on the *tuchases* of bar mitzvah students who can't learn to read their Torah parts. Pray you get the Rabbi for your bar mitzvah lessons, they warn. Pray harder for your poor *tuchases* if you get Cantor Morton.

"We're going to split this bar mitzvah group into ones and twos," Rabbi Abrahms says. His hands stretch across the top of the podium and grip the edge. "The ones will be my students. The twos are Cantor Morton's."

Cantor Morton's head rises so quickly, I expect his neck to snap. His fleshy neck-pillow gets sucked back in and his eyes open. I don't see them open, they just are. Without any noticeable lids or lashes, they remind me of the big-eye CBS TV emblem glaring dark in the squares of his black-framed glasses, searching for the poor half of the twenty who are about to be tagged as twos. We fidget and sweat in our little chairs— those eyes can stare at all the students at once.

Myron Edelson is not the brightest student in our class and almost got his own remedial bar mitzvah training class, but he shouts "One!" from his spot in the front row, his chair farthest left as we face the stage. Maybe Rabbi Abrahms planned to start from the other side, but Myron isn't taking any chances. Matthew Bernstein sits stunned in his chair to Myron's immediate right.

"Do-over!" Matthew begs, but "One!" shouts Simon Weiss sitting to Matthew's right. Matthew slumps in his chair as the counting procession continues without a do-over. Fred Mussman, like he'd rather be punched in the face, counts out "two" from his chair in front of me.

"Sorry," Melinda Levinberg says, watching me. I smile at

her as the count makes it to her chair.

"One," she says, like I'm her hero.

"Two," I say back to her, like a farewell.

•   •   •

Cantor Morton leads the ten twos to his office, a drag-foot slithering line of down-turned faces. "I'm a number two," Matthew Bernstein grumbles behind me. The shoelaces on his dress shoes are loose, and they click along the gray-tiled floor sounding like nervous fingers tapping. " Number twos are nothing but dumps," he says.

I know enough to ignore Matthew while we follow Cantor Morton. Cantor Morton can hear an ant crawl along a sidewalk across the street. Sure enough, Cantor Morton presses his arms down on Matthew's shoulders and tells him he's going first in his office, and he's not going to get a partner for his bar mitzvah. He's going to go solo.

Matthew's hand is buried in Cantor Morton's grip. While Matthew trails behind into Cantor Morton's office, he looks back at us with slanted, pleading eyebrows. We can't help him. The wooden office door, with its smoky glass center, pulls shut and thumps out a deep pop of authority. Matthew's gone.

Cantor Morton's office is across from the picture of the hand reaching down through the heavens, the clouds, and lightning, pointing at Abraham. Our nine faces, the faces of the remaining twos, stare into the picture as we settle to the floor and lean back against the hallway wall.

"I think that's the mighty hand of Cantor Morton point-ing down at poor old God," Fred Mussman says. The rest of us shoot pity-looks at Fred for saying that. Inside his office, Cantor Morton's super-hearing is always on, and his back is probably stiffening, his ears figuring out who said that— *Fred Mussman!* Cantor Morton knows. We know he knows. Fred realizes it too late.

"Damn," Fred says, hanging his head. He seems to melt

into the floor as his curse word floats in the air outside Cantor Morton's office.

"Who wants to be a one?" Melinda Levinberg says. Her sudden voice and beautiful face hover over us. Not waiting for her to choose, Fred hops to his feet and gets going down the hall. He looks back as if to make certain his escape is for real, then turns the corner toward Rabbi Abrahm's office.

"Why didn't you go?" Melinda says, stepping between me and Steven— *Shlomo*— Fishbine. With her back against the wall, she slides to the floor, and I watch her tan skirt hitch up a little against the brick as she settles beside me.

"I like Cantor Morton," I say, aware of the man sitting beyond the door.

"You're full of it," she says back. Hearing words like that come out of Melinda's mouth is like watching a beautiful flower spit hockers. "You like *me*," she says.

Steven Fishbine leans past Melinda to look at me, and the other twos lean forward past him. I can't get myself to talk with my heart pumping so hard. Somebody starts singing, *Melinda and Jeremy sitting in a tree...*

"How're you getting home after this?" she says, bringing her eyes near mine. "I'll wait for you, okay?"

... *K— I— S— S— I—N— G!*

The smoky glass in Cantor Morton's office door rattles. Maybe Matthew Bernstein's gonna be crashing through it in a second. Instead, he walks out, pale, kinda wobbly, clutching a pamphlet and a small record. His eyelids stretch apart as wide as those on the shocked Abraham on the wall.

"Eighty-eight lines," he mumbles. "In Hebrew!"

Cantor Morton appears behind Matthew. "Me-lin-da Le-vin-berg," the Cantor says, showing us he knows Melinda made herself a number two and freed Fred Mussman.

"I'll wait for you," Melinda says, standing.

Cantor Morton places his arm over Melinda's shoulders and scowls at her, for allowing Fred Mussman to become a one, for talking in the hall— then he scowls at me— for giving me a little bit of a Mr. Stiffy. It's the strangest thing having that little Mr. Stiffy while Cantor Morton booms at me, "You are last!"

"She sacrificed herself for you," Steven Fishbine says. He looks at the closing office door then smiles at me, more like a grimace. The remaining twos wear the frightened face of Abraham. We all know Cantor Morton hears everything, and that Steven Fishbine is going next.

•   •   •

If he isn't tucking his chin down, pushing his plump glob from his neck, Cantor Morton looks serious and almost normal, but only almost 'cause he's a little odd around the edges. His eyebrows look trimmed and sorted one black and gray strand at a time to make them checkerboard over his glasses. Cantor Morton's hair is thick and silver and combed over from the left side of his head so carefully and precise that a thin line of his scalp, his part, points arrow-sharp at me.

Cantor Morton is, I'm thinking, a gray man. The skin on his square face isn't sagging, but it looks weak and pale, like it might slip off. He has no lines around his mouth or eyes, and his chin and cheeks are smooth, as though someone had run fine-grit sandpaper over his skin. Only his forehead shows anything that looks like an expression. It's like looking at the front end of a stack of folded bath towels, and it makes his otherwise gray face seem to ask the question, *What's wrong with you, Mr. Rosenberg?*

Sitting in a swivel chair beside his desk, Cantor Morton watches me through his square-lensed glasses. Even when he turns to pick his *Soncino Pentateuch* off his desk blotter, his lidless dark eyes stare directly at my face like one of those spooky portraits where the eyes are made to follow a person walking through a room. I strain my eyes to keep from blinking, to see if I can out-stare him. I can't, of course. My eyes sting and water, and beg to blink, and I give up.

"What are you do-ing?" he asks. His deep voice booms and separates each syllable into its own word. He makes my last name, *Rose-and-berg*, sound as if he's adding something together.

I shrug my shoulders.

"*Ee-nun-see-ate* all your words, Miss-ter Rose-and-berg. Your shrug does not tell me a thing."

"Sorry."

He raises his hands, palms up.

"Sah-ree," I say, enunciating.

"When is your bar-mitz-vah?" he says.

"I have been as-signed May twen-tee-sev-enth," I say like a rat-a-tat-tat on a snare drum.

"Vah-ree good," he says. He lowers his hands to his stomach. "Ee-nun-see-ate each part of each word from your die-ah-fram. Speak each part, each let-ter, as though each one lives as its own word. One does not mum-bull through the say-cred books of Moe-suhs." He smiles an odd, rectangle smile, and dimples appear beside the corners of his mouth, deepening as though a fishing line hooked to the inside of his cheeks is being reeled in.

"Miss-ter Fish-bine said that I talk like the *Lost In Space* row-baht. I do not know what that is. I am con-fah-dent that the row-baht ee-nun-see-ates vah-ree well."

I'd rather have him yelling and screaming at me, then I would know exactly what he's thinking. His smile shows me nothing, and I figure it's shaped like a rectangle 'cause he has no muscles, from lack of practice, to pull the corners of his mouth up.

"Your bar-mitz-vah date is the sev-en-teenth of I-yar, and your Tor-rah read-ing is B' hu-ko-tai, Le-vit-i-cus, twen-tee-six three through twen-tee-sev-en thir-tee-four. Your Haf-tor-rah read-ing is Jer-e-mi-ah six-teen nine-teen through sev-en-teen four-teen." He hands me a pamphlet and a record. "I will call you when I think you should have it mem-or-ized, no soon-er than two weeks from now."

"Two weeks?" I know I sound pathetic. "Don't I have a partner— a part-ner?"

"Not at this time, Miss-ter Rose-and-berg. If one comes

ah-long, I will let you know. Un-til then, learn to ee-nun-see-ate all the por-shuns I have marked. I ex-pect you to re-cite it all oh-ver the tell-a-phone to me. Then ahf-ter that, we will learn the voice-ings."

"Sing over the telephone?"

"Ee-nun-see-ate, Miss-ter Rose-and-berg!" He leans forward. "I see we need to work on your pahs-chure."

I straighten my back against my chair.

"Your muh-ther, of course, will be home in the eve-ah-ning?"

Cantor Morton's voice goes up, like a sparrow's peep, with his question about my mother, as do his checkcrboard eyebrows, although the rest of his face stays frozen. It's like watching a Clutch Cargo cartoon, I'm thinking, when Clutch Cargo's frozen face is supposed to be laughing.

"My muh-ther's home by six or seh-ven," I say.

"How is she do-ing?" he says, peeping away.

"Oh-kay, sir."

"I want your muh-ther there with you at the tell-ah-phone," he says, talking deep again, "so that I know you are re-cite-ing from mem-or-ree and not from your Tor-rah por-shun pam-flet."

While I'm no Mookie Waxberg, I've learned enough to know that *reading* from the Torah, *learning* to read from the Torah, is the entire point, the whole honor, of being a bar mitzvah boy. It's not a spelling bee. It's not a memorization contest. Cantor Morton is lying. He's lying 'cause I know for a fact, by legend passed down by Cantor Morton survivors and from my own observations, that Cantor Morton never raises his voice to a bird peep, he never flaps his eyebrows to the sky, and he certainly never does all these things together. Every thirteen-year-old knows when a boy likes a girl in that extra way 'cause they deny it and lie about it and look stupid all at the same time. They raise their voices and flap their eyebrows just like I did in the hall with Melinda Levinberg, just like Cantor Morton's gone and done talking about my mother. He likes my mother, in *that* way— and he says it.

"She is a love-lee wuh-man."

"Please, Cantor Morton," I say, and though I only mean
to think it, anger makes me say it— "Can't you just beat my
tuchas instead?"

My words ring in my ears 'cause you just don't say that
sort of thing out loud to the Cantor. They make him blink—
twice. It amazes me how papery thin his eyelids are.

"I do not beat an-ee-bah-dee, and cer-tain-lee not children! Where does that get star-ted?"

He keeps his face as still as the moment when I first came
in, but his blinking won't stop— they're nervous twitches
trying to keep him from having to look at me, at *my* eyes glaring at *him*. Maybe I don't look as much like my father as
David does, but I still look like him. So I watch Cantor
Morton with my father's face, that's what I'm thinking, and
how Dad's been dead less than eight months, that Cantor
Morton could never be my dad. *You, Cantor Morton, are
almost an old man.*

I don't recognize the voice I hear, unenunciated, normal,
and it sounds pitiful coming out of Cantor Morton.

"I've seen your mother several times at recent bar mitzvahs. I'm a widower, for seven years. Your mother is a lovely woman, that's all I'm saying— and your father's been gone
for a while, Jeremy."

He has no right. He has no business. This isn't fair. I tell
him good and loud, "I don't want to be a number two anymore."

Cantor Morton closes his eyes completely. I bet he can
see me anyway. He breathes in deep and mumbles so I can
hardly understand him— "Nobody wants to be a number
two."

He raises his hands to shoo me away, me and my bar
mitzvah record and pamphlets. His voice is deep and enunciated again as I open his office door to leave. "I do not care
what you say to an-ee-bah-dee. Ee-nuff time has passed and
she *is* a love-lee wuh-man. There is nuh-thing wrong with
what I have said here to-day. I am a wid-oh-er."

I want to say something back, something powerful and mean that will squash him down. Sometime later I will probably think of lots of things to say at this moment, but I close his office door, saying nothing. It was the way he kept his eyes closed, as if thinking about something sad. I imagine being a widower must be the same as being a widow, and I can't say exactly how that feels for Cantor Morton. He seems to feel something about it, so I leave him alone.

•   •   •

Just as she said she would, Melinda Levinberg waits for me outside the synagogue. She clasps her hands together in front of her white parka, and she swings her shoulders about. Her deep brown eyes watch me from below her bangs, like she's sneaking a peek beneath a stage curtain.

"Your face is red. Did Cantor Morton hit you?"

"He didn't hit me," I say. "I told him I want to be a number one."

"Did you do that to get away from me?"

"I did that to get away from *him*."

"To impress me," Melinda says, sighing.

"Right," I say.

"Don't call your mom," she says. "My mom's already here. She can drive you home."

"You made her wait?"

"It's the evening," Melinda says. "It's like a date."

She smiles at me and her lips stay thick. My own lips tingle, telling me they expect to be kissing her pretty soon. They're saying, *You know it will feel good. What are you waiting for?* But my brain thinks of other things, like what Mrs. Levinberg might think watching her daughter walk down the synagogue's steps with a boy showing the start of a Mr. Stiffy poking at the front of his pants. How are boys supposed to go on dates without being so obvious? My Mr. Stiffy's become as regular around Melinda Levinberg as raising the school flag in the morning. I worry about inviting Melinda to my bar mitzvah, catching a glimpse of her sweet face, and there I am on stage waving it about in my summer dress slacks. Everybody will see and laugh, Oh, look!— the bar mitzvah boy really *is* a man!

"C'mon," Melinda says, reaching for my hand. I tug my parka down as low as it will stretch over my pants.

By her mother's car, Melinda says it's all right if I kiss her, but not for too long, and I can't try to touch her tongue with mine. I hadn't thought of that. But I do kiss her. She breathes my own breath in and then breathes into me, and our mixed-up breath steam swirls in the cold air around our faces. I must've done it all right, I figure, 'cause she kisses me a second time. I worry about burping up Fruit Loops breath the whole time. These are things I wish I could tell Dad about. But I don't feel too bad right now. I just had my first real kiss.

I think, 'cause I'm not experienced, and I'm not Jeff Schuber, that it may have been a real *tuchas* passion kinda kiss. At least Melinda's smiling, Fruit Loops breath or not.

• • •

"There is a God!" Karl Grossman, the first bar mitzvah boy on the block, shouts. As dumb as Karl is, the evidence that he's right is obvious to over twenty kids gathering on the baseball field. "Look at the facts," Karl says. "It's sixty-five degrees, it's January 24th, *and* school's out."

It's true. A teacher's scheduling conference falls on today, the warmest January day ever. Even the adults agree.

"It's a goddamn miracle," Arnold Grossman announces from his front porch, his skinny legs showing, from the top of his black ankle socks to the bottom of his plaid shorts, what the color of snow looks like.

So I have proof that there really is a God, a generous God, or at least a God that *can* be generous. Only God could match up a weekday off from school and a sixty-five degree day in January. And sixty-five degrees in January feels like ninety degrees in any real summer month. Bobby Kinder, wearing his black pants and white dress shirt in the ball field, quickly tic-tac-toes three X's with his hand at his forehead, then to his face, then to his chest.

"Play ball!" Karl Grossman commands, and he yells out a cheer joined in by the other older boys. The smaller boys, including David, and Cheryl, the only girl wanting to play, seem kinda nervous wondering if they'll get to play ball. There're too many kids for two teams. "We can't have four kids playing center field, not today," I overhear Karl Grossman whisper to Skyler Jenner.

Some of the kids are gonna get cut from playing ball on the only summer day in January that anybody can remember. Karl and Skyler, of course, know that *they* won't get cut 'cause they've made themselves the captains. But nobody can play baseball right away in our field without doing some work on it first.

A whole stretch of open fields line the south side of Ellerson Street, although every third field has a twin set of metal power line towers standing ten stories tall. We used to make the field across from the Bowers' house our baseball diamond, but some of us began bouncing baseballs off the Bowers' roof when we started turning eleven. Then we switched to the field by the Edens Expressway, but too many foul balls landed there and the police came by to tell us to move our game somewhere else. Skyler Jenner told the policemen we could play there 'cause his dad was a lawyer.

"He's only a real estate lawyer, kid," one policeman said, rubbing his pocket badge. Skyler Jenner seemed embarrassed by that, or scared that the policeman knew exactly what his dad did in his lawyer office.

We since moved our ball games to the field across the street from Bup Miller's house. That had been our original ball field. But when the Switzers moved out we didn't want Bup to play so we avoided it. The police officers' orders kinda gave us no choice 'cause we liked the Bowers and didn't want to break any of their windows. That doesn't seem to be a problem to us when it comes to Bup's house.

The usual Loblolly Avenue kids have come out to play
January baseball, and I notice kids from other blocks have
snuck in, like this game might make a newspaper headline. It
feels so unusual, so historical, to play baseball in January in
our field, all comfortable in shorts and T-shirts, except for
Bobby Kinder in his long black pants and white button shirt.
I don't see Bup Miller and nobody goes to get him.

Skyler Jenner's out here wearing his Dick Butkus number
51 jersey and matching shorts and a Bears helmet cocked
back the way pro football players do when they're waiting on
the sidelines talking to the coach. The helmet's capitol *C*
emblems look ear-like on his head. He wears a football helmet to our baseball game 'cause he can, 'cause he's Skyler
Jenner, and everything he does is right, like we all should be
wearing football helmets to baseball games 'cause they have
more protection than regular baseball helmets. "Just go
ahead and ask my dad," Skyler says to let the rest of us know
we're stupid for not wearing football helmets to a baseball
game.

Through his facemask, Skyler looks at me in particular—
"Just go ahead and ask *my* dad," he says again, smiling his
confident smile.

I think of what Big Ben said about the Jenners when he
gave all those balls he'd collected off his forbidden lawn back
to me. "The parents are fractions when it comes to being nice
people. And when fractions multiply, you get something even
smaller."

I laughed along with Big Ben 'cause it felt like I was supposed to, not 'cause I understood his joke about multiplying
fractions and the Jenners. Watching Skyler Jenner examine
our ball field, scratching above one of the *C*'s on his helmet,
I think I understand what Big Ben meant. It makes me laugh
for real a couple of years after Big Ben made his joke.

Crabgrass and other weedy things, clumped together
dead, are thick, long, and scattered about our ball field. It's
mined with dog turds, some of them left recently and others
as hard-looking as stones. There's no way to hit a ground ball

without the ball burying itself before reaching the pitcher's mound, or careening off clump after clump, changing directions from right to left or back to home.

"I dub this place Dog Crap Corner," Mookie Waxberg says, waving his hand like a magic wand over the field. Mookie's taken to wearing a fancy white silk *kipah* paper-clipped to his hair, and so has Dahveed standing next to him. Their baseball mitts look brand new, not 'cause they are but 'cause Mookie and Dahveed enjoy doing Jewish things more than playing baseball.

I brought my electric lawn mower to cut the infield 'cause Karl asked me to, 'cause my gas mower's shot, 'cause nobody else would bring a lawn mower. My electric mower, all rusted up and puny, looks pitiful sitting in the ball field. We stand around the mower, about twenty-five of us, waiting for something to happen.

"Where're we gonna plug it in?" Cheryl says.

"Just start it up," Karl says.

"It's not our gas mower," David says. "That one's not working anymore."

"How about a car battery?" I hear from a face I don't recognize.

"Where're we gonna get a car battery?" Dahveed says.

Skyler says, "What were you thinking of, Rosenberg?"

I hate the way Skyler Jenner calls me by my last name, like it's some sort of curse word. "Everybody's house has an electrical cord," I say. "Go get one."

I don't mean to sound like some sort of starting gun, but the neighborhood kids scatter home for cords. Cheryl, David, and I stay by the mower 'cause we already brought the one cord the mower comes with. We also have to protect it from the kids that remain, the ones who don't live on Loblolly Avenue. There're five of them, one bigger than me, all studying the mower like they want to spit on it.

"It'll work," I say.

"I think it's gonna blow up," the smallest one says. He's got his eyes all squinty, even when the sun goes behind a cloud, and one eyebrow rises up at the outside, that Mr. Spock eyebrow. "These guys aren't any good with lawn mowers," he says to the tallest boy.

"Are these the ones that killed Dad's lawn?" the tallest boy says. He's talking like he might want to do something about it. David steps behind me. Cheryl steps in front.

"We didn't kill your stupid lawn," Cheryl says. "Your dad's a cheat."

The tall boy moves forward. I place my hands on Cheryl's shoulders to hold her back.

"In about five seconds," I say, "there's gonna be twenty boys back here from *our* block."

Cheryl raises a fist. Slamming doors crack at the air, the hurried exits of kids with electrical cords rushing back to the ball field before the summer day in January begins to end.

"Let's go," the tall boy says. "He's gonna set the weeds on fire with that mower." The other boys groan how sucky my electric lawn mower is. As they leave, one of them steps on a dog turd and curses at our field.

"I could've beaten them up," Cheryl says. She smiles a little, her bright blue eyes moving side to side like she's looking for something on my face. "What you said was pretty smart, though." David steps out from behind me and Cheryl's bit of smiling ends. She tsks at him and turns away.

"I'm sorry," David says. "I'm just too little."

Folding her arms like a tough guy, Cheryl stands with her back to David and me. The wind blowing through her hair makes all the dark curls move about. They're tangling up, each curl lost among a thousand other curls.

"It's all right, David," I say. He is little, but not much littler than Cheryl. I guess Dr. Bondurant and Kelly Kinder might say *Told you so,* that it's obvious how hard it is for Cheryl to see David with Dad's face, especially when David's such a chicken.

Skyler Jenner returns first and with the longest electrical lawn mower cord. "It can do our whole lawn from one socket," he says inside his cocked-up Bears helmet. The cord is thick, yellow, and new, and comes with its own carrying case. He sneers at the thinner cord that comes with my mower, all bandaged up every few feet with black electrical tape. He hisses when I hook our two cords together, "You better not run mine over."

Mookie and Dahveed return with an orange electrical lawn mower cord with two electrical tape bandages and a regular extension cord. Karl and Charlie connect two electrical lawn mower cords and a cord that starts out brown, leads to a wad of electrical tape, then finishes out as a white cord. They also bring a knee-high guitar amplifier with its own twenty-foot cord and an outlet built into the amplifier to extend another cord from. "I play the tuba," Karl says. "I don't care if we break this."

"Looks like enough," Bobby Kinder says, laying down a green electrical lawn mower cord, an extension cord from a lamp, and another white cord with a little Jesus night-light built in near the plug.

"How do you know we have enough?" Cheryl says. "Where's the socket?"

"Bup's house," Skyler says.

"But that's not fair," David says. "He's not here. Nobody's asked him to play."

Skyler thumps a fist on his Dick Butkus number 51 jersey. "It's the closest house. I'll plug it in."

"But it's not fair!"

"Nobody cares about Bup," Skyler says, figuring we all agree with him about Bup Miller. "He's just a goof and a liar. He can't play with us."

David aims his pleading eyes at me— *guilt rays!*—to let me know I should ask Bup to play ball, or at least protect the Millers' electrical outlets from Skyler Jenner. David knows we have secrets about Bup, about his father, and that we made promises to Bup, serious promises. We haven't been good about our promises to Bup. These thoughts are obvious on David's face, bubbling up into pouts and scowls and forehead wrinkles. Skyler Jenner doesn't understand and teases that David's about to cry.

"I'll call the police," David says.

"For what?" Skyler says. "They're just electrons, you little baby." Skyler gathers the mess of cords and looks for the end plug. "We're just borrowing some of Bup's electrons, running them through the mower, and sending them right back. We're not stealing anything, the police will just laugh at you. Maybe they'll arrest you for being such a crybaby." And he adds, "That's what *my* dad told me."

David's eyeballs kinda spin around wondering about electrons. Skyler Jenner, confident in his Bears helmet and what his dad tells him, finds the last cord and starts walking toward Bup's house.

"Do you think the police know about electrons?" Bobby Kinder asks all nervous. Like he's full of guilt, Bobby frowns at his plastic Jesus night-light resting near the bottom of the unwinding pile of cords.

"It's not fair to Bup," David groans again and again.

"But it's not stealing if we're just borrowing the electrons," Karl says.

"How do we know for certain it's not stealing?" begs Bobby.

"His dad's a lawyer," Charlie says.

"He's only a real estate lawyer," Mookie Waxberg reminds us. "I don't think he helps out crooks."

"He's never helped out *your* dad," David says to Karl.

Karl nods and looks like he's thinking about it.

Skyler Jenner cuts through the bushes lining Ellerson Street along Bup's backyard, carrying the lead end of our cords to the house. His facemask turns side to side a few times, then he jogs to a spot next to a pipe running along the bricks. Gone. Rising, he bops himself on top of his helmet so it falls over his head, like a coach has just called him into a game. He waves and Charlie Grossman flips the switch on my lawn mower.

"This still isn't fair to Bup," David says louder than before.

"Nothing's happening," Mookie says, watching the mower.

Karl says, "It takes a few minutes for the tubes to warm up in the amplifier."

"Look at the Jesus!" Bobby Kinder stutters. He crosses himself, like before, tic-tac-toe, three in a row.

We have more cords hooked up than we need and the Jesus cord is still wrapped up in a small pile near the amplifier. The night-light Jesus begins to glow in the face, then fades, then glows a little brighter, and fades again, but a little less than before.

"It's only the amplifier warming up, idiot," Karl says to Bobby.

"What's that moaning?" Dahveed says. We look around, at the field, at each other, hearing nothing. Then a sound rises from the ground, deep, like something's vibrating.

Bobby says, "He's angry!"

"Who?" Karl says.

"Jesus!"

The little Jesus night-light flickers bright and dim, and the thumps beneath it are as heavy as Frankenstein footsteps.

"Who's moaning?" Dahveed says again, like he's mad someone's playing a joke.

David says, "This isn't right."

Cheryl grabs David by the arm and jerks him to look at her. "Do something about it or shut up," she growls, and drops his arm with a quick snap.

David's jaw wobbles about, stunned that Cheryl's said something to him, and touched him, too, even if she wasn't at all nice about it. He watches her for a moment, then stares at his hands. They begin to ball up, those little hands, and David faces Skyler Jenner stepping over the Ellerson Street curb back into right field.

"It's the lawn mower moaning," Mookie says to Bobby. "It's trying to start up— and the amplifier's thumping. It's not Jesus. Jesus isn't God!" Mookie says that loud, and again, directly into Bobby's face— "Jesus isn't God!"

With that, the two wimpiest older boys on the block begin to fight. It's hard to see who throws the first punch 'cause they both miss and fall to the ground.

"What kinda stupid fight is this?" Karl snorts, standing over Mookie and Bobby. "I bet you're both sitting in dog crap."

A *whack* carries across the field. Skyler Jenner's got his hands on his Bears helmet, a *C* emblem facing forward more than it should. "Goddamn!" Skyler wails.

With red on his knuckles, David balls his fists again. Skyler Jenner moves toward him but David runs behind Skyler and whacks him on the back of his stupid football helmet.

"Goddamn it, Rosenberg!" Skyler grumbles in his off-kilter helmet. "Are you nuts? I'm gonna clobber you!"

"I hate you!" David yells. "I hate your stupid dad and your stupid house and your stupid parties and your stupid everything!"

As David swings another punch, his right sneaker slips up in the air, showing a brown glopping of dog turd. He falls hard to the field.

"I don't think it's safe to play ball here," Charlie Grossman says.

Skyler Jenner spins about looking for David through his helmet. He finds David flat on his back. David kicks at Skyler and swipes dog turd across Skyler's Dick Butkus jersey.

"Turd on number 51!" Skyler roars like a dive-bomber. "After I beat you up, I'll sue!" He's on David, straddling his legs to pin him down, and whacks David's ears.

Karl Grossman tries to stop me from running to David, holding my arm and saying, "Let them go. It's funny."

"Getting bar mitzvahed hasn't improved you much," I say, and I whip my arm from his grip.

Nobody else moves to help David. They all like Skyler Jenner, I guess, even when he's slapping my brother on his ears as hard as he can. Maybe they don't like Skyler Jenner at all but are too afraid of him and his lawyer dad. I'm sure none of them knows why David wants to save Bup's electrons from Skyler Jenner. Who would do anything for Bup Miller?

As I run, something whizzes by my head. It sounds like a hard pitch meant to brush a batter back. It strikes Skyler Jenner in the helmet. A ball-sized rock falls to his legs and he keels over, clutching his Bears helmet now showing a sharp dent in the center of a *C.* He's screaming, "Goddamn! Goddamn!"

"I call Cheryl Rosenberg as my pitcher!" Karl Grossman shouts across the field.

Cheryl's curly hair falls over half her face, letting one eye show through. That eye beams on the fallen Skyler Jenner, her tongue working at the corner of her mouth, and her right arm rests at her left knee just as it should when it's finished uncorking a fastball.

Along with Skyler's cursing, the electric mower starts going all out, whirring and shooting out chunks of dried-up field weeds. The amplifier thumps along and shakes the Jesus night-light glowing bright on the ground in front of the speaker, the Jesus hands palmed together in prayer. Within these noises, a whining siren begins. Bobby Kinder and Mookie Waxberg are the first to run by me.

"Policemen!" they say.

Karl Grossman follows. "Skyler's dad is wrong about electrons!"

Kids scatter across Ellerson Street, and the cap-gun sound of slamming screen doors begins again.

"You're in trouble now, Rosenberg," Skyler Jenner warns David, standing and taking off his helmet. "My dad will see to it."

"Then stay!" David shouts, angry and refusing to cry. "Let's see what the policemen do to electron crooks!"

But Skyler Jenner doesn't stay. He runs across Ellerson Street and makes to cut through Bup's yard. He stops at the chain of cords pulled through the Millers' bushes and runs away, away from the evidence, it seems, into the alley.

"Your dad's a liar!" David screams standing up. "And you're stealing Bup's electrons!"

Cheryl walks to David, not trying to look at him, but not looking away either. She stands by him. For one short moment, she stares right at him.

"I didn't win," David says.

She studies David's messed-up hair and his red and hot-looking cheeks— like Dad's face when Dad would come back from riding the Hydra Glide on a cold day.

"I don't care that you didn't win," Cheryl says so quiet I can barely hear her through all the other noise.

She looks to the alley and begins to follow Skyler Jenner's path, walking as easy as a person can walk. Kicking stones in the alley, she moves toward home, until the siren and lawn mower drown her out.

We wait in the field for the policemen, David and I, with the lawn mower whirring away, and the guitar amplifier thumping, and the little plastic Jesus night-light with its glowing hands in prayer. The siren screams its way toward us as if it were struggling to reach higher-pitched notes.

"It's like the train," David says. "The train that rumbles by at night. It starts out all quiet. But then it gets so loud and mean sounding. It makes my bed rattle, and I have to ask you if somebody's moved the tracks right up to our house. And I ask you if we're going to get run over by the train this time, and you always say, you know, 'Shut up and let me sleep.'"

"I don't think the police will run us over."

"I don't think so either. It just sounds like they want to."

A boxy station wagon appears on Ellerson Street, turning right from the street farthest east of us. The station wagon's familiar white metal and wide red stripe down the middle is polished so well, it reflects light even though the sun has gone behind clouds. David reminds me, but I already know.

"It's the car that took Dad away."

The ambulance speeds along, its wheels squealing with the sirens, certain that it knows where to go. It passes by us and tugs at the electrical cords stealing electrons from Bup's house. The lawn mower winds down, the amplifier stops its thumping, and the Jesus night-light flickers and fades away.

"We broke our promises to Bup," David says, tugging my arm.

"I know."

We walk through the field, angling toward the front of Bup's house. David's limping a little.

"Are you okay?"

"Yeah," he says, looking down. "I'm just trying to rub dog pooh off my shoe."

"Maybe Mr. Miller's not dead yet."

"If he is or he isn't, we have to keep our promises to Bup."

"He's alive," I say.

It's a selfish thought 'cause I can guess real easy how bad Bup's feeling about David and me if his dad is dead, and we haven't been visiting, and we can't get anybody to go to the funeral 'cause everybody's mad at us for ruining our only winter baseball game in history.

We walk too slowly. At the corner of Ellerson and Loblolly, across from Bup's front sidewalk, the ambulance men are already helping Mrs. Miller into the back, trying to avoid the feet and legs of the body lying in the middle. An arm reaches out of the ambulance and pulls on Mrs. Miller's waist. She hits her head on the top of the ambulance and stumbles forward. Another man in a white coat rushes out of the Millers' house and slams the ambulance's rear door shut. He hops around to the driver's side and gets in. The siren blares again, whining away, deepening, then fading to a whistle, until there's nothing left except the echo of it in my ears.

"Did you see if it was really Mr. Miller?" David says. "The sheets didn't look like they were covering a fatso."

"Maybe the stomach cancer ate Mr. Miller up," I say, remembering Brian Yellen. David nods but his eyes keep darting about.

"Bup's always been a good liar," David says.

David crosses Ellerson Street and runs to the Millers' house. I follow, trying to catch him, to stop him, but I don't try hard. We've broken our promises to Bup, important promises. There's nothing we can do to make things worse, so I decide to let David go on. I follow him to the Millers' side door. It isn't far to run at all, but David and I breathe so fast and deep standing together on the stoop 'cause it's hard wondering what we're about to see. My heart's pounding in my head and my skin feels like it's a heating pad turned on high. David's face looks as red and hot as I feel.

As regular as a person can sound, David says, "Hello, Mr. Miller."

On the other side of the screen door, Mr. Miller holds his arms up, tangled in the sleeves of his overcoat, trying to get his hands through. His body is as big as always and fills the width of the screen door. His eyes bulge out at us, bloodshot and teary.

"I thought stomach cancer was eating you up?" I say. They're words, like the thunder-farts in church Bobby Kinder described, that hang out there all stinky and out-of-place, and they float in the air making everybody uncomfortable. "I'm sorry," I say.

"Me?" Mr. Miller says, leaving the house, still struggling with his coat. He walks past us kinda clumsy and forgets to close the house door. He hurries down the walk but suddenly stops, twists about, and pats his pockets for something. "My keys, my keys ..." he says, breathing quick, stepping back toward us. His face, rounded and puffed up, looks confused and lost. His eyes dart about and tears flow down his cheeks. He wipes his tears with his hands but the drops keep coming. He's watery and wet everywhere as if everything inside him is trying to leak out. At the stoop, he stops and watches David and me closely, then shuts his eyes and begins to sink into his overcoat, lowering himself to the ground, to his knees.

"I have only one child," he says. His voice stutters. "I only have *Bupkis*."

Boys who've watched their father die are different from other boys, I figure. Mr. Miller, fallen to the ground, soaked in tears, is like a science experiment. It's our turn to watch instead of being watched, to see what it's like from the outside looking in. I wish I could cry for Mr. Miller and for Bup. It's not that I don't feel sad or anything, 'cause I do. I feel real bad about it. But when you've seen it already, and all you've been doing all year since then is trying to survive it, crying just doesn't happen so easy anymore. I have to say I also feel jealous of Mr. Miller. I'm jealous of all his tears. I'm wishing I could cry like Mr. Miller. I'm wishing David could cry now, too.

•   •   •

David expects to stay home from school in the morning. That doesn't happen. Bup isn't our father, after all. "He's not even our dog!" Mom says kinda mean when David begs a third time.

So David goes to school the morning after the miracle summer day in January, expecting to get arrested for something, for breaking promises to Bup, or for stealing electrons, or for hitting Skyler in the Bears helmet with his fists, or for hitting Skyler in the Bears helmet with a rock even though Cheryl threw it. David knows he's an *accomplice*, he looked it up in the dictionary long ago after watching *The Fugitive*.

But nobody gets arrested for anything. Everybody gets their electrical cords from the field, and I get the electric lawn mower back to the garage without the police or Skyler Jenner's dad showing up. Not even a phone call from Mrs. Jenner. David's done something nobody on the block has done before. Although Cheryl and Bup both knocked Skyler about, David's challenged Skyler *and* his dad, called Skyler a thief and his dad a liar in front of everybody. It's got kids talking.

"Did Mr. Jenner come over and beat David up?" Bobby Kinder says next to me on the school bus.

"Is David going to jail?" Mookie Waxberg says in the school cafeteria.

"Is David being taken away someplace?" Karl Grossman says calling after school.

They don't ask David these things. Maybe they're afraid of the boy that takes on Skyler Jenner and his dad.

"No," I tell them. "Skyler Jenner and his parents stayed away from David the next day, didn't even try anything at school."

Bobby, Mookie, and Karl can't believe it. *David called Skyler a thief and his dad a liar— and nothing's happened?* I tell them what Big Ben told me, *Mr. and Mrs. Jenner are fractions and they multiplied and Skyler Jenner is even a smaller number.* Mookie Waxberg understands what I'm saying 'cause he's the smartest one. Bobby Kinder pretends he knows and Karl Grossman just coughs and hangs up the phone.

Mr. Miller calls two evenings after our miracle day in January, asking for me. Mom holds the phone with one hand covering the mouthpiece. "Why would Mr. Miller call for you?" she asks. Her eyes look tired, even through her glasses. She tries to blink away the fact that she's ready to go to bed way too early again. Her tired eyes give her face that television policeman, I-don't-believe-anything-you're-saying grayness, so I just shrug, expecting her to give up and go to bed, but she doesn't. She talks to Mr. Miller herself.

"Mr. Miller, could you tell me what you want?" She uses her work-telephone voice, I guess to sound awake. A deep voice rumbles through the mouthpiece and Mom turns away from me, grunting and repeating a bunch of *I sees* and *uh-huhs.* "That's all right, Mr. Miller. I'll tell him." She begins to hang up but quickly brings the phone back to her ear like she almost missed saying the most important thing.

"Please tell Bup to get well," she says, then hangs up.

"Bup's not dead?"

It's a reasonable question under the circumstances, but Mom looks at me like I'm some sort of oddball.

"Why didn't you tell me Bup was sick?"

"I didn't know," I say. "I thought Mr. Miller had stomach cancer. That's what Bup told me."

"Adults don't get juvenile leukemia."

"Bup lies a lot," I say, probably not a good thing to say about a boy that's sick with such a long-sounding disease.

"Why would Bup say his father's got stomach cancer?" I know by her fast way of asking her question that she isn't expecting an answer, and I'm not going to call Bup a liar again. It's *me* Mom's not believing. Mom takes off her glasses and rubs them on her shirt. Without her glasses, her eyes, though open, beg for sleep. "You're keeping secrets from me, Jeremy. I'm tired, but I'm not stupid. I'm too exhausted to find out your secrets. I wish you'd tell me. It would make things easier for all of us." She waits a few seconds, watching, waiting for some sort of answer out of me. "Again with the shrug," she says using Grandma Elaine's Yiddish voice.

"Can you tell me what Mr. Miller wants?"

I expect Mom to bribe me— my secrets for her secrets. She smiles a little so she's probably thinking the same thing. Like she's said, though, she's too tired to find out my secrets.

"Bup wants to see you as soon as he's home from the hospital. Mr. Miller said he's going to be all right but nobody can say for sure when he's coming home." Mom folds her arms and shakes her head. "And Mr. Miller wants to talk to you, personally. He wouldn't tell me what for." She tsks, "Keep your secrets from me, Jeremy. I'm only your mother."

She turns and walks away from me.

"I don't know what Mr. Miller wants, Mom," I say, "Really, I don't." She walks to her bedroom and closes the door. Her television set goes on and the voice of the weatherman says he's expecting a few inches of snow. Then the drums of *Daktari*.

•   •   •

"Bup's not dead?" David says when I tell him about Mr. Miller's call. "Even after they took him away in *that* car?"

"Ambulance," I say.

David sits up in bed, shaking his head back and forth like he can't believe it. I guess he's thinking it isn't fair that Bup could survive the white and red ambulance, and Dad couldn't. It's something you think about but don't say out loud.

"It's late, David. Go to sleep."

Through the spaces between the shades and the window, I see snowflakes, more like snowchunks, zip by, falling at a sharp angle in the glow of the Ellerson Street lamp. January miracles are over. Bup Miller got the last one.

•　　•　　•

Standing on the street corner waiting for the school bus isn't the easiest thing to do this morning. For one thing, Bup's house is right there and with the curtains opened up and all the lights off, the big picture window in front reflects back at us all black and plain, like the house is dead. Mr. Miller's big ugly Chrysler has been gone the last two days now. I think all of us at the school bus stop feel something weird about it, except for Dahveed and Hannah Waxberg, who Mookie says are home with bad colds. Even Skyler Jenner can't look at the Miller house for more than a second.

We're all quiet gathering there until David announces the news like he's Walter Cronkite, "Bup's got leukemia!" Cheryl tells him to shut up 'cause everybody already knows.

The most uncomfortable thing about this morning is all the snow. It's worked its way up to our ankles, and then a little more. It's as if I can see it rising, like a flood, every minute that goes by. We've all got our galoshes on, boxy and clutzy and the color of car tires, so that's how bad it is. Nobody likes galoshes. They turn our feet into Herman Munster feet, and the cheap tinny buckles don't line up so well, making it practically impossible to buckle them over our pants. The top unbuckled buckles *ching-ching* along when we shuffle around in them. And it's not like we can take regular walking steps in galoshes 'cause they're so bulky that it's hard to feel where they begin and end even on our own feet. Besides, who wants to put on something called *galoshes* unless they have to? — *ga-losh, ga-losh,* like wearing mud and gooey garbage on your feet. The snow begins to spill over the tops of all our galoshes.

That's the worst thing about standing at the school bus stop this morning. Even our galoshes can't handle all the snow.

David's taken a spot near Skyler Jenner. Both of them stand with their mittened hands stuffed in the pockets of their puffy winter coats, their book bags dangling over their shoulders. They look down the length of Ellerson Street, waiting for the school bus, ignoring each other even while their breath steam mixes together in the air and snowflakes over their heads. David sneak-peeks at Cheryl every other moment, as if he wants to know if she sees where he's standing, standing so near *him*. David's coat makes him look almost as wide as Skyler Jenner, but not as tall. Both have their jaws clenched tight and their parka hoods pulled down to their eyebrows so they can hardly blink. They look like robots. We all do in our winter clothes, coats and galoshes.

"It's like a cold war," Karl Grossman says to me about David and Skyler.

Karl's winter breath steam blows by me, smelling of rotting bacon and eggs. I wonder if he brushes his teeth after breakfast. Mookie Waxberg starts chattering away about how cold it is and moves his galoshed feet in place like he's one of the Three Stooges making to run but never quite gets going.

"Can't you cover that thing with a hat?" Bobby Kinder says to Mookie without looking at him.

Mookie raises his mittened hands to feel for his *kipah*. Snow piling an inch thick on Mookie's *kipah* falls off in the shape of a circle and disappears in the snow on the ground. "Don't get me started," Mookie says to Bobby Kinder.

"All you need is a mug and you can start hopping around asking people for quarters," Karl says, staring at the top of Mookie's head.

"Shut up," David says pretty loud. "Bup Miller's got leukemia."

"Stop it with Bup Miller," Cheryl says. She makes a snowball in her mittens. When she throws it at David, it turns into dust.

Charlie Grossman elbow-nudges Karl. "If you hold it ten seconds in your hands," Charlie says to Karl, "it will stick together." We all hear Charlie and start bending over to grab some snow. Charlie is the first to throw. He throws his snowball at Karl. Only a piece makes it to Karl's face, the rest of it falls apart.

"You idiot!" Karl growls. "Why'd you throw it at me?"

My snowball, holding together pretty well 'cause I counted fifteen seconds, gets Karl in the nose. He drops his snowball to blow pieces of snow out his nostrils.

"Karl doesn't have a snowball ready!" Mookie announces. The rest of us launch snowballs at Karl. They hold together, catching Karl in the face and neck.

"It's melting down my back!" Karl says, and curses. He reaches into his hood, dropping his book bag, trying to dig snow out. Charlie's got another one ready and it hits Karl between his eyebrows. Karl lets loose with his *goddamns!* and Charlie turns to Mookie, saying, "Doesn't it feel good to do this to Karl?" Mookie nods and launches another one, along with Bobby. Charlie's had to live with Karl all his life. I guess Charlie considers what we're doing a favor.

Every time Karl faces us, another bunch of snowballs hits him somewhere in the head, so he keeps his back to us and huddles down in his coat. Spinning about, Karl growls like a bear, his arms out, his face muscled up tight, and throws himself at Charlie. Their puffy parka coats collide at the chest and send out one of those odd made-up television *Batman* fight noises— *THUH-WHUMP!*

Charlie Grossman is large and rounded, but Karl's got

more weight to him, so it's Charlie who goes down on his butt in the snow. He disappears into it. Karl falls on top of him, growling, sweeping the snow around them on Charlie.We keep throwing our snowballs at Karl, trying to hit him in the face. Of course we're also probably hitting Charlie, but only by accident 'cause we can barely see him buried in the snow and Karl dog-paddling over him. Charlie's trying to spit up snow and catch his breath and tell Karl to get off, but his hard laughter keeps getting in the way.

"I ... can't ... breathe!" Charlie hacks out.

"Get off him!"

The command is loud and certain. It's David, looming his robotic parka over Karl. David's got one of his furry mittens, caked in pellet-sized ice-balls, rolled up into a fist. It looks dangerous, like the ice-balls are metal spikes. David coughs and lowers his voice. "Get off!"

The snow frozen to Karl's eyebrows and under his nose makes him look like he's wearing an old man mask, and he grits his teeth ready to bite David's fist off.

"Leave him alone," I say.

Karl growls, "Your brother's gone crazy!"

David hasn't gone crazy. He's trying to get Cheryl to hate him less, his quick peeks at her give him away, and he's willing to get pounded for it.

"Get off!" David says in that deep voice he's made up.

"Crazy!" Karl says, rolling off Charlie.

Cheryl flings a snowball squeezed tight to the size of a shooter marble, striking the center of Skyler Jenner's nose.

"Goddamn!" Skyler says, but he knows enough not to try anything with Cheryl.

"Thou shalt not take thy Lord's name in vain," Mookie says.

"That's right," Bobby says.

"Just damn, then," Skyler says, trying to sound tough.

"*He* knows what you mean," Bobby says.

"I call time-out with the snowballs," I say.

"That's not fair!" Karl says. "I didn't throw any yet!"

"I second the time-out," Mookie says.

Karl starts working up a curse word, but Bobby stops him. "Two time-outs called. It's official." Even bigger kids are supposed to stop for official time-outs. It's true everywhere all the time no matter what.

"I call evens," Karl says, and throws a snowball square against Bobby's cheek. "Now I've thrown mine— now it's even— now it's an official time-out."

"I've never heard of 'evens,'" Bobby says.

"He really wasn't hurting me," Charlie says, sitting up from his hole in the snow.

David says, "Sounded like it to me."

Snow continues to fall thick over our heads. Like pellets, the flakes are large and heavy enough to thump against our parkas. Our down-turned faces huddle in a circle, and clumps of snow melt from Karl Grossman's hair and slip over his cheeks to the little dent in his butt-chin. Loblolly Avenue is disappearing from us, swallowed up by the snow. Just the Millers' house remains. The Jenners' house looks like its shadow, and my house and the houses across the street and down the block are gone. Snow in the sky, snow in our faces, snow on the ground— it all looks the same up or down. If it weren't for my galoshes feeling heavy on my feet, and the Millers' house on the corner, I'd think we were floating in a cloud.

From the bus stop to the Jenners' house, a person can hide themselves in the snowfall. But somebody's coming, without galoshes, without a parka. We turn our parka-hooded heads, like periscopes, except Mookie, who knocks another round clump of snow off his *kipah*.

Sally Jenner crosses Ellerson Street and nears our circle at the school bus stop corner. She's got her arms folded tight against her sweater, her bare hands stuffed firmly in her pits. Snow gathers on her everywhere, clinging and clumping and piling up, but her hair flip stays as firm as concrete and collects snow, a moat of white around a castle. She crinkles her nose and speaks only to her brother.

"I told you so," she says.

She takes Skyler by one of his mittens and pulls him away from us. They turn gray passing the Millers', then become shadows themselves standing on their front porch. Their shapes melt into their house.

"I guess they'd rather we turn into snowmen before telling us school's canceled," Mookie says clicking his tongue.

"School's canceled?" David says.

"You don't know for sure," Karl says. "You know you can't *always* trust the Jenners."

"I'm going," Cheryl says, but she doesn't move.

"If she's going, I'm going," Charlie says.

"What if we're wrong?" Bobby says.

"We can always come back out," Mookie says.

"What if the bus comes when we're gone?" Charlie says. "We'll be in big trouble."

Cheryl says again, "I'm going."

We stay huddled in our circle, not sure of what to make of things. It's kinda new not trusting the Jenners, I mean all of us not trusting them at once. We stand there, in snow spilling over our galoshes, and snow making piles on all our hoods and Mookie's *kipah*. We stay at the corner, not trusting the Jenners until Mr. Grossman comes running out in the same shirt and shorts he had on two days before when it was warm.

"The wind's blowing the goddamn snow up my shorts!" he says, chomping a cigar. "Get in your houses before my *yarbles* fall off and my farts freeze!" And with that we leave our school bus stop, trusting Mr. Grossman, who always tells the truth more plainly than Mrs. Grossman wants him to.

"What are *yarbles*?" David asks me.

My parka rustles as I shrug.

"I hope Hebrew school's not canceled so Mr. Grossman can explain."

Cheryl's throwing snowballs at the Jenners' picture window. Mr. Jenner stands in his lawyer's business suit and tie, wearing a snowball smacked against his chest, if only the glass hadn't gotten in the way.

February

I'm beginning to think WCFL should fire Barney Pip right away. He's no better than Cheryl, picking his favorite record and playing it every chance he gets. Now he's playing *Winchester Cathedral*, but only after playing *I'm A Believer* at least three times in a row this morning. David insists on keeping the radio tuned in, waiting to hear Barney Pip announce that School District 57 is closed for another day.

"That includes Eisenhower K-8, you know," he says.

"I know."

Of course School District 57 will be closed. It's gonna be closed all week. I'm not sure we're ever going to school again.

The wind keeps blowing that white stuff around, God almighty! Barney Pip shrieks as if he's the only one that knows something so obvious. *It's a number one record twenty-three inches and it's not going away anytime soon! Speaking of number one records, heading into its sixth week atop the Pip charts...* and *The Monkees* start singing to me for the fourth time this morning.

"Does Davy Jones play an instrument?" David asks.

I look up from my bed and see David sitting there on the edge of his bed staring into the dim light glowing from his clock radio. He's crinkling his forehead, looking serious in his Batman BVDs.

"It's not even six. Go to sleep."

The guitars in *I'm A Believer* bop around between two notes, and David bops his head right along with them like he can't help it. "Dahveed says none of *The Monkees* plays anything. They're just faking it."

"How would Dahveed know?"

David's bony shoulders rise. He scratches his head. "It's just that on TV, they only show Davy Jones shaking a tambourine and singing. Mike plays the bass. Peter plays the guitar. Mickey plays the drums. Davy Jones just shakes tambourines. That's way too easy if he's not gonna sing."

"Right," I say, tugging my covers to my chin.

"So why is Mickey singing this song? He's already busy playing drums."

"*Fake*-playing drums."

"Why isn't Davy Jones singing this song?"

"He sings."

"Just the doo-doos," David says. He raises his pointer finger and listens to Mickey Dolenz sing, *What's the use in try'n'*— and then the others —*doo-doo, doo-doo*— and Mickey —*All you get is pain*— and the others— *doo-doo, doo-doo.* "Why do they even bother with Davy Jones?"

"He's supposed to be the cute *Monkee*."

"How would *you* know?" David says, squinting at me.

"I've seen his face postered all over Cheryl's walls."

"Oh." David bops his head some more to the radio. "I don't go in there anymore."

"Right," I say.

Don't worry, everybody. Pip will play that song at least twice during the six o'clock hour. Barney Pip blubbers along probably thinking somebody might really be worried. *Right now, Pip's got your list of school closings. Sit tight, it's a long one!*

"Please, please, please," David says, tugging at the elastic around his BVDs.

I get up to pee and David stares into his radio, cranking

up the volume. As I walk the hall, the school district numbers bounce around high and low but don't land on 57, not
yet. *School District 118 is open!* Barney Pip says. *How about
that?* It gets David to squeak a nervous, "Oh no!"

I look at the clock on the tank as I pee, remembering my
personal best record of fifty-five seconds. David said he's
gone over a minute at least ten times. "You've got a small
hose so it just takes longer to pee through it," I told him. I
shouldn't've said it. It might bother him one day if he ever
sees a guy like Jeff Schuber in his gym class.

No pee-breaking records this morning.

Mom's TV is on, telling her about hogs and sheep and
cattle and prices per bushel of corn and wheat from South
America. And I hear David's worried voice again. "Oh no!"

The beginning of morning comes through our living
room and dining room windows, enough so I don't need to
turn on lights and I don't bump into things. I need to see if
my shoveling job from yesterday got blown over again. My
hands are a little raw and I don't want to do any more shoveling. There's the *L* Volume World Book Encyclopedia David
left open on the coffee table at the page he reads over and
over again. David didn't know about the *e* before the *u* in
"leukemia," so I had to help him look it up. Page 191. "Please
help me with some of the words," he said. So I read to him:

*Leukemia is a serious disease of the white blood cells
of the blood. The disease is a purposeless, continual
growth of white blood cells. Some scientists believe
that leukemic cells may have lost their enzymes
that regulate their growth.*

David interrupted. "What disease *has* a purpose," he said
like he was angry at the book, and he ordered, "Go again
where it says 'treatment.'"

*Doctors use various means to produce periods of tem-
porary improvement. But there is no known cure for*

*the disease. Blood transfusions, cortisone, and certain
chemicals called antimetabolites may be useful in
retarding the disease. However, the abnormal growth
eventually returns, and causes the death of the
patient. Chronic cases often go on for five years or
more.*

"I don't get it," David said. He took the encyclopedia
from me and tried to read it himself, running his fingers over
the neat columns and paragraphs. "It's not good for Bup, is
it?"

"No," I said. "Not if he's telling the truth this time."

"That ambulance took him."

"It did."

"How old's this book?"

"A couple years maybe."

"Do you think somebody might've found something out
since?"

"I don't know."

"Maybe we should go get a newer encyclopedia."

"Maybe," I said just to say it.

Now there's a lump in the *L* Volume Encyclopedia and
the binding's broken at page 191 right where David's been
leaning and pressing down and learning how to read *lym-
phocytes* and *metabolism* and *plasmocytes*. David wants to
go to synagogue and pray for Bup, but even the Waxbergs
don't go. They say it's closed like every other place. So David
prays at home, his own prayer for Bup Miller— *Dear God,
please let this be a big lie like everything else Bup's said
before.* And I watch David pray to our God defeated by snow,
unable to keep the synagogues open. I guess I keep changing
my mind about God. One thing's for certain, God isn't regular about things. You can't predict much about God.

I open the living room door to see how my shoveling's
held up, and there's the surprised face of Missy Grossman on
the other side of the screen window. She's squinting in the
cold, cradled in Karl's parka and hood. The wind tosses the

bottom of her house robe around her legs and Karl's clutzy galoshes. Through frost sticking to the screen window, Missy Grossman looks like a ghost, but it's me that's scared the ghostly looking Missy Grossman. She huddles even more into a turtled-up ball in Karl's coat, hiding, I'm thinking, from the fact that I've caught her at something. She slips a white envelope into the mail slot at the side of the door.

Missy Grossman kicks her way through snow drifting over the walk and steps into old boot prints that make stairs up and down the piles of snow built by snowplows. She struggles across the street, wobbling, slipping twice, and steps into the boot prints in snow piles on her side of the street. Not once does she look back.

I reach into the front hall closet and pull the envelope through the inside mail slot— *Loblolly Avenue loves the Rosenbergs.* I count fifteen fives.

David taps me on the shoulder. "No school!" he says running in place. He blinks at the envelope and keeps yabbering like it's no big surprise, "I'm going back to sleep!" and ponies to our bedroom.

I count the money again, searching for the two ones, but I don't find them. Would Missy Grossman come all the way here in the cold and snow to take two ones and leave the fifteen fives behind? This morning's envelope and money send energy into my hands, vibrating and sparking miracles against my skin, that's how it feels. *Missy Grossman*, I whistle out. Like God, it seems, Missy Grossman isn't predictable either.

• • •

Mom isn't happy about going to work today, not that I'd expect her to be happy about working at a place called International Minerals. She assures David that although there's nothing there nearly as fun as the animals at the animal hospital, International Minerals is not the same kinda place as the Bedrock Quarry on *The Flintstones.* She's not out tossing big stones around in the cold. "Look at my business suit, David," she says, touching his cheek. Her fingertips shake a bit as she tries to calm him, her eyes dim and tired. David smiles, but it's forced, I can see, and he tries to keep himself from flinching away from Mom's nervous touch.

"Oh, it's cold out there," Mom says, putting on her scarf, coat, and boots. Her business suit is buried under her blizzard clothes. She looks out the picture window at our pitiful Bel-Air, all stickered-up on the sides with Cheryl's flower-power stickers, carrying snow on the hood, roof, and trunk as square as suitcases. Plows have pushed even more snow against it. Big Ben Lipshilts and Arnold Grossman work to shovel the plowed snow away. At least Mom didn't put the car in the garage when the snow fell. It's gonna take forever to get the snow out of the alley.

"What is it about Arnold?" Mom says. While Big Ben is as large as a bear in his winter clothes, Arnold Grossman is out in his shorts again, freezing his *yarbles.* David asks if we might get to see one of Mr. Grossman's frozen farts.

"I guess crooks can do anything they want to do," David says.

"Mr. Grossman's not a crook," Mom says.

"That's what he tells us."

"Oh, David— Arnold Grossman says lots of things." She places her hand on top of David's head and David leans into her coat. She's trying to keep her fingers still, but they twitch about in his hair. "He's a bankruptcy receiver," Mom says. "He takes the property of people and businesses that run out of money and sells it for them so their bills can be paid."

"But what do people do without their stuff?"

"They go out of business, I suppose."

"Where do the people live after Mr. Grossman's through with them?"

"They manage somehow, David."

"Did you give Mummy the envelope money?" David says, looking back at me.

"Of course I did," I say. "*I'm* not a crook."

"I know, I know," David says. "I don't want Mr. Grossman to sell *our* stuff."

"The two ones aren't there," I say.

"I didn't take them!" David says, spinning around.

"I know you didn't, honey," Mom says, kissing David on the cheek. Even her lips seem to shake. Mom slips her hands into thick leather gloves. Motorcycle gloves for the Hydra Glide. I catch her watching them, looking sad. For a moment, she smiles, just a little, and it makes her face, the one she's lost, show as though it's pushed through from the past— young, beautiful, fresh, and calm— my mother's face, the way I want her to look forever.

"You kids are lucky," she says, blinking herself to attention, and the smile, that face from before, is gone. "Five closed school days in a row," Mom repeats, adding again how lucky we are. The twitching returns, small twitches in her lips and her sleepless eyes. I think Mom wishes she were like us, a child on a school's-off snow day, she'd be home and have that smile I love.

In one way or another, Bup Miller's domino theory keeps my own thoughts in the past. I wonder how bad it would be if I just left this thing about Dad's first domino alone. That would be selfish now, I think, 'cause I saw Mom's face, that good face. It's still there somewhere. David thinks we can get it back, and I'm the man of the house whether I want to be or not.

Mom slips going down a plow-made snowdrift and Arnold Grossman tries to catch her. He slows her down enough so it probably didn't hurt her when she landed, but she's there on her back on Loblolly Avenue. Big Ben rushes over to help Arnold get Mom on her feet. I turn away not knowing if that look on her face as she lies on the street is the old one laughing or the new one crying.

"I still think Mr. Grossman's a crook," David says. "Only crooks can wear shorts outside today."

"Right," I say, leaving him at the picture window.

I peek in Cheryl's bedroom without knocking or asking

permission first. She's not there, and her parka and galoshes are gone from her closet. I go to find her.

•   •   •

When the weathermen say it snowed twenty-three inches at O'Hare Airport, that doesn't matter much. On Loblolly Avenue in some places it only snowed a few inches while in other places it snowed over eight feet. At my house, it snowed over eight feet by our back door, the corner ends of the front of the house, and up and over the west side of the garage. The wind that came with the blizzard swirled things around so much, it's as if all the houses on the block now sit between the peaks and curls of Dolly Madison cake frosting. Some of the time the sun's been shining, melting the snow a little. The snow freezes again overnight, making the wavy white surface crusty to the point where I can sometimes walk on deeper parts without falling through.

With the sun out, there's more light, it seems, beaming up from the snow than down from the sky.

I put on Dad's gray-tinted motorcycle goggles 'cause I found them in the front closet, 'cause I can, 'cause they're so tough. The frame around the curved oval lens sits on the tip of my nose and almost reaches back to my ears, and I make it fit by drawing the back strap as tight as it will go. Whatever my galoshes and parka coat do to me, Dad's motorcycle goggles make everything else look cool.

At the base of the pinners porch, new snowdrifts, like fingers stretching, begin to cover up my shoveling job again. I face left, then right, then left again, and find Cheryl's galosh prints skimming across the snow crust. I step off the sidewalk, on top of the crust, and follow Cheryl's prints through Dad's goggles, listening to the hollow-sounding thump my galoshes make on the surface. Tomorrow's Groundhog Day and the groundhog won't see his shadow 'cause he's not gonna be able to get out of his hole.

There's a ridge of snow, a white, four-foot miniature

model of a mountain range, running the length between my house and the Jenners' house. It serves its purpose, I'm thinking, keeping them away from me. I don't want to see them. This ridge should stay here forever, if only snow could stay snow in July.

I have to wade through the shallow part of this ridge, between it and the snowdrift blocking my side door. I feel my galoshes begin to fill with snow and squishy slush as I push through. The crust held Cheryl up. I fall through it. She's hardly as light as a ghost, I'm thinking. Her lightness is simply a lie.

Over the last four days, Cheryl's been tunneling. At first her tunnels collapsed as soon as she dug in sideways only an inch or two. But in the last two days, the surface has become crusty enough to allow her to dig out the guts of the soft stuff and stay safe under the hardening surface. Her main opening begins at the back of the house beside a large dumping of dug out snow and a stick holding a cardboard sign on the outside that says, *Cheryls Only!* I kneel down and enter the tunnel made for Cheryls only.

I don't get three feet before the tunnel curves right, and I follow the path of knee impressions around the bend. My parka-puffed head and shoulders scrape along the insides, making small sheets of snow tumble. Although there's only one way to crawl, I'm losing sense of where I am. It's the whiteness around me, even through the goggles, and it's my own breathing echoing back at me in the tunnel. The tunnel takes me to bricks, probably garage bricks, then turns back sharply on itself to the left. It drops a little, to the tips of grass browned by winter cold. The Cheryls Only tunnel couldn't be all that long, maybe fifteen to twenty feet, but it seems to take forever to get to the end of it.

Cheryl's galoshes.

As I inch closer, I see she's in a space large enough for her to sit up. Hopefully there's room for two just in case there could be more than one Cheryl in this world. I have my doubts.

"I hear you," she says. "You're not allowed in here." Her voice sounds convinced that sooner or later she'd be found out. We both know how snoopy David is, and she looks surprised when I pull my parka hood and Dad's goggles off.

"Hello," I say. "Are you Cheryl?"

"Maybe I am," she says.

Her own sunglasses and hat lie at her side, her parka unzipped to her waist, and she rests against bricks, against the house, I figure. There's enough room to sit against the bricks with her. In this space, the snow walls glow around us. Not bright, not dull. More like the light from regular fixtures in a living room. Cheryl's little body is warm, like it's the furnace to this place, this little igloo at the end of the Cheryls Only tunnel.

"It's a neat tunnel."

"Hannah and Dahveed helped me build it."

"Where are they?"

"They're not allowed in. They're not Cheryls."

"Did you tell them that before they helped you build it?"

Cheryl shakes her head. All her curls are filled with millions of tiny snow crystals and her motion makes many of them fly out, float for a second, then fall.

"That doesn't seem fair," I say.

Cheryl glares at me. I should know better about fairness.

A picture of three smiling men, astronauts, posing in their space uniforms, is poked into the snow wall with a small pencil. It's cut out from the front page of the January 28th Chicago Sun-times, and I know who they are without looking too close— Astronauts Grissom, White, Chaffe. Beside them is a picture of their burned-out Apollo space capsule, and then another picture poked into the snow wall of a child no bigger than David, hugging a wife of one of the astronauts.

"Is Mom still taking you to see Dr. Bondurant?"

Cheryl clenches her jaw tight.

"Is it doing any good?"

She shakes her head and a million snow crystals fly away

from her curls.

I lean back against the brick wall and fall into her shoulder. Her breaths are deep and they stutter when she exhales, as though she's trying to keep from crying.

"Cheryl," I say as nice as I can, "will you tell me one thing, just one thing about what's happened to you since Dad died?" Snow crystals brush against my cheek. I try again. "I'm not Dr. Bondurant, I'm your brother. I won't blab, I won't tell anybody. I'll get up and leave this tunnel right now if you say so, for good, but please tell me one thing. After all this time, will you please tell me one thing? Anything?"

Cheryl's stare moves to follow a tear falling down my cheek. I feel it reach my chin as I wonder how that one tear, after all these months of shutting down, finally worked its way out.

"I was supposed to go with Dad to Atlanta," Cheryl says, and she lowers her head to her mittened hands.

"It was a school day," I say. "You couldn't've gone with him."

"He asked me and I could've gone!" says *Daddy's Little Girl*.

She tied Dad up in knots with her voice and her smile and her tears. She's right, I know. Dad would've taken her if she really wanted to go, and there's nothing Mom could've done to stop it, even on a school day. I wait for Cheryl to raise her head. When she does, I see her face muscles pulling in, tensing, her skin flush and hot.

"Why didn't you go?" I say, and the tears come out of her as fast as tears can flow.

She tells me like a rat-a-tat-tat, "'Cause he let David help him in the basement instead of me— I was mad at him— and he let you use the drill with him, not me— and then he asked me to go with and I told him to go away— *go away* was the last thing I said to Dad before he left!"

"You didn't kill Dad."

Her chin drops with her voice as she confesses, to herself, it seems. "All I had to do was make him stop— just for one bathroom— the whole thing would've been different!"

Bup Miller, I'm thinking. Bup Miller and his domino theory.

"What if David or I went with Dad? We could've stopped
it, too."

"But he asked me!" Cheryl says, thumping her mittened thumb against her chest. "And I said no 'cause I
was being ..." She leans her head back and sags, her tears
falling unwiped.

"David and I are trying to find out who to blame for
real," I say. "If I thought it was you, I'd arrest you right now.
But if it was you, then I'd have to arrest David for helping
Dad in the basement. And I'd have to arrest me for using the
drill instead of you. And I'd have to arrest Mom for not letting you use the drill, too, then Big Ben, and the Grossmans,
and the Yellens, and the Waxbergs— if any one of them had
come by the house before Dad left, slowed him down, hurried him up, something, none of this would've happened.
The police can't arrest so many people— there'd be nobody
left on the block."

I can't say that Cheryl's got me under her control, not the
way she had Dad, but that doesn't mean I can't do what Dad
would do right now. I've learned what to do. I put my arm
over her shoulders, hitting my mitten against the ceiling of
our igloo shelter along the way. It snows on top of us for
some seconds. Little ice crystals stick to Cheryl's face, and a
few flow along with her tears to her chin.

"You look like an angel," I tell her, like Dad often told
her, like he would if he were alive today. "You didn't know,"
I say. "You had no way of knowing. It's not your fault."

Her little body, fluttering, fills her parka, then deflates.
Biting into her mittens, pulling them off with her teeth, she
pinches the picture of the astronauts in their Apollo space
suits and tugs it off the snow wall. She brings it close to her
face, and her eyes twitch back and forth.

"Dead astronauts," I say. "Walter Cronkite cried on TV."

Cheryl says more thoughtfully, "Dead fathers." She drops

the picture. "Every day, Jeremy, I feel like I'm the only one."

For all these months since Dad died, it's my heart I've heard beating in my chest, they're my eyes watching the house fall apart, and Mom falling apart with it. I see the rooms without my father. Just the pictures of him, looking more distant and of no use to me except to bring my heart's pounding to my ears. I've lost him— *my* father.

With my arm over her shoulders, squeezing, I feel like I'm soothing my own feelings. We cry together as David scampers about over our heads.

"Hey! Where are you guys?" he calls out, his voice booming into the tunnel.

The snow roof creaks and pops beneath David's footsteps and the snow inside begins to crumble. "Hey!" he booms louder, and a crack and pop send a pile of snow down on our heads, along with one of David's galoshed legs. We grab his leg and bite it, but not too hard, and David wiggles it hard, yelling at us to stop. Of course we don't stop, and he struggles to free himself from our hands and our little bites.

The snow roof and David fall on us now. All I hear is Cheryl's laughter, pounding into the air, loud enough to reach the entire length of Loblolly Avenue, and everything else seems to stop to listen to the collapse of the Cheryls Only tunnel.

•   •   •

I've done it. I've uncorked Cheryl's mouth.

She's sending waves of information stored within her head that keeps coming and coming, much of it boring and uninteresting. Guess I asked for it.

David and I sit on the floor in her bedroom. Despite Cheryl's invitation, David remains nervous and uncertain about his safety in her room. We listen to her as she sits perched on a pillow on her bed like a queen before her subjects. She promises David that she won't hate him in any strange way anymore, that ever since he stood up to Skyler

Jenner, she's decided she should only hate him like a normal sister regularly hates a pesky little brother, no more, no less.

"Just don't hit me in the face," David begs. "That's where I look like Dad, you know."

Cheryl shakes her head a bit and the melted millions of snow crystals fall as globby water drops from her hair, her curls still there by the thousands, but not nearly as tight. Cheryl lets us know just how silly she thinks Dr. Bondurant is.

"She was trying to get me to tattle on you, Jeremy."

"About what?"

"She thinks you're mean to Mom."

Cheryl keeps on yapping. She places no more importance on what Dr. Bondurant said about me and Mom than anything else. Dr. Bondurant's thought stings me in the brain and makes me think about the mean things I've said to Mom. I think about all the mean things I've *thought* about her, and how I don't pay much attention to her these days. Sometimes I find myself wishing for Mom to go away, that it would be better if we lived in Grandmaland with Grandma Elaine and Grandpa Erwin.

What would it be like for Mom to watch David, Cheryl and me taken away by someone else 'cause she couldn't manage, 'cause she couldn't keep up, 'cause she needed monthly envelopes of money? Maybe Mom, when she sees our faces, can only think of our father, her husband, and so she goes to the television set glowing black and white in her bedroom until her blue eyes darken, and she turns gray as a shadow and disappears.

Cheryl slides off her pillow to the floor. David flinches, not knowing if this is one of the regular times Cheryl's supposed to hit pesky little brothers. She steps barefoot to her desk, leaving images of the arc of her feet and little toe ovals on the wood floor. "I found these under Mom's bed," Cheryl says, showing me two brown bottles. Dr. Bondurant's name typed at the top of the labels might as well be skulls and crossbones.

"Val-ee-um," David reads as though he's making fun of the way Cantor Morton talks.

"It's terrible candy," Cheryl says. "It smells bad and tastes bad and puts you to sleep and wakes you up feeling dizzy."

"You've eaten these?" I say. Cheryl lets me take the bottles. "I don't think that's a good idea."

"I only took one, and only 'cause they look like candy." She gags her tongue out. "But they don't taste like candy."

I narrow my eyes and say as important-sounding as I can, "Promise me you won't take any more of these. Promise!"

"It made me sick and dizzy and real sleepy, Jeremy. You can have them." Cheryl inspects the bottles. As if revealing a secret, she whispers, "I think Mom's trying to forget about us."

"Mummy's not trying to forget about us!" David says.

I dump the little candy-yellow pills in the toilet. They hit the water making the sound of hail and turn the water the color of piss. I know that this doesn't solve anything or stop Mom from getting more from Dr. Bondurant. Still, I feel something good when I watch the pills spin together in the center of the swirl and flush away.

She'll have to deal with us tonight, I'm thinking, without her Val-ee-um.

• • •

David sits on his bed this Groundhog Day morning turned to his radio, listening then slumping his head as he hears that all schools, *All of them*, Barney Pip barks with his gut-rumbling laugh, are open.

"What kinda holiday is Groundhog Day," David whimpers, "if you can't stay home from school?"

There's something odd-feeling about going back to school after missing so many days. It's like you're supposed to take out the garbage, but you don't, and it piles up, and you can see it and smell it, but you manage to ignore it. Then the garbagemen come, and suddenly you're running around in your pajamas getting all that built-up garbage out to the street. The garbagemen watch you as you haul out the junk, the gunk, the smelly stuff and the personal stuff— they can see the leftovers of what you ate and what you did. The garbagemen see you, and they know about you as you run around in pajamas hauling out all that garbage. Like that, my teachers will see that I didn't study. I know I won't be the only one, but most of the kids will have done their work, and some will have read ahead, and they will be smarter than me, more ready for eighth grade.

My homeroom teacher is gonna ask about what we did on our blizzard vacation. It's gonna happen. And after everyone else talks about snowball fights and snow fortresses and snowmen and television and studying, it will be my turn to stand up and say that I told my nine-year-old sister not to eat any more of Mom's Valium, that I flushed the pills down the toilet, and that for the first time I can remember, Mom got the wooden spoon out and used it on me for real.

Mom couldn't get to sleep, and she wouldn't explain why, she just told me I already knew why. She paddled me and I didn't beg her to stop, not a whimper. What good would it've done to say anything knowing I hardly talk to her at all anymore? She'd just've paddled me more. I deserved the paddling, for letting all the garbage pile up.

Cheryl knocked on my door after my spoon-whipping, leaned her head in and whispered how sorry she was about the wooden spoon *and all that.*

"What're you thinking?" Cheryl said.

"I still love Mom."

Cheryl smiled and closed my door. It's as if Cheryl thanked me without saying so.

Maybe somebody else's mother would do better with our circumstances. Others might do worse. There's no test you can take ahead of time. David didn't understand dying. Cheryl thought she was to blame. With Mom, I figure, she just loved Dad, loved him a whole lot, with *tuchas* passion. Who am I to say what's normal for Mom when she lost Dad and their *tuchas* passion? I do love her. She can't beat it out of me. And it's not as though she paddled my skin off. I felt her holding back and the regret in each swing.

I don't want to go to school. When I show up, it will be with all my piled-up garbage. People will watch me and know something about me, personal but obvious, I won't even have to say a thing.

David's dressed for school. He pulls my blankets off me.

"Have you got my-tushy's-stuck-a-tosis?" he says, laughing.

He's growing up. He can laugh at his childish past. I really am feeling a little stuck.

•   ·   •

It doesn't take my-tushy's-stuck-a-tosis to get out of school. I avoid Mom all morning and she doesn't seek me out. She leaves for work, I get on the bus, ride to school, walk toward the back of Eisenhower K-8 where there aren't any windows, and keep going.

The streets and sidewalks are as low as the valleys of the Grand Canyon, surrounded by straight walls of white three to eight feet high. Don't need my galoshes on the shoveled walks and streets. Galoshes would just slow me down making this walk to Skokie Valley Hospital. David had his tonsils removed there. It's not that far unless you're wearing galoshes. Since I knew what I was gonna do this morning, I have plenty of room to stuff my galoshes in my bookless book bag. My toes feel cold in my Keds, but I'm moving along pretty fast and warming up. I'm free. One more school-off day, I figure, to see Bup Miller. I have to go, so I'm going, and even the consequences if I'm caught ditching school aren't enough to stop me.

Whoever built Skokie Valley Hospital must've liked rectangles. It sits there, with its flat roof, tic-tac-toe frame, and three stories of windows, an immense rectangle a full block long. It's a puzzle— how many rectangles can you find within the big rectangle? I count over a hundred rectangles on the Simpson Street side alone. It keeps my mind busy as I walk.

Another rectangle, I think, opening the glass entrance door. A woman, as old-looking as Grandma Elaine, but not nearly as friendly, sits at the information booth wearing a white hat with sharp-folded corners— with her hat and face, I count two more rectangles. As I stare at thick gray hairs poking out of her chin— doesn't she know?— she tells me that Bup Miller's room is 203A. Bup's glob of a head might be the only thing that's not rectangular in this place.

Elevators in three-story buildings are determined to take forever to get to where you want them to go. I suppose if they went any faster, they might overshoot the top floor and hit the roof. I've counted all the rectangles I can in here, twice, and the bluish-white light makes me feel as though my sight is getting fuzzy around the edges. When the elevator door opens, I don't see a rectangle. It's a pear-shape blocking my way, one giant pear among all the rectangles.

Mr. Miller pulls me out and squeezes me into his furry blue sweater. His belly kinda mushes around me. I don't hug him back. I can't hug him back the way he's lifted me off the ground like a rag doll. What to make of Mr. Miller? His body heaves and quakes as if he can't make up his mind to laugh or cry.

"Come with me, come with me," he says so excited. "You just missed Mrs. Miller. Bup will be glad to see you! He's going to be fine, he's going to be okay. You'll see how good he looks."

Bup looking good? Mr. Miller must be as bad with the truth as Bup. He takes me by the hand, yabbering on about Bup, and leads me down a building-long hallway polished shinier than a bowling alley lane.

It smells odd when we pass by the rooms. Food, I'm thinking, that's what I smell, but it's mixed in with another smell, the smell of getting ready to get a shot. And a third smell, a faint smell of used diapers. It's the mix of smells I remember from the other hospital, in Chicago, where I visited Dad. Dad complained to Mom about it. He called the place a dog kennel— *The medicine, the food, and the shit are smelling the same to me, Grace!* It's not like he hadn't said curse words in front of me before, and he knew I'd heard them all from Grandma Rosenberg. He seemed so determined about it, though— *Get me out of this shit!* The hospital was glad to see Dad go. The doctors didn't mind kicking him out and dropping him off at our house, still in his body cast. It's not like we could pay for much.

My stomach's curling up, I'm sure an x-ray would prove that. I wonder if Mr. Miller hadn't been there at the elevator whether these smells would've been reason enough to keep me from seeing Bup.

"Here's his room!" Mr. Miller says as though he's surprised he found it. A nurse works at a cart across the hall, dropping pills into cups. She's as pale as her white uniform, puffed up like a two-section snowman. It's hard to tell how old she is the way the blue-white hospital light makes her face blurry. She frowns at me, though. It's easy to see how old I am, and I'm not in school.

"Excuse me," the nurse says, holding pills in cups and pushing her shoulder against the door to room 203. Her voice reminds me of how Mom answers the telephone at International Minerals, like she has to pretend to be in a good mood all the time. "Please wait in the hall until I've finished with 203B." It's a business smile she gives us, and it's gone as soon as she begins to turn away.

"That's for the poor fellow in bed B," Mr. Miller says. "He's a lot worse than Bup."

Mr. Miller bends down toward me and grins a foot from my face. People don't ordinarily look any good that close up. Mr. Miller sure doesn't. His balled-up cheeks look like torpedoes aiming at me, and little blond hairs poke out the tip of his nose, and there's all that sweat, millions of tiny balls of water collecting over his eyebrows. His smile stretches out farther. Can't figure what I've done to make him so pleased with me.

The nurse reappears and nods that it's okay for us to go in. "Thanks for coming," Mr. Miller says, and leads me by the hand into Bup's room.

How did Bup Miller get so bald? It's impossible not to notice and impossible to keep from looking at the top of his head. It shines as bright as a lighthouse, reflecting the bluish-white hospital lights better than the polished floor. For the first time I can think of, Bup Miller looks like something in particular, like Charlie Brown, except Bup's missing the one and only hair curling on Charlie Brown's forehead. I feel my insides wanting to laugh at the sight of Bup lying on his hospital bed with that light bulb of a Charlie Brown head.

"He looks good! —doesn't he look good, Jeremy?" Mr. Miller says.

"You look happy to see me," Bup says. His voice rasps and he tries to clear something from his throat. He says a little more clear, "Are you happy to see me, Jeremy?" As a liar, Bup shouldn't expect an honest answer to such a hard question.

"I'm a little nervous, Bup," I say, "to tell the truth." A skinny tube needles into Bup's wrist and a thicker stub of a tube pokes from his left nostril. And again, my eyes flick up to the whiteness of his head.

"Sometimes I have a little trouble eating," Bup says, pointing to the tube in his nose. "This is my N-G tube. It's like a straw. You'd think they'd pour in a milk shake, but they don't. I don't know what they call the garbage they put down this thing. I think N-G stands for nothing good." Bup looks down at his bedsheet, shaping creases beside himself that make a mummy out of his legs. "I'm a little nervous, too," Bup says.

"You told me it was your dad."

Mr. Miller coughs and sits down on the vent sticking out from Bup's rectangle window. Simpson Street is beyond him, a football field length of snow away. The distant cars pass behind his body and take a little longer than I expect to reappear on the other side of him. "We had this conversation,

Jeremy," Mr. Miller says in a stern voice directed at Bup. "Don't you think you should apologize?"

Mr. Miller wouldn't be so nice to me if he knew what I convinced Bup to do at the Hebrew school and that I broke my promises to him as easy as if I had never made them. I figure Bup hasn't told his dad a thing about searching for first dominos. Just 'cause Bup lies all the time doesn't mean he can't keep a secret. I tell Bup not to apologize and that only makes Mr. Miller smile even harder.

"Bup looks pretty good, doesn't he, Jeremy?"

"Dad— I'm bald and I stink," Bup says, telling the truth.

"You look better than before," Mr. Miller says.

"You should have seen me before."

Two honest answers from Bup in a row.

Beyond the curtain draped around the other half of the room, a moan starts out as low as a whispered *Oh,* and works its way up like a trombone slide, blowing louder— *Oh!*

"Not again," Mr. Miller says, rubbing his chin. "I can't believe they put Bup in this room. It's impossible to sleep!"

The moaning *Oh!* hovers around a high note, fluttering away. It reminds me of the frozen car engines up and down Loblolly Avenue trying to start after the blizzard. The engine inside 203B's curtain won't turn over and the moan dies down only to rise and try again.

"Day in, day out!" Mr. Miller says almost shouting. "They shouldn't put Bup in this old man's room in the first place. I don't care how crowded the Juvenile Ward is."

"I'm used to it, Dad," Bup says. Seeing Bup's eyes sagging below his shining scalp, I doubt Bup's made it to saying three true things in a row.

"The pills will kick in, Jeremy, sooner or later," Mr. Miller says as though he thinks I'm ready to run out of here. I stay despite 203B's pitiful moaning, despite the sickening mix of hospital smells. It's interesting to hear Bup Miller tell the truth two out of three times.

"Leukemia stinks," Bup says, telling the truth again. "I

said Dad was sick 'cause I wanted to know how it felt. I wanted to know how Mom and Dad were gonna feel, you know, about me dying. I thought I could learn that from you, since you'd been through it."

Mr. Miller reaches into his pants pocket for a handkerchief. "You just fell out of remission," he says. "That's all." He blows, inspects his collection, and stuffs the handkerchief back into his pocket. "The doctors say there's a good chance he'll go home, Jeremy. He'll go into remission a second time." 203B raises his voice again, his one word, but it sounds tired, drugged.

"Oy!" Bup says, laughing. He grimaces and pinches his N-G tube. The skin around it is rubbed raw. "It sounds like an *Oy!* to me."

"It does, Bup," I say.

"The pills are slowing the old man down," Mr. Miller says. "He'll stop moaning altogether pretty soon."

Bup rolls his big Charlie Brown head toward me, adjusting his nothing-good tube and wincing. Bup's face shows an intelligent look, not the hope his father talks about.

In this room, I see Bup's future is more my father's and Mr. Miller's more like mine, only in slow motion so I can watch, so there's time to ask questions. I wouldn't ordinarily ask, but I have to. It's an opportunity and I can't stop myself.

"How does this feel, Bup? Do you think you know?"

Mr. Miller begins to cry. He buries his head in his hands and starts heaving his shoulders.

"I'm sorry I did that," I say to Bup. "I didn't mean to do that."

Bup grins at me like I've done him some big favor. His voice is still raspy, but there's something different about it, older, I'm thinking, not a boy's talk, more like a father's. "It's always going to be sad for Mom and Dad," he says. "I'll make it less sad. That's what I'm trying to do."

From a drawer in a table beside his bed, Bup pulls out a book, a large book with a shiny blue and white cover. Bup's arms shake and I help him bring his book to his lap. I recognize the book right away, the *Soncino Edition of the Pentateuch and Haftorahs.*

"I'm gonna get bar mitzvahed," Bup Miller says. "Cantor Morton stopped by and dropped this off. I asked him to train me."

"Why, Bup? Why would you do that when you don't have to?"

"I want to," he says all sure of himself. "You asked me so I told you. This is how I feel."

"But you're only eleven. They won't let you read from the Torah for two more years."

Bup's hospital gown slips down his arms. His arms are thin and have no shape to them. "They're making an exception," he says, "under the circumstances." He smiles like he's landed a ping-pong ball in Bozo's bucket number 6. "I'm a number two!"

"Nobody wants to be a number two," I say.

"That's what Cantor Morton told me."

Cantor Morton, I say under my breath, watching Bup nod. "You said you were a hooey."

"You feel lots of different things," Bup says, repeating my deepest thoughts, "when you're a boy in my position."

Bup starts quoting Genesis without reading from the *Pentateuch*. He's been studying for a bar mitzvah that might never happen, and he's probably much more ready for it than I am for my own.

"You're going to go into remission again," Mr. Miller says, walking around the foot of Bup's bed. He takes me by the hand and leads me away from room 203A. "Bup starts falling asleep when he does that."

The hospital hallway is busy with nurses in white uniforms, pushing their carts filled with pills in cups. It's like the whole place is waking up. Mr. Miller has a question for me and he takes me to a private lounge beside the elevators. It's meant for visitors, but we're alone.

"Bup's getting bar mitzvahed, Jeremy," Mr. Miller says, his face teary and red. "It's true. He's getting bar mitzvahed this spring." I try not to give Mr. Miller a reaction, but it's as hard as biting into a lemon, then pretending you didn't— you can't keep from twisting your face up. "I'm not making him do it, Jeremy."

"He doesn't *have* to?— he *wants* to?"

Nod your wet and red face all you want, Mr. Miller. I won't believe it. Getting bar mitzvahed is a requirement, a ritual, like getting spanked when you're born. It happens 'cause you have no choice about it, being a Jewish boy in Skokie. You've got to go up on stage in the sanctuary and read from the Torah and pray you make no mistakes. Every kid in the audience is waiting to hear your mistakes and add them up. It's a show for them. And you pray, as the bar mitz-vah boy, that puberty doesn't get you right in the voice box while struggling through the Hebrew that the adults around you think is sacred. All the kids in the congregation pray as well. They pray that puberty does get you right in the voice box, right at one of those juicy, *ahch*, Hebrew ee-nun-see-a-shuns, with Cantor Morton right beside you ready to whack your *tuchas*.

Mookie and Dahveed want to get bar mitzvahed. They love being really Jewish. The rest of the Jewish boys on Loblolly Avenue simply know, without asking why, that we can't make it to fourteen without first getting bar mitzvahed when we're thirteen.

"He's doing better," Mr. Miller says. "He'll go back into remission. But, you know— spring. They're letting him do it this spring. They'll let him be eleven and be a bar mitzvah boy. He feels he needs it, Jeremy." Mr. Miller pulls out his handkerchief again and blows and stares at his catch once more before putting the handkerchief back in his pants pock-et. "I need it, too, Jeremy. You understand? I feel I need it now, too."

Should I tell Mr. Miller to trust his domino theory? It can't predict the future, but if God knows the future, He isn't telling people about it when there's still time to do any good with the information. The domino theory can explain things, especially the bad things, even if only after they happen. It makes no excuses for having the bad news ahead of time but doing nothing to stop the bad things from happening. Bup ought to stick to being a hooey.

"We all need this," Mr. Miller insists, a convert to Bup's need to get bar mitzvahed. I want to warn Mr. Miller that getting bar mitzvahed has got nothing to do with religion. Even Karl Grossman was pronounced a bar mitzvah boy, that's plain proof enough. It's a requirement on Loblolly Avenue before Bup can turn fourteen. Don't depend on God to let Bup make it to fourteen. The World Book Encyclopedia, 1964, *L* Volume, at page 191, says Bup's not likely to make it to fourteen, bar mitzvah or not.

And then Mr. Miller asks me, "Would it be okay if Bup is your bar mitzvah partner? It's Cantor Morton's idea."

"A double?" I say.

"If it's all right with you."

A miracle, I'm thinking, owing to the domino theory. Bup gets sick, feels a need to get bar mitzvahed— *clack clack*, go the dominos— I get rid of half my bar mitzvah lines. I'm certainly sad about Bup, it's just funny how things work out.

"That's fine with me, Mr. Miller."

Mr. Miller rubs his hand across my cheek and kisses me on top of my head like I've done him a big favor. I feel a chill run down my spine— guilt, nagging guilt, that Bup's leukemia eases my bar mitzvah burden. Guilt is God's last hold on me, I believe. It's the one thing the domino theory can't seem to explain.

"You know, Jeremy," Mr. Miller says all serious, "I'm not sure how many people would show up just to see Bup's bar mitzvah. I'm glad you're agreeing to do this."

"People would show up for Bup, Mr. Miller," I say. I say so 'cause I feel sorry for Mr. Miller, that he recognizes the truth. There might be the regular religious people in the sanctuary, like the Waxbergs, they always show up for Sabbath. It's interesting what the Millers know about themselves. They seem to accept that people don't give them a chance 'cause they're fat or look like scarecrows or lie all the time.

The Millers started with no religion, with being hooey-ish. At their worst moment, they take up being Jewish like it's the last and best thing they can turn to. I started out Jewish but when I needed God, God did nothing for me. Bup can have half my bar mitzvah. He can have it all if that could happen. I've got no use for it. I just need to be allowed to turn fourteen.

•   •   •

When I walk home, I call Mr. Trauby and he confirms it— Bup Miller is scheduled to get bar mitzvahed. Mr. Trauby corrects my grammar, "We say, *become* a bar mitzvah, not *get* bar mitzvahed. It's a transformation of sorts," he explains, "not something you buy in a store."

"Jewish puberty?"

"Jeremy," he says, his voice falling away from the phone.

"Like magic?"

I feel mean. I can say anything I want to, to anybody. I've searched Mom's room so that every kid in this house can honestly say they did it. Found one bottle with Dr. Bondurant's name typed on it, freshly opened, full, with a ball of cotton still in it smashed to the side, like Mom was in a hurry to get to her piss-yellow pills. She left it under her box spring, her fake mattress, just how I've hidden one of Mr. Grossman's dirty magazines under my mattress.

"How are things at home?" Mr. Trauby says. He talks the way a loving father would and sends my thoughts spinning in circles again. "I can give you that information, Jeremy. Are you ready for it? Do you still need it?"

"Who killed my father?" I say, closing my eyes.

"It's not that simple, Jeremy. I'd like to talk to you about it in person."

"Can't you just tell me now?"

"I'd need to explain it to you. It's not a matter of one

name or one thing. I'm afraid this will be difficult for you. In person, Jeremy," he says, commanding me.

"I won't do this with my mother there, Mr. Trauby. You can just tell me and I'll decide what to do."

Mr. Trauby's breath pushes through the phone loud enough to tickle my ear. "I have to tell you, Jeremy. I think your mother already knows. She knows what I do."

"How can you say that? She doesn't know. She can't!"

"A lawyer from Skokie made the same calls my friend did, but over six months ago. Jerome Yellen. Does your mother know him?"

"Yes, Mr. Trauby."

"Then she already knows, Jeremy."

"Right, Mr. Trauby." That's all I'm able to say. He keeps his fatherly voice talking— *Do you want to meet with me? Do you still want to know? How's Bup Miller? Is the double bar mitzvah with him all right with you? Are you all right, Jeremy? Jeremy?* — "Right, Mr. Trauby," to everything he says, and I hang up. I can't say anything more.

In this living room, a space that's opposite the dining room, I sit on the couch where I first heard the news. *His heart stopped and he died.* That sunburst clock ticks at me, rolling along. It doesn't care. It's keeping time.

According to Mr. Trauby, Mom already knows about Dad's first domino. She knows, and I still don't, and it hasn't made a bit of difference to her or this family or this house. My house is a museum, that's what it is, and not a popular one like the Museum of Science and Industry. It's one of those museums that nobody comes to visit 'cause nobody wants to. It's too dusty and creepy and dull. I'm like one of those old security guards putzing around an old, tired, empty museum, waiting for something to happen, pretending something might happen even if it takes forever. I need to make something happen.

I call my mother and tell her I'm home from school, sick, never made it, threw up in a pile of snow nobody can find, nobody can investigate to see if I've lied. Her voice, as usual, is at first polite, a business voice. When she recognizes it's me, she sighs and says, "Right, Jeremy. Take some Pepto-Bismol. Go to sleep." She'll call the school up, sign the note, whatever is necessary. "Feel better," she remembers to say, and hangs up.

I call Bup's hospital room and tell Mr. Miller that I'll do it, I'll double up my bar mitzvah with Bup. But since I've done Bup this favor, I ask Mr. Miller not to tell anybody I visited Bup today, and Bup shouldn't tell anybody either. Mr. Miller asks me why and I tell him I'd like to keep this double bar mitzvah thing a secret, a surprise for as many people as possible. Whether Mr. Miller really agrees with me or not, he says he does, and he promises not to tell, and I hope, at least, that Bup Miller didn't learn to lie by watching his father.

After thinking about it long and hard, I call the Hebrew school again and ask for Cantor Morton. He's in, and he ee-nun-see-ates, "Hell-oh."

"This is Jare-ah-mee Rose-and-berg," I say.

"Oh!" he says using that odd bird peep. "What can I do for you?"

It's hard to say this, to tell him exactly why I called. It seemed so easy to do when I was dialing, before I heard his enunciations and felt his reputation through the phone choke the courage out of me. It's not like I forgot, but with my courage gone, my idea doesn't seem so smart anymore.

Something about that sunburst clock ticking along encourages me, so I tell him the last thing in the world I thought I would ever say— "You can call my mother." Possibly he didn't hear me 'cause the phone's so quiet. I say it again, louder. "Call my mother, tonight if you like. I'm serious."

"Oh!" he says — *peep peep*, "I heard you the first time."

For my mother, Cantor Morton will be quite the new domino. When she sees those lizard eyes bugging and that lizard neck wobbling, and hears that lizard talk peeping, Mom will freak at the lizard asking her out on a date. Better than what she's been doing— she needs to be freaked. She'll grab the wooden spoon and take it to the synagogue to investigate. She might pull me and David out of Hebrew school and cancel my bar mitzvah. Who knows what will happen when a new first domino like that explodes? — like an atomic bomb, I think.

"Thank you for your per-meh-shun. I know how hard it must be for you."

I wish he hadn't said that before hanging up. It gives me that familiar guilty feeling. I hate that.

One more new domino before I'm through. I open Mom's Valium bottle and pull out the cotton ball. In its place, I leave a note on a scrap of paper over the pills. I have several things in mind to write on the note, a lecture, a plea, a curse word about Dr. Bondurant. I write *We love you, Mom,* and underline *We* three times. I place the bottle back beneath the box spring near the corner of her bed, exactly where I found it.

There can't be any one first domino, I decide. Things are far too messed up for any one first domino to get all the blame. I've stuck in my own dominos and sent them in another direction to see what happens. I lean back against the couch and close my eyes. That clock still ticks away the time. It never stops.

•   •   •

She enters my room late tonight, much later than when she used to regularly come in to tell stories and tuck me and David in. I keep my eyes closed to pretend sleep and my ears sharp to listen to what she does when she thinks I'm not aware of her. She walks like she's trying not to wake us, but of course our shagless wooden floor creaks a bit — old bones, I think. Her steps, the creaks, make it to the side of my bed. I feel her, her breathing, her stare, moving up and down my fake-sleeping body.

She whispers my name and she sits beside me, pressing the mattress down so I roll against her. Through my blankets, she's warm, and her eyes, I know, are busy moving about, examining my face.

"I'm so exhausted," she says, continuing with her whispers, and she says she's sorry. Her hand gently strokes my face, from my alert left ear to my fake-sleep drooping jaw. "Okay, Jeremy," she says. "Okay."

She leaves the room without going to David. She knows, I'm thinking, that the note in her pill bottle is mine. David the Spy speaks from his own fake-sleep. "What did you do?" he says all worried. I don't answer 'cause I think of so many different things to say, one right after the other, that nothing comes out. He asks again, but all my answers clog themselves up and I fake-sleep a grunt, moan, and a rustle beneath my cover.

I find Dr. Bondurant's pill bottle by my pillow. Even though I smell the bitterness of those pills, the bottle is empty. Remembering Mom's gentle touch at my bedside, I am hopeful now about *my* domino theory, about my new first dominos.

"Just don't snore," David says.

We wait for our fake sleep to become real sleep.

•　•　•

Mom gets a Valentine's Day card in the mail from the Skokie Jewish Congregation. David shows me how to open the envelope and seal it again using steam from the teapot. "I watch *The Man From Uncle*," he says. Pretty clever. Just a bunch of hearts with *Be My Valentine*, and no name. I put it on her pillow before she gets home from work.

Our American school teachers advertised Valentine's Day for over a week, taping bright red and pink heart decorations of all sizes to the chalkboard and windows, dangling even more of them from the overhead tube light fixtures— they make floating heart shadows on our desks and school books all day long. Mrs. Goldbeck hung a *Be My Valentine* banner over her desk.

Melinda Levinberg lets me know I didn't get her a

Valentine's Day card. I failed to see the consequences of that coming.

"How could you miss it?" Melinda says to me after the Eisenhower K-8 Valentine's Day card exchange.

She has red and pink and white Valentine's Day cards sticking out of her stuffed book bag, none from me. I hold the card she gave me in my hand, sucking the little candy heart I found inside it. The candy had printed in red letters over the pale pink candy, *Only You!* She signed her card to me, *Love Mindy.* Her sweet face, with only the slightest adjustment, zings her disappointment in me right to the center of my gut.

"There'd better be something in my mailbox when I get home!" she warns.

There wouldn't be anything in her mailbox from me.

Now Melinda Levinberg holds mittened hands with Leonard Schlictman during recess, huddling together in their bulky parkas and sneaking kisses behind piles of snow. At Karl's school band concert, Mr. Grossman says about Leonard Schlictman, "What a fat ass *he's* got! — there's a difference between a fat ass and a good *tuchas.*"

Leonard Schlictman plays the bassoon and wears glasses. Never wears blue jeans. Leonard wears pants that businessmen wear to work, pulled up a little too high and clamped too tight across his lower belly by a skinny black belt, the same belt every school day. I think he smells like Bugles corn chips. Arnold Grossman announced his fat ass. But Melinda Levinberg holds hands with Leonard Schlictman and, other than shaking her head when I see her in American school and Hebrew school, she ignores me.

Valentine's Day, like Groundhog Day, doesn't keep you from having to go to school. Asking somebody to *Be My Valentine* is just so weird for a boy my age to say, I think. What does that mean? I got Valentine's Day cards from all sorts of people I can't stand, even boys, including one from the hairy ogre Jeff Schuber— *Be Mine!* it said with pink hearts circling the card. Everybody got a Valentine's Day card from Jeff Schuber. Nobody I know wants to *Be His*. Valentine's Day just can't mean much at all is what I see. What might *Be My Valentine* mean hanging over Mrs. Goldbeck's desk? A promise to give me an *A*? Doubt it.

Being dumped for Leonard Schlictman makes me look in mirrors too often, searching for things wrong with my face and finding them. There's a freckle on my cheek where there shouldn't be, an eyebrow that's shorter than the other one. I find my first pimple, a small purple dot on my forehead. It sits there like a warning, that there's more coming, that puberty holds a secret number of pimples beneath my skin waiting to sprout. I worry about my body and whether I have, or will get, a fat ass like Leonard Schlictman's. Things would've been easier for me if only I'd given Melinda Levinberg a Valentine's Day card.

On my way to Hebrew school with Karl, Charlie, and David, and Mr. Grossman chomping his cigar as he drives, I think of Melinda. In my mind, I make her hair turn green, then fall out completely along with her teeth. I put a wart on her nose and cross her eyes. But the truth sneaks back in and I see her as she really is. I get my Mr. Stiffy. After Hebrew school, I'll have to go to bar mitzvah class where Melinda is a number two. She did that for me and will remind me of that fact with her look that just kills me inside.

"Why do I still have to go to Hebrew school?" Karl Grossman whines. "I already got bar mitzvahed."

"Because I say so," Mr. Grossman says, wiggle-wagging his cigar about in his mouth.

"So?"

"Why I ought to crack you," Mr. Grossman begins, but he makes no move to crack Karl, and Karl doesn't flinch. "Because your mother says so," Mr. Grossman adds, lingering over "mother" like it's a reminder of something so obvious and dangerous that Karl shouldn't forget.

"Damn," Karl says. "At least I'm done getting bar mitzvahed."

"*Become* a bar mitzvah," I say, surprising myself. Karl

sneers into the back seat at me to let me know I'm weird. I say Mr. Trauby's words. "You *become* a bar mitzvah, you don't *get* bar mitzvahed. It's like a transformation."

"You've transformed into Mookie Waxberg," Karl says, grunting out a laugh. "Where's your sheenie beanie, Rosenberg?"

"Quiet," Mr. Grossman says, but he keeps driving and Karl ignores him.

"Where's your beanie?"

"It's a *kipah*," I say.

"A kaput?" Karl snorts. He starts buzzing spitty letter *P's* between his lips— "*P, P, P, P*— kaput!"

David's parka makes crinkling noises, the sound of balling up a potato chip bag, as he turns his hooded head toward me. "What do you become?" he says all serious.

Mr. Grossman lifts a hand off the steering wheel and removes his cigar. He turns his head to Karl, just for a second, and says, "A bar mitzvah's not supposed to be easy. It means you've learned something about being responsible, about being Jewish. It means ..." Mr. Grossman holds his breath to make sure he has our attention "... that you've grown up and become a man."

"I started getting hairs on my sac after my bar mitzvah," Karl says.

"Goddamn," Mr. Grossman says.

It's the weakest swearing I've ever heard and not mean at all. It's as though Mr. Grossman's sorry about something. Maybe it's his own fault for raising Karl or for teaching us about sex on the way to Hebrew school.

"You know Karl was born too early," Charlie says. "A lot too early. Mom says he didn't even weigh three pounds."

"Shut up," Karl says, thumping Charlie in the chest.

Charlie says to his brother, "I'm only trying to explain you."

"*Become* a bar mitzvah," Mr. Grossman says, repeating my words and sticking his cigar back in his mouth. "I like that. You're a regular defender of the faith, Jeremy."

"Are you gonna wear a *kipah* like Mookie and Dahveed?" David says.

"When I have to."

"Why not all the time?"

Karl says, "When I took mine off after my bar mitzvah, it felt like I still had it on for a whole week, like somebody had their hand on my head all the time."

"Maybe it was God telling you to put it back on," Charlie says. "Maybe He was still giving you a chance to become something."

"Right," Karl says.

"I don't want to wear a *kipah* all the time," I say to David. "I'm not that Jewish."

"How Jewish are you?"

"Not enough to wear a *kipah* all day."

"Kaput," Karl says.

"Goddamn," Mr. Grossman says. "You *were* born too early."

"We're Jewish enough," I say.

David crinkles his parka sleeves, folding his arms across his chest. "We'll see after your bar mitzvah. We'll see what you really become."

"Check your sac now and then after, Rosenberg," Karl says. "You'll see the change."

Unfortunately for Mr. Trauby, Karl's idea of the bar mitzvah change is stronger in my mind than Mr. Grossman's. It seems an odd time to require responsibility from boys, a serious religious responsibility, when everything in the world makes me think of Melinda Levinberg and Mr. Grossman's magazines and my own changing body.

The eight boys and four girls in this class sit fidgeting while Mr. Trauby asks his questions about what a *mitzvah* is in Jewish life. We each wear a tiny pimple, Myron Edelson wears three, as a mark of some kind, a badge to show we're all wondering about sex, not Hebrew things, not *mitzvahs*. Only Melinda Levinberg is clear of pimples, but her two new little booby nubs are obvious to me. Even when I don't look at them, I sense them. I know they're there, growing, and I can't keep from thinking about them pointing into me, wondering what they might feel like, and the bottom of her short skirt marks the line between good and evil, I think. Melinda Levinberg shakes the air around her.

Mr. Trauby answers his own question with more questions.

"Is it more important to do good things out of compassion, or because we do them as a commandment from God? Should we revere people more who volunteer, or people who have followed religious commandments without fail?"

Mr. Trauby folds his hands together on his teacher's desk, wearing a brown suit, white shirt, and tie. His black hair is cut so close to his head that it seems as though he's wearing a knit winter hat with ear holes cut out. It makes his Jewish face look more Jewish, his nose, his chin, his skin, just as he described to me, David, and Bup. His face announces his Jewishness. It's not that I'm thinking he's ugly. Just the opposite. His face is defined, he looks like what he looks like. He's Mr. Trauby, a man who has sex with the beautiful Mary Trauby. I can't figure out what I look like. I worry I'll never have sex in my whole life.

"Are you more impressed with the volunteer of good things, or the dutiful follower of God's commandments?"

I wonder what the class must look like to Mr. Trauby, our pimples lit up extra purple beneath the white glow of the florescent classroom lights, our eyes swirling as we think about our bodies. He gives up waiting for a volunteer in this class. He calls on Fred Mussman to answer using Fred's Hebrew name, *Moshe*. Moshe, I know, stands for Moses. Moshe has a pimple rising below his ear.

"The volunteer —" Fred answers, sounding more like he's asking a question.

"Moshe, are you just picking one out of two, or have you thought about this based on your studies?" Mr. Trauby must know we hardly give much thought to the little bit of Hebrew we study. I guess he pretends otherwise.

"The volunteer," Fred says more like an answer this time.

"Anyone else?" Mr. Trauby says. Fred droops his head. "Students, there's only one other possible choice."

"The volunteer!" Steve Fishbine says.

"I already said that, moron," Fred shoots back at Steve.

"I didn't say you were wrong, Moshe. Perhaps Shlomo was thinking about it and agreeing with you." Standing and turning to Steve Fishbine, Mr. Trauby asks, "Is this your conviction, Shlomo, or did you simply forget that Moshe had already picked the volunteer?"

Steve drops his stare to his desk. "I ... can't remember," he says, and we all stop wondering about sex long enough to laugh at him.

Hearing *Shlomo*, of course, always makes us laugh at least a little. *Shlomo* stands for Solomon, the wise King Solomon, who threatened to split babies in two to discover real mothers. My American school bus driver is the skinniest person I know and he tells us to call him Tubby. Calling Steve Fishbine *Shlomo*, Solomon the Wise, is like that, it makes us laugh even harder.

"You can't lie to me, can you, Shlomo?" Mr. Trauby says.

"No," Steve says.

"Why not?"

"You're a Hebrew school teacher."

"You fear me?"

"I'm afraid of what you can do to me."

"I won't beat you up, of course." Mr. Trauby smiles. "I'm not Cantor Morton."

"I'm afraid you'll kick me out. Then I can't get bar mitzvahed."

"Praise Shlomo for his sense of obligation!" Mr. Trauby says, throwing his hands up in the air. "Who here really wants to become a bar mitzvah?" Mr. Trauby scans his eyes over the twelve of us. Myron Edelson raises his hand. Our stares follow Mr. Trauby as he steps from behind his desk and marches quickly to Myron. Myron's elbow crooks a bit as Mr. Trauby leans his face down toward him. The elbow crooks even more so that it looks like Myron's riding a bicycle and signaling for a right turn.

"That's only a half-truth, Pinchas," Mr. Trauby says, examining Myron's arm. "Tell your Hebrew school teacher the whole truth." Myron Edelson's arm collapses to his lap.

Mr. Trauby straightens and announces, "*Kiddushin* 31a, 'Greater is he who is commanded and carries out an act, than he who is not commanded and carries it out.'" Mr. Trauby returns to his desk and speaks to us quietly. "A *mitzvah* is a commandment of God, something we must do regardless of our opinion. If we choose voluntarily to do a good deed today, that does not mean we will always do that good deed each and every day. But when we feel obligated, feel that a good deed must be done because God commands it, we will continue to do that good deed for the rest of our lives.

"For some of you, your bar mitzvahs and bat mitzvahs approach. As far as I can tell in this school, only four out of the twenty bar mitzvah students truly want to go through with it, and not one of that four is in this class. Don't think I don't know it. Don't think I didn't have the same thoughts as you when I was your age. I preferred radio mysteries to the Sabbath, playing soccer to *shul*, but I felt obligated to obey. You all feel obligated, to your parents, to God, maybe to me, like Shlomo and Moshe. You are all children of Israel, though you sit here waiting for class to end, wishing you could be in front of your television sets. It's all right. You are merely following God's commandments to honor Him and your parents *because* you hate to be here but are here nevertheless."

"So if you *like* coming here, you're less Jewish?" I say pretty snappy.

"Yitzchak," Mr. Trauby says to me, "you're thinking again. Good."

I hate my Hebrew name. I hate the sound of it. Mr. Trauby's been using our Hebrew names 'cause our bar mitzvahs are approaching. "Try to get used to them," he said.

Yitzchak. It sounds to me like someone's trying to clear

their lungs to load up a hocker. "Your Hebrew names are historical, they make us remember, they sound endearing," Mr. Trauby said the first time we laughed at *Shlomo*. Mr. Trauby said his own Hebrew name reminded him of a deli sandwich. "Can anyone try to guess what it is?" Solomon the Wise blurted out *Hoagie!* "It's Ruben, Baruch Ruben," Mr. Trauby said, laughing. "I'm a deli sandwich!"

"Why can't we be both the volunteer and obey the commandments?" Melinda Levinberg says. "Why's it such a big deal?" Her question gives me an excuse to look at her without making her mad.

Mr. Trauby raises his hands to dismiss us. "Think about it and ask me next class, Yocheved."

Melinda's question and my question seem logical to me, and they sink Mr. Trauby's nice-sounding speech. I can't stand how these speeches drip out and leave us with more questions. Sitting firm in my chair, I raise my voice. "Can you answer me, Mr. Trauby?"

The students are out of their seats and begin gathering their books, and I freeze them with my question, a demand for an answer out of Mr. Trauby. Even Melinda Levinberg, half turned from her desk, has her eyes and booby nubs pointed at me longer than since Valentine's Day. I ask again, hearing my voice turn snotty, "Is somebody less Jewish because they like coming here?"

"Ponder it, Mr. Rosenberg, and tell us at our next class what you think."

Think? — I think Mr. Trauby doesn't have an answer, and I keep my stare on him to let him know that. He's acting like I might give up, shuffling some papers together and doing other fake busywork. I ask him, louder than before— "Tell me."

Fred Mussman makes his way out the door. His seat is closest to it. The rest of the students seem caught between Mr. Trauby and my demand for a complete answer.

"We'll discuss this in private," Mr. Trauby says.

"Now?"

"If you would like to."

With a wave of his hand at the other students, Mr. Trauby lets them go. They leave me alone with Mr. Trauby.

Mr. Trauby waits behind his desk, staring at his hands for close to a minute, maybe more. He turns his head to the door, listening to the rising then quieting hallway hum of students freed from their Hebrew school classes.

"Yitzchak," he says, "for months I've waited for you to talk to me. I've had you in my home, with my family, shared my food— there are few things more sacred than that. My hand has been extended to you all this time. But you have said so little. Why now are you asking these questions? Why in this class with all my other students?"

I shrug.

"*Oy vey iz meir!*" Mr. Trauby says, staring at the ceiling and in that Yiddish way that means to tell me he's talking to God. "Maybe if I invite a crowd, Yitzchak will speak to me." He returns his stare to me. "Why don't you repeat that question of yours, Yitzchak. What was it— are you less Jewish if you like coming here, was that it? And I told you I wanted you to think about it."

"I'm tired of thinking about it."

"Thinking about it for five minutes tires you out, Yitzchak?"

"No, Mr. Trauby." I slouch in my seat.

"How long have you been thinking about it?"

"Forever."

"That's a long time for a thirteen-year-old."

"Tell me, Mr. Trauby, how Jewish am I?"

"You're Jewish."

"You said I don't look Jewish."

"I was only paying you a compliment." I see he's laughing at something, at himself, I suppose.

"Why do you say things like that?"

"I know what I look like. People make up their own minds about what Jewish is supposed to look like. I guess I just fit what such people want to believe. But being Jewish, or anything really, depends upon what's in your heart and mind, and your deeds in your daily life. On the outside, I think I'm too ugly for any religion. But there you are, Yitzchak, looking so much the opposite of me, so handsome even with that little pimple on your forehead, like you could sing *White Christmas* in a Hollywood movie, yet you're Jewish. How can that be?"

I raise my hand to my forehead and touch my purpled-up pimple.

"Mr. Rosenberg, some answers can never be definite. They can never be exactly the same for everybody. If that were true, if we understood everything without disagreement, particularly about God, there wouldn't be so many different ways to believe in God by so many well-meaning people."

"You don't know?" I say. "You don't know about God?"

"I know my own thoughts about God."

"Tell me."

"The joy is in the journey, not the conclusion. I don't have a conclusion to give you because I'm still living the journey. There's a Jewish proverb— If I knew God, I would be God. Who am I, sitting at this old desk, to tell you anything truly definite about God? He's God, I'm just a person."

"How can I be Jewish if I don't know?"

"You feel obligated."

"I feel guilt."

"Hardly a difference there, Yitzchak." Mr. Trauby stands and gathers his books. "Yitzchak," he sighs. He manages to make that name sound sweet. "I have no right to order your obligation to embrace God. But by your obligation to your father, his memory, and your family, you are a follower of God's commandments. You feel obligated because that's the way you are. You can't help it. I honor you, Yitzchak, for your obligation to your family even if you think you don't like being Jewish. But you are, as I know God, a Jew as much as I can be myself. It's not a matter of degree.

"And your obligation to your family is why I think it's

best for you to talk to your mother about what happened in Atlanta. I'm your Hebrew school teacher, maybe your friend one day, but I'm not your family. Talk to her. I think you know I'm right, Yitzchak." He snuggles his books under his arm and begins to leave. "Go to your bar mitzvah lesson."

I watch Mr. Trauby as he reaches the classroom door.

"I don't hate being Jewish," I say as if begging him to believe me.

"Of course, Jeremy," he says smiling. "Try not fighting that guilty feeling so hard. If you listen to it, it might turn into something better."

Mr. Trauby turns out the classroom light. He leaves me in the dark after making being Jewish into such a mystery so I have to keep coming back to Hebrew school. It's the same as a TV show that gives some interesting information but finishes with *Stay tuned next week for the exciting conclusion!* It seems with Hebrew school, the exciting conclusion never gets here.

• • •

David and Karl wait for me on the steps leading away from the sanctuary. David is dressed as Mordechai, a hero of the Purim holiday, who convinces his beautiful cousin Esther to tell King Ahasuerus, who Esther won in a beauty contest, not to kill all the Jews. Hard to believe that Purim is supposed to be a fun holiday considering how the Purim bad guy, Haman, was no better than Hitler. At synagogue, the littler kids love to dress up in their Mordechai costumes— a three-pointed cardboard hat, a tinfoil sword, and a Purim tin box noisemaker called a *grogger*.

While Karl sits on a middle step outside the sanctuary, blank-staring, his jaw drooped against his fist, David stands on the step behind him with his Mordechai hat slipping over his eyes, his tinfoil sword raised, and his *grogger* tin can cranking about on its little stick, sounding like Moe crunching Curly's head in a vice. "Haman!" David shouts at Karl.

"You are evil!" and twirls his *grogger* by Karl's ear. In a second, Karl's tossed the *grogger* down the steps. David raises his tinfoil sword and hoots at Karl, "Die, Haman! Die!" anointing Karl in the cheek with a slap of sword-shaped Reynolds Wrap.

"Don't do anything to him," I say to Karl. "He's only playing."

"If he rattles that shit at me one more time I'll shove it down his throat." Karl speaks as he pleases among Hebrew school students, teachers, and parents walking about the lobby. The shadow of the Rabbi could move in from behind to hear the bar mitzvah boy cursing outside the sanctuary. Karl doesn't care. I see Charlie standing by the front door entrance, carrying his own *grogger*, silver sword, and three-pointed cardboard hat. He's leaning his head against the long skinny window built into the front door.

"Dad's here," Charlie says. He shoves his chubby parka shoulder against the door. The wind blows Charlie's cardboard hat off his head, and he drops his *grogger* and sword on the floor of the lobby as he leaves.

"They're mine!" David calls. His face is hot and filled with play as he rushes by me to pick up what Charlie has left behind. Behind Karl, Cantor Morton appears at the top step, and Karl stands so lazy, letting out his lazy talk.

"He better not rattle that shit in my father's car."

Holding his sacred *Pentateuch* in his hand, Cantor Morton is a statue atop the staircase. He casts his lizard eyes down upon Karl's back as if wishing him to leave by the strength of prayer. Karl carries nothing but his coat on his shoulders, no Hebrew schoolbooks of any kind.

"There's nothing to flunk here," he says, passing me. "Bosses won't ask about Hebrew school grades." Karl turns his hang-jaw face back to Cantor Morton and then to me, smiling out even louder, "None of that Purim garbage in my car."

I give David his *grogger* and, with Charlie's already in his hand, I ask David to give one to Mr. Grossman. "I think he'll like it for the drive home. Hurry," I say. "Go to the car and give it to him!" David leaves with his two cardboard hats, two swords, and two *groggers*, shouting to Mr. Grossman that there's *groggers* for everyone.

"Rosenberg!" Karl's face winds up like he wants to do something to me right there in the Hebrew school lobby. I see his eyes level with mine. I've gotten taller, I realize, and my puberty and my pimple, I think, make me look more like a challenge to him. He zips up his parka. "I'm telling my dad not to come back to get you."

"That's all right," I say. "I've got a ride home already."

"No you don't, Rosenberg. You're gonna freeze walking home." He leaves me in the lobby and goes to his father's car.

Through the door window, I see the parking lot lights shine against Mr. Grossman behind the steering wheel. I see his smile, his curly-haired head turning back to David, and then his eyes staring at the *grogger* gift as he joyfully spins it about. Karl slumps against the front passenger window, raising a middle finger to me. It was worth it, I think, though I have no ride home.

"Yitz-chak!" Cantor Morton commands. I follow his dark figure 'cause I must, 'cause I fear him, 'cause of guilt, 'cause of obligation.

•　•　•

The ten twos gather on the old sanctuary stage in hard wooden chairs with our aching backs straight and our eyes forward as directed by Cantor Morton. We are here to learn about cantillations. These are the trope, the symbols and the squiggles beneath and above the Hebrew lettering. The trope tell us how to sing our bar mitzvah portions, our blessings, and Torah and Haftorah passages.

Cantor Morton demonstrates each symbol, his voice deep and full, like one of those yawn-sounding opera songs I pass by on the radio dial as I tune in to find the Beatles. I notice his paper-thin eyelids closing, his body swaying with his voice as though forming the shape of the trope he sings. The ten twos slouch in our chairs to relieve our backs, and stiffen again only as Cantor Morton finishes, and his eyes reappear from the depths of his trope. He smiles, satisfied with himself, and begins another trope, a long one filled with the rises and falls of a roller coaster that never wants to end.

Cantor Morton raises his palms upward and clenches his eyelids shut as he continues. The ten twos know we are in for a particularly long trope, and we slump in our chairs again to catch our breath and relieve our aching backs. Our entire class heaves from trope to trope, falling as Cantor Morton loses himself in his songs, rising when he turns to us when he finishes, enunciating out, "Do all the stew-dents un-der-stand?" We nod knowing we are doomed at some point in the class 'cause we don't understand at all. But in the meantime, we take our chances when he sings, relaxing from our painful bar mitzvah "pahs-chure."

I sit behind Thelda Dachman. As her name suggests, she's fat, really fat, so fat that I feel safe hiding behind her while Cantor Morton gets lost in his tropes. I relax my back and write my note to Melinda Levinberg: *Dear Melinda*— cross out. *Dear Mindy*— cross out. Get to the point, I think. *I'm sorry, Mindy,* I write. *I've had a lot on my mind as you probably know.*

Cantor Morton begins a new wailing trope that at first sounds as deep as a basement and seems determined to climb to the top of a skyscraper, taking all the time it needs. I cross out my sentence. It doesn't seem right to use my dead-father boy situation as some sort of advantage. I place my pencil tip to my bar mitzvah notebook and feel tingles in my brain. Should I write it? I wonder. Do I mean it? What does it feel like to write these words? — *I love you, Melinda. I'm sorry I forgot to send you a Valentine's Day card. I'd send you a thousand now if I could go back in time. Please be my valentine even after Valentine's Day.*

These are the words I write. This is what I think about in bar mitzvah class. I tingle in my brain, my pimple, my heart, my stomach, my helpless little Mr. Stiffy. And as I study the words, Cantor Morton's trope hits the top of a skyscraper, and it leaps skyward, to outer space, before falling, falling in small steps as though it wishes it could float with the clouds forever.

"Yitz-chak!" Cantor Morton booms beside me. I raise my eyes and see heads on stiff-backed bar mitzvah "pahs-chures" twirling toward me. Pitying stares anticipate the proof that Cantor Morton does in fact beat the *tuchases* of disobedient bar mitzvah students. Cantor Morton hears everything and sees through his eyelids. He fools us into thinking his tropes protect us from his superpowers. I am fooled. *My love note to Melinda*— his fingertips press the paper!

"Yitz-chak! I have been stan-ding here for all-most one min-ette. What are you do-ing?"

Melinda Levinberg's stare is on me from the left end of the front row. I wait for pity in her face, but find only that hard look she makes with a twitch of a face muscle. Can't pick out exactly what she does, but it flattens my gut just thinking how she's gonna look at me when Cantor Morton starts to read my note to her, to everybody, out loud in bar mitzvah class. The sound of paper tearing from my notebook scratches my ears. Unable to run, frozen in my chair, I sit on display, soon to be entertaining the number twos with Cantor Morton's whacks upon my helpless *tuchas* while he demon-strates his tropes using the words I have written.

Cantor Morton raises my love note in *his* hands to *his* unblinking lizard eyes. What am I thinking? How could a note change things? It's too late for notes. Melinda thinks Leonard Schlictman, with his fat ass and Bugle corn chips smell, and funny clothes and glasses, is better than me. How can I think a mere trope can keep Cantor Morton from read-ing my note through Thelda Dachman's thick body? Head hunkered down, shoulders slumped, I shut my eyes and wait for the agony to begin while the remaining number twos have their permanent, most memorable bar mitzvah class experience made at my expense. I feel my pimple glow as bright as a beam from a lighthouse.

"Oh!" Cantor Morton says, reading. He crinkles the page and brings it to his nose, moving his nose across the paper like a pointer. Thelda Dachman makes a gagging noise, probably 'cause she's in a spot to see that bulging neck thing of Cantor Morton's poking out— my note hides it from me. I see only his eyes darting about behind his glasses as though he's busy checking my spelling letter by letter.

Then the miracle happens, proof of God if Mr. Trauby could have the opportunity to explain it to me. Cantor Morton folds the paper and lowers it to my lap. "Nev-ahr mind, Yitz-chak," he says. "Vah-ree good, Yitz-chak." And he steps away smiling as though I have done something wonderful.

Cantor Morton begins another trope, longer than any before, swooning along as he makes his way to his place in front of the class. I stiffen my back and remain that way out of fear and confusion. Keeping good "pahs-chure" is my way of thanking him.

For the entire class, Cantor Morton doesn't ask us to sing his tropes. He is happy to do it by himself, his eyes closed, his voice fluttering. Maybe a miracle is involved, but my doubts search for something more practical. This, I imagine listening to his soaring voice, is where Cantor Morton keeps his own thoughts.

• • •

What a nightmare! Here I sit trying to figure out how it became real. To my right is a car door, locked, with me inside a big black Cadillac. In front of me is the metal dashboard bulging at my face like knuckles on a fist. The dark length of the hood stretches out to the horizon of the road. I can't see where we're going! I hope Cantor Morton, driving with his gloved hands gripping the steering wheel, understands my directions home.

I expect an odd smell from Cantor Morton, or maybe an old smell. He's odd and old. People like that, in small closed-up places, always have an odd, old odor, like they're evaporating ancient blood. My Finkelwitz grandparents have their smells, of boiled chickens mostly. My Rosenberg grandparents smell dusty. And Mr. Yellen, though not as old, but looking as old as grandparents look, leaves his serious business paper smells behind in my dining room every evening he studies our lack of money. But Cantor Morton smells like soap, clean, freshly showered, and he has a light scent of aftershave I'm afraid my mother might like. I've given him my blessing to call her, and now I've told him how to find where we live. He asked me as I stood in the synagogue's lobby bundling myself up for the freezing walk home, "Do you need a ride home, Jeremy?"

There was no enunciation in his voice. His words seemed to care about whether I might turn into a popsicle. Maybe it was his hat, a hat with a rim so wide it could almost be a cowboy hat if it weren't made out of fuzzy felt. And maybe the dim light inside the lobby of the closing Hebrew school played tricks with his hat. The shadows warmed his face, gave him a smile with friendly folds and wrinkles showing in the right places. I worry now that in a dim light, wearing a hat, Cantor Morton might seem almost handsome to my mother.

I don't want to freeze making the long walk tonight after bar mitzvah class, but that alone would not have made me accept Cantor Morton's offer to drive me home. Curiosity made me accept Cantor Morton's offer.

Still, I hold on to the inside door handle, an escape hatch. Cantor Morton has electric locks in his Cadillac. He uses them. I swear I see all four lock tabs fall at once, thunking me in secure. With a woosh of air, my body falls into the softness of the leather seats, gripping me around my parka and jeans. Trapped!

Inside his car, Cantor Morton's face swims in light and shadows from the streetlights we approach and pass. Am I witnessing Cantor Morton's secret identity, his Clark Kent, his Bruce Wayne? Away from the Skokie Jewish Congregation, Cantor Morton might be a mild-mannered something or other. He might have a name other than *Cantor*.

"I sent your muh-ther a Val-en-tine's Day card," he says, squeezing the steering wheel.

"She has not said an-ee-thing to me."

"I for-got to sign it."

I grunt slowly, "Oh," probably not as surprised sounding as I should have grunted.

"I for-got to sign the card. I for-got to write my name on the re-turn ad-dress, too." His hat rim shakes side to side. "I did not ee-ven put my name ah-bove the re-turn ad-dress," he repeats as though he can't believe his own words. "I sup-pose send-ing an un-signed Val-en-tine's Day card is not much dif-fer-ent from not send-ing one at all."

"Right," I say.

"You think that was stew-pid of me?"

"No, sir."

"Of course it was stew-pid of me."

"Yes, sir."

"Do you think it was stew-pid of you?"

"Yes, sir."

We stop at the red light at Peplow and Church Streets, and the click from the Cadillac's turn signal beats in doubles, matching the pace of my own heart. I don't know what Cantor Morton was thinking mailing his unsigned card. Maybe he was nervous 'cause he was feeling the same things about my mother that I feel about Melinda Levinberg. I only want Cantor Morton to bug out his lizard eyes and neck at my mother and speak in his lizard voice to scare her like a monster popping out of a dark closet. Hadn't thought much about Cantor Morton's feelings.

With the green light, Cantor Morton turns left on Church Street, the winter wind howling into the Cadillac's big grille. The lights on Church Street make the snow piles glow, and the thin sheet of winter crystals coating the pavement shimmer gray-white. Twin paths in these crystals lead straight as railroad tracks toward Loblolly Avenue.

"I want to change your bar mitz-vah less-ons," Cantor Morton says. "If it is all right with you, I would like to meet with you at Miss-ter Bup Mill-er's hos-pit-al room."

"Yes, sir."

"If you do this, you will not have to go to the less-ons with the ah-ther twos. I sup-pose that makes you a num-ber three."

The other Hebrew school students might wonder whether I'm in a remedial class, Karl Grossman's remedial class, 'cause I'm stupid or getting punished for my note.

"Of course," he says, as if I've always known, "you will still learn the en-ti-er Tor-rah and Haf-tor-rah pore-shuns, Jare-ah-mee, not simp-lee one half. I wor-ee ah-bout Miss-ter Mill-er's health. You will have to be pre-pared. We all will."

Cantor Morton rattles my domino theory. I'm mad 'cause Bup's leukemia *of course* isn't getting me out of half my bar mitzvah studies, and I'm mad that my brain can even think such selfish things. I try to slide down in my seat, but Cantor Morton's Cadillac won't let me. I've been sucked up like a fastball hitting the heart of a catcher's mitt. It's what Cantor Morton probably orders his Cadillac to do to me.

"Is this your street?" he asks, already turning on his blinker.

"Yes, sir. Now four blocks down."

"I will in-form you of your sched-u-al as soon as I talk to Miss-ter Mill-er's par-ents and hos-pit-al staff."

"Yes, sir."

Cantor Morton weaves his Cadillac between cars parked on both sides of Loblolly Avenue. The snow piles make people park them farther out from the curb. He says, "Did she say an-ee-thing?"

"My mother?"

"Miss Lev-in-berg."

"No, sir. I did not give her the note. I still have it."

"For-get ah-bout notes, Jare-ah-mee. You should talk to her in per-son. She cer-tain-lee can throw out notes. But she has to hear the words if you speak them face to face."

Cantor Morton stops his Cadillac beside our flower-stickered blueberry blue Chevy Bel-Air. Even in the dark, I see where rust begins to poke around the edges of the doors and wheel wells. Tilting his hat brim low, a shadow over his face, Cantor Morton inhales as wet-sounding as a straw sucking drops from the bottom of a glass. "I wrote notes like that to my wife," he says, "but only after she was gone." I don't recognize his voice, low, mumbly, and weak. It *is* his secret identity, I think— no enunciations. "I had problems remembering Valentine's Day cards and birthday cards and anniversary cards. I didn't think they were important. Now I can't even remember to sign them."

"How did your wife die, sir?"

"Badly."

"That's not what I mean, sir."

"That's all I'm telling you."

"Yes, sir."

"Talk to Miss Levinberg, Jeremy. Tell her face to face. That's what you need to do when you forget to send a Valentine's Day card." Cantor Morton raises his head. His eyes glow through his glasses, focusing beyond me, on my house. "Is your mother home?"

"She's probably sleeping, sir," I say like I'm telling a secret only 'cause I have to. "I mean it. She does that, sir. Even this early."

"Ee-nun-see-ate, Miss-ter Rose-and-berg," he says, almost shouting. He straightens his shoulders forward. The door locks pop open and he laughs like he doesn't mean what he's saying, like he's laughing at himself. "Ee-nun-see-ate!"

"I un-der-stand, sir," I say, and I open the door before he can re-thunk the locks. I gather my notebook and bar mitz-vah lesson pamphlets and push open the Cadillac's door all the way. It taps firmly against the Bel-Air, but I don't expect Cantor Morton will say anything about it. He's too busy freaking me out with his secret identity.

Cantor Morton's been a widower for over seven years. Might be getting close to eight years.

As the Cadillac waits until I reach my unlit pinners porch, I wonder about the consequences of becoming a widower. Based on what I've seen of Cantor Morton, the consequences of being a widower for over seven years is that it makes you strange. Who would marry him now? Yet he wants me to follow his advice about Melinda Levinberg, that I should talk to her face to face. I can't help but feel that it's the kinda thing a father would say to his son.

• • •

"Where did you get that?" I ask David.

"Get what?" he says, looking up from his math workbook.

David likes to do homework in bed sometimes, in his BVDs, shirtless. It's kinda like a uniform for him. Can't seem to study at home any other way. His tiny belly sticks out to the edge of his workbook, and his deep belly button, folded horizontal and down at the edges, gives me a toothless frown. I barely see it at first on top of his brown hair, but David's desk lamp makes the material shine a bit. The *kipah* is there, its seams dividing it into sections like the top of a basketball.

"Where did you get *that*?" I say, thinking Karl's *kaput*. I point at David's head. David reaches to touch it.

"Oh," he says. "I got it at Hebrew school."

"You stole a *kipah*?"

David's face clenches up as if he believes I'm ratting him out to God. "I didn't steal it! I found it on the floor outside the sanctuary!"

"You picked it up off the floor?"

"Hey!" he says, lecturing me. "I kissed it fifty times first before I put it in my pocket!"

"You don't do that with *kipahs*," I say. "You do that with

American flags that touch the floor."

Again he raises his hand to it and pets it a bit, just the way Mookie and Dahveed do it. "How would *you* know?" David says, slapping his workbook shut.

"I know about American flags and fifty stars and kissing a flag fifty times if it touches the ground. A *kipah* doesn't have fifty stars."

"It's got ten commandments. I kissed it five times for each commandment." David shakes his math book at me like he's holding some sort of proof.

"Are you gonna wear it all night?"

"Dare you to knock it off!"

"Are you gonna wear it to regular school?"

"I might."

"I wonder what the other kids will say."

"I don't care. I'll stand with Dahveed."

"Will you wear it in the shower?"

David falls back on his pillow and turns his head away. "I'll kiss it fifty times again when I put it back on."

"Five times Ten Commandments," I say.

"That's right," David says, reaching to turn out his desk light.

Our bedroom goes black and I hear him rustling his arms around, probably reaching to pet his *kipah*. His voice scolds me in the dark. "You're as bad as Karl Grossman."

"Wearing a *kipah* isn't like putting on a hat," I say. "You're supposed to know something first."

"What do *you* know," he says, not at all like a question.

"Can you tell me the Ten Commandments?" I say.

"Don't snore," David says. "I wish that was a commandment for *you*."

In the morning, David leaves his *kipah* at home. Whether he forgot it or not, I don't know. The Loblolly kids stand at the school bus stop in our regular winter parkas and hoods, except for Mookie and Dahveed, who touch and adjust their *kipahs* every few minutes. David watches them without making a face, bad or good.

I think all Jewish boys on Loblolly Avenue get that feeling about wanting to wear *kipahs* at some point early on. I got it 'cause it seemed fun to be Jewish, like a game, with Hanukkah candles and Purim plays and sugary macaroons, and Passover stories as exciting as mystery adventures, and *Sukkot* parties in huts made out of corn stalks, and a new year right in the fall in addition to the American January new year. It's fun when you're little. But then it gets serious, and we learn how Egyptians and Pharaohs and Philistines and Hitler and a policeman in Atlanta don't seem to like us for whatever reason. It becomes work. It makes you look different, I guess, wearing those *kipahs*.

MARCH

The month of March comes in like a lion, goes out like a lamb, so everybody's saying on TV and radio, in the newspapers, and at school, both American and Hebrew. Cheryl's English assignment was to write an essay on the meaning of *In like a lion, out like a lamb.* The essay, according to Mrs. Gastert, had to be concise. On pale-green, inch-wide-lined grammar school notebook paper, Cheryl wrote for her third grade teacher— *Just when I think it's turning into spring, March doodies more winter on me.*

Cheryl taped the paper next to the refrigerator handle, showing the bright red *See Me!* note written across the top.

"What did Mrs. Gastert say?" I asked my sister.

"She said it was very concise."

Winter doesn't want to let go of March. Few afternoons make it over freezing, and the plowed-up snow piles that have aged all February still tower more than twice my height at street corners and in parking lots. They're concrete tough. Walking on them barely leaves a mark, and they squeak beneath shoes and galoshes like chalk breaking on a blackboard. A rare warm afternoon makes them glisten and sends water flowing down cracks in their sides as though they were mountains in miniature with creeks and waterfalls. But nighttime comes and the temperature falls. By morning, the snow piles are still there, sharpened at their peaks, frightful daggers, their steep sides as slippery as an ice rink and impossible to climb. There's no fun in them anymore.

And it's not just the snow piles, it's dangerous everywhere. Big Ben slides his car into the back of Mom's Bel-Air and the front bumper falls off Big Ben's Cadillac.

"Christ," he says about that. He kicks at his fallen bumper and stubs his toe and slips to his butt all at the same time. You'd think a Cadillac could beat up a Chevy any day, but Mom's Bel-Air, with its streaks of rust and Cheryl's flower stickers, holds up just fine. Nobody can find a scratch.

"If Big Ben hadn't said 'Christ' in *that* way," Bobby Kinder says, examining Big Ben's car, "it wouldn't've happened. Looks like all its teeth are knocked out."

"Big Ben said 'Christ' after, Bobby," I say. "He said it *after* he lost his bumper."

"He must've been thinking it before he said it."

"Why would he do that if the accident didn't happen yet?"

Bobby tilts his head about for a moment before he clears matters up— "It's why Big Ben fell, that's what I mean. He shouldn't've said 'Christ,' and he wouldn't've got injured." It sounds to me as though Bobby Kinder is trying to force mismatched puzzle pieces to fit together.

Big Ben's on the same floor that Bup used to be on at Skokie Valley Hospital, except now Bup's in the Juvenile Ward 'cause they found room for him and he couldn't stand that old guy's constant moaning. Big Ben moans a bit himself whenever he has to move. He's got one leg raised up in a sling dangling from wires and pulleys and an overhead metal beam. His black hair is clumped to one side and he's got sleep lines mashed into the right side of his face. "Traction," Big Ben says. "It's 'attraction' without the 'at,' and it hurts like hell."

Sitting on the window air vent, watching Big Ben strapped to his bed by the leg and hip, I feel the warm air turn on and rush through my jeans. I tell Big Ben about

Bobby Kinder's idea why his hip is broken.

"'Christ?'" Big Ben says. "I said 'crap!'" Big Ben starts feeling around his chest for a cigarette, but his hospital shirt doesn't have any pockets. "Christ," he says flopping his head back on the pillow. "You watch out for Bobby Kinder." Big Ben shoves an index finger toward me and I sense the force of it through the air. "He'll try to convert you."

"Convert me to what?"

"To a Christian!"

"How does he do that?"

"He makes you believe in Jesus Christ, that's how."

"Jesus Christ?"

"The first Jewish boy to convert."

"To what?"

"To a Christian."

"So Jesus Christ was really Jewish?"

"All the Christians make Him out to look like an Aryan, but He spoke better Yiddish than your Bubbie and Zadie put together."

"What's an Aryan?"

"Don't get me started."

"How does Bobby Kinder make me believe in Jesus Christ?"

"By making you eat those church cookies. They make you into a Christian— a *Catholic* Christian!"

"Bobby hasn't made me eat any cookies. I can't see how an Oreo's gonna convert me anyhow."

"Just watch out if he does."

"Right," I say just 'cause he's Big Ben, even if he's talking crazy. "It's just something Bobby said about you falling down, that's all."

"Religion's just the caveman's way of explaining lightning," Big Ben says, hunting his bed sheets for a pack of cigarettes. His face strains at his middle and pointer fingers— his cigarette-holding fingers— holding no cigarette, twitching them like scissor blades. "Christ," Big Ben says under his breath, and I can't tell if he's swearing at his empty fingers or praying for cigarettes.

Mom comes into Big Ben's room with David and Cheryl following her like ducklings. They chew at their vending machine food. It's as though David and Cheryl are on vacation, having Mom out of the house with us, but Mom still looks like that moment just after you wake up, all dozy and wishful for another hour's sleep. She feels enough guilt about Big Ben and his beautiful new Cadillac losing to our tough and ugly old Chevy, enough to get her to leave the house on a Sunday to visit Big Ben. Cheryl, in her powder blue dress, and David, in a white shirt and navy blue tie— a real tie *he* put on with the fat part hanging too long— are dressed up formal even though Mom said nothing about it. Cheryl and David have always been afraid of Big Ben, his name, his size, and his sacred lawn. To them, I guess, visiting Big Ben is kinda like going to synagogue, even if it's Sunday, 'cause he's big and has a voice that's deep enough to make your ears rattle.

"He sounds almost like God Himself," David said, dressing for the hospital visit.

"Better take your *kipah,*" I said, sticking my feet through my jeans, "if you really think you know what God sounds like."

David watched me kinda odd, like my words were sinful or violated some sort of Big Ben Commandment, but I had stepped on Big Ben's lawn, got caught, and survived. Big Ben's Cadillac lost to a Chevy. And one fall put him in the hospital. I can't imagine why I was so afraid of Big Ben in the first place.

Mom drops down on the cushy high-back chair beside Big Ben's bed and finishes the last bite of her soggy sandwich. The commode Big Ben would use if only he could get out of bed is beneath the removable seat part Mom sits on. "Christ," she says, drooping her head to her hands. "Christ, Jeremy. Your Cantor's here. He asked me out."

"Out?" David says. "It's cold out."

I feel one of my dominos falling hard on my toes. *What*

happens next? It's my own domino, but I have no control over it! Mom tsks at me, "Cantor Morton said you gave him your permission, so I had no choice, did I? I had to say 'yes' then, didn't I? — so now I know one of your secrets, Jeremy, am I right?"

I can't look at Mom. I fear her eyes may tell me, *Have you forgotten your father already, Jeremy?* I would say back, *No, Mom. I've remembered you.*

"You should go, Grace," Big Ben says. "It'll be good for you."

Mom smiles her beautiful smile, and her eyes shine up as though a flashlight beam is on them. When her smile stretches into laughter, David and Cheryl turn as if to watch a magician pull something unexpected from his sleeve, something wonderful, lost, and almost forgotten. They look stunned as Mom loses herself in her chair, over the hidden commode, forcing herself to breathe. "Christ," she manages to say again. "What's with the Cantor's neck?"

Cantor Morton, it seems, unlike March, has finally made up his mind about something. His enunciations probably hit Mom hard, and those lizard eyes, and that neck— I guess I feel sorry for him. He can't help himself. *He's gross*, according to the beautiful Melinda Levinberg. With her laughter, Mom's tears fall, *Like April showers*, I'm thinking. My head is full of these childish rhymes— *They bring May flowers.*

"Where's he taking you, Grace?" Big Ben says.

"He didn't know anyplace to go," she says, and then like a lizard, "He did not know *an-ee-place* to go."

Mom's eyes drop water harder than a spring storm, her laughter clapping like thunder. Cheryl cups her hands against my ear. "You're not so dumb, Jeremy," she says. "Look at Mom now!"

• • •

The Juvenile Ward has a red-painted sign hanging over the entrance— *Family Only*, it warns. In the adult rooms, the signs warn against more than two guests at a time. Mom, David, and Cheryl fuss over Big Ben without getting arrested, so I enter the Juvenile Ward and watch the nurses ignore me. No alarm goes off. I'm in *somebody's* family, after all. That's what I'll say if I'm arrested.

Cantor Morton's been sleeping, I can tell by his *Pentateuch* and Leviticus bar mitzvah pamphlets piled at his feet and the newspaper sports section blanketed over his lap. He brings his head up from his perfect posture to look at me as snappy as a sleeping cat waking to pounce on a passing mouse. He's been sleeping on the commode chair next to the head of Bup's bed. *Doesn't that particular chair bother anybody?*

"It is not the day for your bar-mitz-vah less-on, Jare-ah-mee."

I say, "It's not the day for Bup's lesson either."

Settled in with his prayer books and newspaper, and his sleeves rolled up, Cantor Morton speaks his crisp syllables, "How-ev-er, Jare-ah-mee," he beats along, "here I am."

Bup sleeps on his back, his poor bald head sinking deep into his thin hospital pillow, the ends curling up around his face. Cantor Morton invites me to take his seat, but he doesn't look at me for more than two seconds. He's busy watching Bup as though he has no choice about it.

I think of all the history of people's business going in commode chairs. The worn edges on Cantor Morton's tell me it's a commode chair with lots of history. These thoughts aren't leaving my mind simply 'cause there's a cushion over the receiving end of it. "I'll sit on the window vent," I say. "I kinda like it."

"Fine," he says, leaving my unenunciated talk alone.

Bup's Juvenile Ward room is warm and lit by a table lamp topped by a coned brown shade. The lamp doesn't attack eyes with blue-white hospital light, but glows yellow as easy as a candle. Cantor Morton's stare drifts to me then darts back to Bup's bald head, forced somehow, I'm thinking, to focus on Bup's face. Bup's body is small beneath his blanket.

Smaller than the last time I saw him. His lashless eyelids stay closed and seem to bubble. They're dreaming eyes, turning back in on his brain and looking inside. Bup's lips move a bit as if he's trying to say something.

Cantor Morton must know what Bup dreams about, or knows Bup's future. After all, Cantor Morton can see through walls and hear distant whispers. While he can't figure out where to take my mother on a date, Cantor Morton can see the sadness of Bup's dream and wears it across his own face.

"My wife died bad-lee," he says, still focused on Bup. "It was vahr-ee slow. Vahr-ee bad."

"Mr. Miller said Bup's gonna be all right."

"I know. He was here with Miss-us Mill-er."

Cantor Morton sounds doubtful. Probably trusts Bup's dreams more than Mr. Miller's words. Can Bup dream truthful dreams? Bup hisses then sucks in a deep breath. He eases to his side, facing Cantor Morton. The blanket over Bup's curling knees rolls along like an ocean wave toward Bup's chest. With his jaw drooped, Bup's hand appears and a thumb finds its way between his lips. A different dream maybe? A nightmare ended? Even Cantor Morton looks uncertain.

"I would like to see Bup Mill-er be-come a bar-mitz-vah," Cantor Morton says. "But I ex-pect you, Jare-ah-mee, to be able to do the en-tie-er Le-vit-a-cus por-shun and Haf-to-rah."

"Yes, sir."

"Do you have an-ee ques-chuns?"

"No, sir."

Cantor Morton sits back in the commode chair and darts his eyes about beneath his television screen glasses, investigating a shadow over Bup's lampshade. Through lips barely moving, he whispers, "How did your fah-ther die?"

His voice doesn't have the pity I hear from other adults. He's already told me about being a widower, so it's fair, I guess, that he asks me.

"Bad," I say. "Quick and bad." It's not the entire truth, I

know, and he doesn't ask me for details, which is good 'cause I don't know the details.

"I am true-lee sahr-ree," he says. "With your muh-ther, I cer-tain-lee do not mean to dis-re-spect you or your fah-ther."

"Cantor Morton," I say, "my mother used to like to go to movies." I figure he can't drive a motorcycle.

"Thank you, Jare-ah-mee."

"And please, Cantor Morton. Try to keep your chin up." He smiles at me with that terrible rectangle smile, the shape of all the rectangles of Skokie Valley Hospital.

"I know this ah-bout my-self," he says, raising his hand to cover his neck. "You, Jare-ah-mee, should start stud-ee-ing your bar mitz-vah," proving he can read minds when he wants to.

Maybe I should tell him to blink more and talk regular, maybe go to Florida for a tan or something. Make himself look less like a lizard. That would ruin my plan, I think, if I made him look okay. Just the neck thing is enough, I decide. If he wants to know more, he can read my mind.

Reading minds and seeing dreams, Cantor Morton has found something to keep him beside Bup's hospital bed, staring so close with his unblinking eyes. When I look close at Bup, even seeing him like this, it's Bup the liar I see. But it doesn't make me mad anymore. It seems to me now that all the lies he's told since he moved to Loblolly Avenue have shown me something true about myself.

•   •   •

The Millers came to our neighborhood and replaced the Switzers. "It's as bad as the Cubs trading Lou Brock back in '61," Skyler Jenner said right away. "They got a bad deal, too." Skyler Jenner was only five back in 1961, so I doubt Lou Brock's trade was anything he knew much about directly. It was probably something his father had told him. But since Skyler Jenner said it, we knew we got a bad deal with Bup, as bad as the one the Cubs made, and the Cubs were always losing more than they were winning.

"You'll see," Skyler said, and when we did, Bup was ugly. With Mr. Jenner standing alongside, Skyler laughed at Bup's head and his pudgy cheeks and the way Bup raised his pants over his waist a bit too high, "Like a farmer," Skyler Jenner said with Bup right there.

We sat on the Jenners' lawn after an it-kid tag game with Skyler and his father in the center. They could've convinced us to hate ice cream. Bup Miller showed up with his big head and farmer jeans and asked to play. "Big head, farmer jeans," Skyler Jenner said right there, "Just like we told ya'," and Mr. Jenner grinned around his pipe.

We all had something funny looking about us, especially back then when we didn't have our Beatles hair cuts to hide our funny shaped heads. Our crew cuts and little Elvis pompadours showed something odd about all of us. But we all knew right away that we were lucky not to be Bup Miller.

"His name is *Bup*," Skyler Jenner said, and we laughed even harder with Bup standing there looking uncomfortable, like he wanted to leave but couldn't. Our block on Loblolly Avenue is where *he* got traded to.

Bup Miller became a liar, if he wasn't one already, when he got traded to Loblolly Avenue. He stood outside our circles unable to get in. We'd play statue-maker, and nobody wanted to spin Bup around. So he'd say, "Look at me!" and he'd pretend to spin himself around, freeze, and make some wild look with his long, pudgy limbs and fat head, even worse than normal, which Skyler Jenner had made us believe was impossible. And it-kid tag went along without anybody ever tagging Bup, even when he made his body an easy target for the littlest it-kids to tag. Bup hung around, pretending he won 'cause he was the last to be tagged. He was never tagged.

We had a game, a pretty dangerous one, I think now. We're not allowed to play it anymore. Skyler Jenner made it up, standing on the street corner outside Bup's house.

"Hit me!" Skyler yelled at Karl Grossman. Nobody hit

Skyler Jenner, not then, so Skyler yelled again, "*Pretend* to hit me, in the head. Hurry!" And Skyler Jenner looked excited at a car heading toward the corner. Karl Grossman swung and missed Skyler's chin by a good foot, and Skyler went down pretty real-looking, I thought, like he was really knocked out. Karl ran away, as instructed, and Skyler stayed there on the ground at the corner of Loblolly and Ellerson with his tongue hanging out. The car went by without even slowing. So did the next three cars. Big Ben's was the last one. Big Ben yelled out his window, "Good!" and kept driving.

"Watch me!" Bup said, rushing out of his house. He stood there at the corner while we ignored him, long enough so the sun began to set, asking for somebody to hit him in the head.

"This is too much," Skyler Jenner said finally, and he left us sitting on his front porch and walked up to Bup Miller. "What did you say, Bup?" Skyler said real tough, challenging Bup to say it again. Bup was large and we weren't too sure how strong he was, but he leaned away from the shorter Skyler Jenner. Skyler leaned in. "What do you want, Bup?"

"*Pretend* to hit me."

Skyler hit him, smacked Bup hard on one of his pudgy cheeks. It sounded like a baby bottom getting a whack. Bup's head rolled to the side and he brought his hand to his cheek.

"Is that what you want, Bup? I think you asked me twice!"

Skyler Jenner slapped Bup Miller on the other side. It's horrible to think about it now, but I laughed then as did Skyler Jenner and the rest of the kids on Loblolly Avenue. We laughed and pointed and faked-hit each other as Bup remained standing at the corner holding his face, dropping his chin. A car approached, still a ways down from the ball fields and power lines, and Bup spun around from the corner and fell in the middle of Loblolly Avenue.

"Crazy!" Karl Grossman said.

By then, the sun dropped below the stretch of fields and the streetlight came on, lighting Bup up on the ground, his fat head, his farmer jeans. Though the car wasn't moving fast, Bup wasn't moving at all. I thought about running to Bup. I think I saw that thought on all the kids' faces, but we didn't move. Skyler Jenner didn't move. I closed my eyelids and pinched them hard and just stayed on the Jenners' porch when I heard the tires squeal.

"Bup! Bup!" — it was the fat bald man we knew to be Bup's father, his big Chrysler's bumper hovering over Bup's forehead. He moved his fat body out of his car so fast, *Like Jell-O trying to run*, Skyler Jenner said, laughing about it. "What are you doing, Bup? Bup!"

Mr. Miller was on him, checking for injuries, finding nothing and beginning to shake Bup's limp body. I didn't understand it then, and Skyler Jenner said it was all just liar's gobbledegook, when Mr. Miller cried out, "You're in remission, Bup! Stay in remission!" Bup suddenly stood up, laughing, and pointed at us. "I'm playing, Dad. They let me play with them. We're fake-hitting!"

Mr. Miller hit Bup for real on his butt and sent him running to his house in front of all of us. Of course we laughed at Bup, even harder than before. Mr. Miller parked his car and shouted at us, "If it was some other car, somebody who didn't live at the corner, he'd be dead! You'd all be arrested!" Skyler shouted something from his seven-year-old mouth that I still don't understand.

"Assumption of risk!"

Skyler Jenner shouted at Bup's father. He'd probably get away with slapping him, too, being the son of a lawyer. Bup began throwing stones at us while we waited for the MaSkokie Day Camp bus, and began to cut halfway through tree limbs. He lied every chance he could get, hanging around the outside of our games, not trying to get in anymore, just shouting out lies about famous people he knew— Tommy John, Ed Sullivan, Paul McCartney, Bobby Kennedy, and Martin Luther King. They all visited him late at night, he said. And he knew all about military stuff and secrets about Communists and Red China, and about being a spy like

James Bond, and having a black belt in judo and karate both. Skyler Jenner slapped around the bigger Bup Miller whenever he pleased. "He's not a very good black belt," Skyler Jenner said after sending Bup running away to his house. "He's just a really good liar."

David was the only one to ask, when Bup stood with his hands in his farmer jeans pockets, watching the rest of us play our games. "What's 'remission?'" And Skyler said to David, "Play with us, or play with him. You can't do both."

"It's nuthin'," Bup said, and he ran to his house, shouting, "Leave me alone!"

"That's easy to do," Skyler said. "It's all just liar's gobbledegook."

Everybody who knows Bup Miller knows he's a liar. He's lied about everything anyone could ever think of. But what else was Bup gonna do when we made fun of him, and his father and mother, and ignored him and never bothered to find out the truth about remission?

• • •

Bup's as still in his hospital bed now as he was when his father shook him on the street after almost running him over. His mother and father come into the room carrying wrinkled paper bags, smelling of food. She looks like a scarecrow and he's fat, sweaty fat, but I've given up on not liking them for that, for a while now, I think. My mother shows up with Cheryl and David, and a nurse comes in to take Bup's temperature. The nurse says, "Five more minutes, okay? Then we're taking him down for a blood transfusion." Mrs. Miller tries not to cry and Mr. Miller takes her bags to set beside me on the air vent. When Mr. Miller smiles at me, I tell him I'm sorry.

"That's all right, there's enough room on the vent, Jeremy," he says through his big face. "You can stay there for the five minutes." Mr. Miller doesn't understand what I'm sorry for.

Cantor Morton gets up from the commode chair to give the nurse room to wake Bup and take his temperature. He looks nervous standing by my mother, dropping his chin then suddenly raising it too high, I think, like he's holding back a sneeze. My mother watches him just a little out the corners of her eyes, waiting for him to blink, I guess. He isn't blinking.

David and Cheryl step to the foot of Bup's bed. They watch Bup getting his temperature taken. At least it's a mouth thermometer.

"Are you giving any blood to Bup?" Cheryl asks me.

"He's not old enough yet," the nurse says, examining her thermometer. "The doctors have the blood in a special place."

Bup's stare circles around his room, trying to watch us all at once. "Big Ben's in the hospital, too," David says. "Upstairs."

"We're here to visit *you*, Bup," I say.

Bup's lips are dry and cracked, but he smiles. *"Mensch,"* he calls me. *"Mazel tov."*

Two men wearing white shirts and pants wheel a cot next to Bup's bed and help Bup slide over to it. We see his legs before they can cover him up again, and Mrs. Miller rushes out of the room. Cantor Morton follows after her.

•   •   •

We don't say much in the Bel-Air, the tough, flower-stickered car that beat up Big Ben's Cadillac. David whispers to me in the back seat, "Bup's turning into Brian Yellen."

Cheryl plops her head back against the front seat and the top of her curly hair spills over, shaking. Her sniffs sound wet. I see Mom's eyes in the rearview mirror staring straight. The third time Cheryl sniffs, Mom raises her right arm and brings her hand gently to those tight curls. I see the calmness in Mom's fingertips.

In my room, I dig for my bar mitzvah pamphlets. I find

them beneath piles of comics about a foot under my bed. The bindings are still stiff when I open them. *Leviticus*, I read from the English introduction. *God instructs Moses before entering the Promised Land.* I say out loud, *Le-vit-i-cus.* I begin to enunciate my bar mitzvah lesson.

•   •   •

Kelly Kinder came home from college and put me in the hospital with Bup and Big Ben. That's how I imagine it now when I think about domino theories. She came home from college and walked to my house— the first domino fell. She wore bell-bottom blue jeans that scraped along the sidewalk, her shoes kicking at the hems as she stepped. Between the bottom of her pale shirt and the top of her jeans wound a stripe of deep tan whispering out a hint at a secret. It was her, I knew, her skin showing right where her hips start to curve round, making the first warm day of the year. She teetered like a seesaw, down on one side, up on the other, then grinding to switch sides. The piled-up snow seemed to sweat as she passed. It shrank from her heat. *In like a lion, out like a lamb.* Spring had arrived with Kelly Kinder.

Through my picture window, I saw Karl Grossman standing on his porch across the street. He came out to watch Kelly Kinder, and dropped his mouth to let all the flies in.

For the first time since the blizzard, patches of grass started to show. They appeared around Kelly Kinder walking toward the pinners porch. Her bellybutton, as narrow as a cat's pupil in sunlight, watched me. She had my attention and took the next step to put me in the hospital. Kelly Kinder told me she's buying Dad's motorcycle, she had worked it out with my mother. She wanted to see it.

"It's not for sale," I said.

"Your mother told me it was."

"It's not."

"She said it was."

"No," I said, and I closed the door on the incredible Kelly

Kinder. From her side, I guess, I slammed the door shut.

Through the door, I heard Karl's voice stumble, "Hi, Kelly. I'm a man now— I've been mar bitzvahed!"

She left my porch, laughing, and I banged my head against the closed door with my imagination following her sweet *tuchas*.

"*B*ar mitzvahed," Karl shouted after her pitifully.

Kelly Kinder was getting more and more powerful, and my puberty seemed to weaken me even as I grew taller. But when it came to Dad's Hydra Glide, I had no idea what Mom was thinking, and I wasn't giving in. Dad drove that Harley as easy as anybody else put on a favorite pair of old jeans. It wasn't made for anyone else, certainly not for the body of Kelly Kinder. I suppose I took the next step to put me in the hospital with Bup and Big Ben when I called Mom at work, but only 'cause of what Kelly Kinder had said.

"International Minerals," the cheery robot-voice said through the phone.

"Grace Rosenberg, please."

Mom told me plain out, "Bar mitzvahs aren't cheap."

"I don't need a party."

"You need a suit and a *tallit* and *kipah*."

"My old suit is fine." David can steal the *tallit* and *kipah* and kiss them for me, I thought.

"Your pants aren't long enough to reach your socks."

"I'll stretch them. I'll close a door on the bottoms and pull from the waist."

"Jeremy," she said, and she hissed that I was embarrassing her at work. "I don't need an old motorcycle— I need a new mattress. I can't keep taking that money forever." She hung up as hard as I had closed the door on Kelly Kinder.

"I couldn't stand it if it's gone," I said to the phone.

I felt the dominos falling, heard them clacking away in my head. I didn't know where they'd take me, certainly not to the hospital, but I followed them as though I had no choice. I passed David in the backyard inspecting a slushball in his hand, compacting it tight, the old snow more gray than white. He eyed the side of Cheryl's head. She heard him, of course, heard his hands squeezing the dirty snowball, and she willed its safe fall to David's feet with a stare that told poor David, You don't want to start *that* row of dominos falling.

"Where're you going?" David said to me with a surprised look on his face.

Cheryl's, "Where did you find those?" sounded excited and childish.

I wore Dad's motorcycle riding coat, black leather with silver snaps in front and at the cuffs, and his *Hogan's Heroes* cap with its eagle emblem and saddle-shaped top and white rim in front. Dad's goggles wrapped halfway around my face, and his black leather mitts, cracked and browned at the tips, reached back to my elbows. I couldn't find his boots so I stumbled along in my galoshes— they were black, the right color, even if they weren't really tough-looking. David and Cheryl ran up to me and together gave me a *What are you doing?* so childlike I felt myself growing into Dad's clothes.

Clack clack clack went the dominos— "I'm starting up the Hydra Glide."

"You're driving it?" David said.

"We'll see," I said, trying to keep my lips straight and tough as I talked.

I stood at the opened side garage door. The after-school sun shined around me and struck the gray tarp covering the Hydra Glide. I learned about this bike before I could make it through the *ABC*'s. To Dad, the details of the Hydra Glide were as important as food, and as sweet as a bedtime story. They *were* his bedtime stories.

The 1949 FL Hydra Glide, he'd start as often as other parents say once upon a time, *with its newly designed Panhead engine*— he'd pause and ask me, *Remember what engine it replaced?* I knew 'cause he'd told me a hundred times before, but I wanted him to say it. *The Knucklehead 61E engine!*— and he cracked his knuckles the way fathers do and rubbed them gently across my cheek. *Knucklehead, like one of the*

Three Stooges, he'd say. *The 1949 FL Hydra Glide, overhead valve 45 V-twin, 1213 cc, four-speed transmission, mounted within its tubular steel cradle, reaching a top speed of what?*

"It'd go one hundred two miles per hour," I said out loud in the garage while pulling the tarp off the Hydra Glide, "if Mom hadn't wanted all those foo foo modifications to make her comfortable."

We weren't going to Niagara Falls without a windshield, Mom would say sitting next to Dad on my bed. *We needed saddlebags and a comfortable seat—* and Dad rolled his eyes— *Only room for one tuchas on that Harley seat on the Hydra Glide.* Dad stole the banana-shaped seat off his old friend Burt's 1947 Indian Chief, with its deep padding and chrome grab rail in the back, and made it fit the Hydra Glide.

And why didn't I get a Chief motorcycle like Burt's? Dad said. Like one plus one, I'd answer, *'Cause its top speed is only eighty-five miles an hour!* I never met Burt. His Chief could never catch the Hydra Glide.

And it had fenders like a woman's skirt, Mom said, finishing Dad's thoughts about Burt's 1947 Indian Chief. *Can't have that,* I said, and Mom rolled her eyes at me and Dad, for being *typical men.*

"Can't have that," I said out loud in the garage.

Black with chrome everywhere, Dad dressed to ride his Hydra Glide as if he became part of the machine. I pushed myself away from the front edge of the Chief seat, back to where Dad would sit, and settled in. I stretched over the black tank to reach the handlebar grips, seeing the speedometer's final number in the circular casing— *A hundred and two miles per hour, Dad? But it says a hundred and twenty!*— Dad said, *It goes a hundred twenty without Mom, saddle bags, and windshield, and with a strong tail wind, a downhill, and a good bean-driven fart.* Mom laughed, disgusted, but I knew where butts pointed sitting on the Hydra Glide and thought, *Why not?*

Cheryl and David stood beside the bike. One of them said, "Are you gonna start it?"

Clack, went another domino. I felt my foot fall to the kickstart and lower the return spring, and my hand reach the tank-shifter knob— *Four-speed gearbox with chain drive—* Bedtime lessons. This bike was for me one day.

Clack!

I dropped the key into the switch on the tank and turned. "Like a Christmas tree," someone said. "A Menorah on the eighth day!" another voice said. The Hydra Glide's lights glowed in the garage.

Somebody closed the skinny side door— *Clack!*— and the only light in the garage came through those block glass windows that shaped sunlight into large raindrops. Dust hovered around me, circling the Hydra Glide. I rose up, stretching to keep my galoshed toes on the kickstart— *One day, you can do this. You'll drive me!*— and I dropped my weight down hard.

"Are you gonna start it?" a voice said.

"It's like the lawn mower," the other voice said. "It needs a new spark plug."

I felt a pain in my shin where the kickstart slapped against it. I climbed my galoshed foot back on the kickstart and brought my weight down hard. I heard a failed putt-puttering and the pain returned to my shin. *Sometimes that happens,* Dad said, apologizing for cursing around the neighbors waiting their turn for a ride. He rubbed his shin then brought his whole body over the kickstart.

"Are you gonna start ..."

The 1949 FL Hydra Glide, hydraulically damped telescopic forks, five hundred ninety pounds (without Mom's foo foo attachments), manly air-flow fenders, chrome exhaust, seventy-four cubic inches, overhead-valve forty-five V-twin— it announces it's a Harley, Jeremy— it rumbles, it growls, it lets you know something wonderful is coming down the street.

It sounds like your stomach, Dad!

It does, Al.

I'm always ready to make it go a hundred twenty, Jeremy, with a tail wind, a downhill ...

...and bean farts, Dad!
Clack!

I worked the throttle in neutral, revving the engine as a tough cloud of smoke chased the circle of dust away. The smoke darkened around me, smelling so much like Dad. I thought I heard a tiny voice say, *Me, Daddy!*

I rushed forward, aiming through my goggles and windshield. I heard the engine reach a hundred and two. My head became dizzy and the air around me got real black like the sun had gone down. Within the roar, dominos clacked away, falling hard, one into the next. I tried to make the Hydra Glide go faster, raising my butt to point in the right direction to make a hundred and twenty.

As I felt myself float in the black cloud, the headlight beam hit Ida Lipshilts in the face. "Why aren't you visiting Big Ben?" I said, but I couldn't hear myself. She started to yell something in front of the Hydra Glide, and I thought how funny it was how Ida could run a hundred and twenty miles an hour backwards smoking her cigarette. The cigarette fell from her mouth and she coughed a fit, and on my way down, that last domino clacked me somewhere hard on the head.

From the garage floor, Ida Lipshilts looked incredibly tall bending over me. Beyond her, I found through the smoke, a bird, an eagle, painted red, blue, and yellow across the bottom part of the Hydra Glide's windshield. It was turned with its wings up so they appeared as one. Then, I passed out.

That's how Kelly Kinder put me in the hospital with Bup and Big Ben.

•   •   •

My poor mother, having to explain me to the parade of neighbors coming to visit all day long in the Juvenile Ward. Nobody can help themselves from eventually coming to the subject I hate most. With a tsk, a shake of the head, a roll of the eyes, sooner or later each one says, with shock in their voice, *What'd you do?* A mother having a son pull this stunt, to his brother and sister as well, poor things, after losing a husband not so long ago— *How terrible,* they all say as if it's required.

The neighbors come in one at a time to sit in the chair against the opposite wall from the foot of my bed. They take their turns at me. From my pillow, their heads hover at various heights above my feet sticking out bare from the end of my blankets, and they each say their piece.

"Your father always wore a helmet," Ruth Waxberg says.

I say, "Not always."

"Your father didn't ride it in the garage," Mr. Waxberg says.

"He ran it in there sometimes."

"He kept the little side door *and* the big door open," Izzy Yellen says.

"Oops," I say.

"Your father was old enough to ride it," Missy Grossman says.

"He stole his first one at fourteen."

"You're not your father," Missy Grossman says back.

"My wife said *that* to you?" Arnold Grossman says. "Why I ought to … wait 'til I …"

"Can I smoke in here?" Ida Lipshilts says.

"He's smoked enough smoke," Mom says.

"I'll visit Big Ben, then," Ida Lipshilts says, breaking a cigarette she's trying to stuff back in her Winston box. "I can smoke up there."

"If it wasn't for you," Mom says, and Ida Lipshilts leaves to smoke her cigarette.

"I'll have Bobby bring your homework," Mrs. Kinder says.

I say, "I have a headache."

One by one they come. Maybe I should send each one to Bup's room. But sending them on to his room would serve no purpose except to make Bup feel worse. I don't care to do that to Bup. Being in a hospital bed is like being in a zoo cage and having people say silly things to you. My visitors' heads float over my feet in the visitors chair, and I pretend to tickle their chins with my toes and kick them out of my room. I do Bup a favor, I figure, by not saying anything about him at all to my visitors.

Between visitors, Cheryl and David sit on the window air vent, enjoying the warm air when it flows.

"We got to miss school today," David says so pleased with me.

"You're concussed," Cheryl says.

"I know it."

"That means you have a brain," David says, "'cause one had to rattle in your head to make you concussed."

The proof that I have one proves I don't use it.

"Look at those pretty colors around his eyes," David says. "Black, purple, yellow — and his eyes are all red."

"He looks like a bandit wearing a mask," Cheryl says.

"What did it feel like?" David says. "You know, Dad's motorcycle?"

I say, "It felt like Dad."

The window vent turns on. Cheryl's blue dress begins to float around her knees and her curls fly up like I've shocked her.

"They took you in *that* car," David says secretly. "The same one as Dad's and Bup's, the red and white car."

"It's an ambulance, David," I say.

"I know," he says. "Dad died and Bup's going to die." David watches me as though he's expecting me to explode. I wish he'd sit in the visitor's chair. I'd toe-tickle his chin and kick him out of here.

Grandma Elaine and Grandpa Erwin show up carrying the Waldheim baskets they use to bring vegetable and fruit plants to grow on our dead relatives. "So, where's your mother?" Grandma Elaine says sitting in the commode chair beside my bed.

"Visiting Big Ben upstairs," David says.

Ahch! Grandpa Erwin says, sitting in the visitor's chair.

His head floats over my right foot's toes, his bald noggin red from the warm room or the outside air or wine or pretty much anything else in the world. David slips off the air vent to sit on Grandpa Erwin's lap. *Ahch,* he says when David plops his butt on Grandpa Erwin's knees. David's head floats over my left foot's toes and I begin trying to kick him out of the room.

Grandma Elaine's face is made up to smile, with red rubbed into her cheeks and her glasses pointed upward at the outside corners. The bubbled lenses magnify her eyes to the size of quarters and catch the blue-white hospital light, spinning it back to me in rainbow colors. Her white hair, released from the scarf she unties and rests on her lap, springs up slowly, like baking cake batter rising to a shape it knows by memory. "So," she says. "What'd you do?"

Grandpa Erwin *Ahchs* before I begin. "We already know, Elaine. Leave the boy alone."

"Maybe he'd like to tell me himself."

"He's concussed," Cheryl says.

"We got to miss school today," David says. I flick my big toe under his chin and try to punt him like a football.

"He'll live," Grandpa Erwin says. David looks at me like he's not so sure 'cause he's seen bad luck with that ambulance. Despite the flick of my toes, David stays put, so I raise my left foot a bit to cover him up completely.

"Tell me yourself, Jeremy," Grandma Elaine says, and her smile doesn't change, like a plot, I figure, to make me confess to something.

"Mom wants to sell Dad's Hydra Glide," I say.

"That's it?"

"I want the Hydra Glide."

"Nothing new," Grandpa Erwin says. "She never wanted that motorcycle."

"That's not true!" Cheryl says from the air vent. "Mom drove it!"

"She drove it for your father, honey," Grandma Elaine says. "She wanted *him,* not the motorcycle."

"But they were always riding the Hydra Glide!" David cries.

"Honey," Grandma Elaine says, turning her smile to David. "There's no *they* anymore, don't you see?"

Cheryl folds her arms, real bossy. "Jeremy said he felt Dad when he was on it."

Ahch! Grandpa Erwin says. "That's too much for me."

"Let me tell you about your mother and father," Grandma Elaine says. She smiles into the air over my bed and hums before she speaks. "Your Grandpa and Grandma didn't like your father at first *because* of motorcycles. His first one was noisy and dirty-smelling, and besides, he stole it from somebody named Burt. Your mother was a leaf hanging in the breeze, shaking on that thing so bad I feared she was doomed to fall off just parked there. But your father had her wrap her arms around him, and she became a bandit. She'd steal every chance she could get to ride that thing with him. It was a hug for her, I know." Grandma Elaine hums again. "I could tell by watching her."

Ahch! "So I should buy us a motorcycle, Elaine?"

Ahch! Grandma Elaine gives back. "It wouldn't hurt."

"I'd like to keep Dad's motorcycle," I say.

"Jeremy," Grandma Elaine says, "after all those years of hugs on motorcycles, what do you think your mother's feeling now that she's a widow? The motorcycle isn't your father, Jeremy. It was both of them."

"*Tuchas* passion," Grandpa Erwin says. His bald head turns pink. "I played cards with your father and Big Ben and Arnold Grossman. *Tuchas* passion, they called it."

I try to nod, and my poor concussed head throbs.

"Let it be her choice, Jeremy," Grandma Elaine says, stroking my hair.

"No!" Cheryl cries. "It's *our* Hydra Glide!"

"And I look the most like Dad!" David says, wagging a finger.

I want the Hydra Glide, too. When it was beneath me, my legs wrapped around it, my arms stretching to the grips, my belly low over the tank, I knew Dad was there. He told me how to throttle, how to shift, and I reached the edge of the memory Dad's body left behind in the Hydra Glide.

I say, "Whatever Mom wants. If she needs to sell it, whatever she wants."

"But it's ours!" Cheryl says, and her curls blow sky high over the air vent.

David and Cheryl snap at each other until Grandma Elaine uncovers her Waldheim Cemetery baskets and sets out bowls of chicken soup and plates of boiled chicken, *kishke*, and those pale *k'naidelakh*. "Let's have something to eat like it's Friday night," Grandma Elaine says.

I lay back and listen to the whining stop and the mushy eating of Grandma Elaine's food begin. I can't eat with my headache and the hospital smells, can't stand to even look at the *k'naidelakh*. When Mom comes back, I'll tell her to sell the Hydra Glide if she wants. It was just the shock, I guess, of Kelly Kinder saying she's buying it.

At night, I dream of the bird with the red, blue, and yellow feathers. I see it's an eagle with that one wing overhead. It turns its sharp beak and clear blue eyes toward me and flexes its muscles to raise that wing even higher. First drawing itself down, the eagle leaps into the sky, pulling two wings away from the one. Unfolded, spanned full, the wings beat together, and the eagle rises above the world. Soaring behind the eagle, I look down at an endless pile of black rectangles toppled all over the ground. From horizon to horizon, my dominos have collapsed, wrecked, covering the Earth. I race the throttle on the Hydra Glide and follow the eagle through my goggles, its two wings appearing stretched across the windshield. I chase it to the moon.

•   •   •

There's a time in the Juvenile Ward, after visiting hours end, drapes are drawn over the rectangle windows, and the biting florescent lights dim, when a patient feels left alone and away from the world. I feel both relief and helplessness 'cause the poking and prodding by well-meaning family and neighbors finally stops— that's the relief. But the poking and prodding by well-meaning nurses begins. They wake you up to take your temperature, they wake you up to ask about your *bowels* and your *urination,* they wake you up to see if you need a sleeping pill. I'm concussed, I explain, and I have to tell the nurse that Dr. Singer told me no aspirin and no sleeping pills of any kind. The nurse checks my chart and apologizes. That's the most unsettling thing of all. Poor Bup, he's been here since the great blizzard of 1967. How many times has he been poked and prodded, and how many times have nurses apologized after reviewing their chart on him? I'm here only one more night, *For observation,* Dr. Singer said. Finally, near eleven, it seems nobody wants to observe me anymore.

I can't say anything good about hospital gowns 'cause there's nothing good to say. They're as dumb as Superman putting his cape on backwards and trying to fly without feeling stupid about it. Standing up in the gown makes my butt feel obvious, like it's sticking out as large as a ten dollar pumpkin. Though moving around makes me feel a little dizzy, I get my sweatpants on as fast as possible. It's good to have my butt covered again, to know that it's not looking like that pumpkin. I wander out, with my backwards cape, sweat pants, and bare feet and make my way to Bup Miller's room.

The hospital halls seem to be set on night-light, still glowing, but dull as a parking lot. Nurses at their stations hunch over their note-taking. I'd like to read my own medical chart. Dr. Singer never lets me read his notes about me, as if my blood pressure and temperature were secrets to be protected from communist spies or other doctors. Maybe Dr. Singer wrote something he knows I wouldn't like to see, like what Missy Grossman said about me— *The boy's not like his father, not at all. Can't even stay on a Harley standing still in a garage, and forgets to open garage doors.* And other topics— *doesn't send Valentine's Day cards, spills all his dominos. Probable future cause of death— doesn't study Leviticus enough in the face of his own bar mitzvah and Cantor Morton — death by tuchas whipping.*

Bup's room is the one with all the beeping. He sits on his own commode chair next to his lamp that glows peaceful light. He has a clear thin tube taped to his wrist. The tube rises to an upside down bottle hanging from a hook in the wall. Bup's ridiculous hospital gown covers him like an apron, with his bony knees sticking out and bonier shins almost knife-sharp stretching long to the floor. Centered on top of his head sits a *kipah,* as shiny black as his scalp is shiny white. His father lies on the hospital bed, facing the window curtain. Mr. Miller's big backside is large enough to paint *Eat At Joe's* across it and still leave room for directions. Mr. Miller takes in a huge breath of air and heaves it out against the wall.

"My mother went home," Bup says. "I think she blames herself."

"Mine did, too," I say to make him feel better. "She's probably blaming me."

"I heard," Bup says. He sees me watching his *kipah* and smiles. "Jeremy, it's Purim in two days, the feast of plenty. It comes late this year. The fourteenth of Adar comes late. I've been here so long, I make every day the fourteenth of Adar." Bup raises his arm to show me the clear fluid dripping into his veins. "You can join me, Jeremy, but there's no macaroons and no Manischewitz wine. All I have is this methotrexate flowing into my body. I have nothing else to give you for Purim, but I give freely of my methotrexate." Bup points to his visitor's chair and I drag it up to sit near him. "You look awful," he says. "And I'll say it first so you won't feel so bad about thinking it. I'm a mess."

"You are," I say.

"Dad's convincing himself I've only lost my baby fat."

Bup's wrist is purple where the tube is taped to his arm, and his joints look large and knobby. Fingertip-shaped bruise marks clutter his arms and neck and face. Not hard marks, but barely visible shadows, as if ghosts or angels are busy inspecting him. And there's a darker bruise in the middle of his right cheek. It's shaped like the kiss Mrs. Miller gave me for eating Cheerios in her kitchen.

"How'd you get in the chair, Bup?" I say.

"I can walk, Jeremy, it's just a little hard."

"From the leukemia?"

"From the shots in my hip." He pulls up his hospital gown to show me.

"God, Bup," I say. "I believe you without having to see it." But I can't keep from looking at the large punctures over his pointy hip bone, surrounded by purple and black shades as dark as the skin around my eyes.

"They're removing bone marrow, Jeremy. You ever suck the center out of a boiled chicken bone? That's kinda like what they're doing to me." Bup talks about himself as plain as a scientist. "They're also poking me in the back, too, Jeremy. They're trying to put that methotrexate anywhere they can fit it in. Would you like to see?"

"I believe you, Bup."

"They're pumping methotrexate into my spine and brain. No Purim macaroons and wine for my spine and brain. Plenty of methotrexate."

"Don't show me, Bup. I believe you."

Bup continues to smile at me, broader now, I think. "You've said it three times now, Jeremy."

"What did I say three times?"

"That you believe me."

Bup leans his head back and chants what Hebrew school students say for Purim, to separate the good guys from the bad guys— "Blessed is Mordechai! Cursed is Haman! Oh, how I long for a *grogger*!" Bup gargles his throat hard and Mr. Miller rolls to his back, snorting out rumbling snores. "Blessed is Mordechai! Cursed is Haman! Oh, God, help me, I can still tell the difference!" Bup raises his wrist and stares at the tube where it buries itself beneath the tape. "More methotrexate! Oh, Jeremy, I can hardly eat. How can I celebrate Purim properly?"

"You're acting crazy."

"Look at me, Jeremy." Bup waves his hands up to his head and across his body. The tube in his wrist and the nothing-good tube in his nose make him look like a stringed-up puppet. "Tell me why a boy who looks like me can't act crazy?"

"You're right, Bup."

"Jeremy believes me for the fourth time! Blessed is Jeremy! Cursed is ..." Bup freezes and stares at something in the air. "Damn," he says finally. "There're too many."

"I'm sorry, Bup," I say.

"I know you are, Jeremy. But now, today" — Bup lifts his wrist and clear tube of methotrexate higher— "I drink to you on Purim!"

"You've converted, Bup?"

"I have."

"What happened to being a hooey?"

Bup drops his tubed arm to his lap and stares at his wrist as if in a trance, watching the methotrexate flow in. In the glow of his shaded lamp, the bruised finger-shadows appear to move over his face and arms. He closes his eyes, looking calmed by the light touches. "Being a hooey doesn't work, Jeremy," he says. He opens his eyes, still aimed at the methotrexate. "There's nothing in it to feel. There's no Purim."

"What about the picture on the wall, of God pulling tricks on Abraham? You said that was mean and that no God would do that. Remember what you said, Bup?"

"Cantor Morton told me not to think about today, but what it was like back then. Fathers sacrificed sons as often as they wanted. Every time it didn't rain enough, somebody's kid got it. God's telling Abraham He doesn't want human sacrifices. That's the shock if you were alive back then. Not that God asked Abraham to do it, but that God ordered him to stop. It wasn't a dirty trick at all, but God undoing a dirty trick."

"That made you Jewish?"

"It made me ask Cantor Morton more questions. A hooey doesn't stop to ask questions."

"And what did you learn?"

"That each answer makes me ask more questions. It doesn't stop. Cantor Morton says it's not like knowing the alphabet or one plus one. Asking questions is more important than thinking you know all the answers about God."

"That's all I get in Hebrew school, a bunch more questions to the one I ask, and it drives me crazy. It sounds like a bunch of hooey to me, Bup."

"You've converted, Jeremy?"

"Maybe I have."

"I can yell at God," Bup says, beginning to smile. "I can yell at God and complain and sometimes win."

"Win what?" I say.

Bup's eyes narrow, then close. "I'm not gonna win this," he says. "Not likely." With his deep breath, shapes of ribs poke through his gown. "That's five times, Jeremy," Bup says. "Five times in ten minutes you should believe me."

"I believe you, Bup."

"I like God being a little not-so-perfect, Jeremy. I couldn't stand to think God planned this to happen to me. So I've won, Jeremy, 'cause I'm all right about this, 'cause yelling at God makes me feel all right."

The old Bup changed his looks with every blink, as shapeless as a lumpy block of clay. Now he's as light as a butterfly, as though he could flap his silly hospital gown in a breeze and float away.

"I've run out of methotrexate," Bup says, watching the clear bottle hanging above his head run dry. "I guess that means Purim's over. But I'll have more tomorrow, Jeremy. You can stop by for more Purim tomorrow."

"I'm going home tomorrow."

"But tomorrow's Saturday," Bup says. "You can come back with a *grogger*."

I bring two *groggers* on Saturday. Bup and I spend the

afternoon confusing the morning nurses and then the afternoon nurses with our *groggers* and their cranking noises we can do as slow as a dripping faucet and as fast as a zipper zipping up. I visit when I can, driven there by Mr. and Mrs. Miller, and sometimes Mom drives me and brings David and Cheryl and Grandma Elaine and Grandpa Erwin with their chicken soup and *k'naidelakh*, which both Bup and I manage to eat and keep down. We do our own Purim play that David runs like a cops-and-robbers game, and David always refuses to make himself the bad guy. We play until we wear Bup out, and we leave him to take his methotrexate. Bup reminds me that our practice bar mitzvah run-throughs begin in April and asks David if it's all right for me to bring the old reel-to-reel so Bup and I can hear what we sound like.

It's a good idea to use the reel-to-reel, I guess, so we're not shocked by our own voices for the first time at our bar mitzvah. But when Bup asks for the reel-to-reel, I can't keep from feeling that Bup has told me the truth about his leukemia, that he's not likely to win.

Each visit, as I'm ready to leave, Bup and I yell as loud as we can, *Why! Why! Why!* and David and Cheryl start laughing until nurses and orderlies and doctors and other patients come piling into Bup's room. Our cheeks glow red and our smiles begin to hurt our faces even as we're kicked out once again for causing a ruckus.

"See, Jeremy?" Bup calls out after me. "You feel it inside?" I turn and find him covered in his lamp's warm glow, the shadowy finger-bruises stroking his pitiful pale skin. As if in prayer, he says, "Jeremy, don't be a hooey."

April

Grandpa Erwin, of course, not liking the Cubs, thinks April Fools' Day was invented for Cubs fans— "And for good reason," he says, as if explaining an answer anybody but an April Fool should already know.

On every April first since he could talk, Skyler Jenner boasts to the kids gathered on his front porch that the Cubs are sure to win the World Series, saying it like he's Jack Brickhouse announcing they've already won it. "April fool!" David shouts at Skyler Jenner this April first.

"I'm no April fool," Skyler Jenner shouts back. David doesn't flinch when Skyler Jenner defends his Cubs. "The Cubs will win it!" Skyler says, pointing his finger in the air. "This time for sure!"

David says, "You sound like Bullwinkle Moose just before he's pulled the wrong thing out of his hat."

"Wrong hat!" Bobby Kinder says with a squirrelly high voice.

"Get off my property!" Skyler Jenner says. "No it-kid tag! Get off!"

"Mr. Fraction," Mookie Waxberg says, stepping away.

"Mr. Fraction!" Karl Grossman says, staying there with one foot solid on the Jenners' porch. Karl refuses to leave and says, "You're not a number one. You're a less-than-one."

The real insult to Skyler Jenner, of course, is that it's Karl Grossman doing the insulting. Whether Karl Grossman understands what Big Ben means by his Mr. Fraction nickname for the Jenners, we all know it's pretty bad to be called something stupid from the mouth of the stupidest kid on the block. That, I think, even Karl Grossman knows.

We wait for something to happen between Skyler and Karl, but Skyler wusses out and says he's calling the cops. He spins around on his heels and darts into his house. The cops don't come and we sit on the Jenners' lawn in a circle, pulling grass out as we please, trying to whistle through blades of grass held stretched between our thumbs. Dahveed says we don't need Skyler Jenner to play it-kid tag. Charlie Grossman wants to know whose idea it was to play it-kid tag in the first place— *Skyler Jenner's*, we all decide. "Well, I don't feel like playing that," Charlie says, and the *me-neithers* follow until we've all agreed with Charlie. It sounds more like a decision about Skyler Jenner than a vote about it-kid tag.

Skyler Jenner's face is at his living room window screen yelling at us to get off his lawn. Sally Jenner stands behind him, appearing faint through the screen. She talks on the telephone, giggling and twirling the cord around her wrist, proving she's talking with somebody other than a policeman. We stay where we sit, pulling up grass from the Jenners' lawn. We decide to play it-kid tag, but the Jenners' house is off-limits, considered poison, an immediate foul in the game. It's clear to me that Skyler Jenner has become what Bup Miller used to be on Loblolly Avenue.

•   •   •

Missy Grossman chooses April Fools' Day to tell me the entire truth about the monthly envelopes, the fifteen fives, and the absent two ones. I read someplace that April first used to be New Year's Day. But long ago some king thought it was too depressing and dark in the winter and that people could use a good party, so he changed New Year's Day to

January first for no good reason other than cheering up the dead of winter. April has its own things going for it— it's when winter weather really ends, not March, and it's when tulips bloom, and the lawn needs cutting, and girls' clothes get *better* more on a regular basis. April feels like it's promising a long summer, and that school's gonna end, and even bar mitzvahs will be over. April doesn't need to begin with a New Year's party. I read all this in the 1964 World Book Encyclopedia, I think, or maybe it was at school someplace, all except for the girls' clothes getting better more regularly. I've been figuring that out on my own.

I sit on the Grossmans' porch after being voted referee of the it-kid tag game 'cause I can't play it-kid tag yet in my condition. I look like a raccoon or a bandit with a mask, and although I don't get headaches anymore, Dr. Singer's ordered me not to run around for another week or two. There's not much to do refereeing an it-kid tag game. There aren't any rules except the new one about staying off the Jenners' property.

Across the street, Cheryl's darting around Big Ben's lawn using the sidewalks, risking getting spotted and caught by an it-kid rather than by Big Ben even while he lies tractioned-up in his hospital bed. It's a habit we have. Cheryl's saddle shoes clip-clop on the cement, and Hannah, the it-kid, appears from behind the Kinders' front bushes and makes her way toward Cheryl. Hannah Waxberg wears her Keds— she's silent as she creeps up behind Cheryl and throws herself on Cheryl's back.

"You're it!" Hannah shouts.

Cheryl whines, "Aw, shoot!"

Hannah frowns and shakes her head. "Don't swear on Sabbath."

"I said 'shoot' not 'shit,'" Cheryl says.

Hannah and Cheryl stand there debating whether or not "shoot" is the same thing as "shit," and Karl Grossman's voice comes from somewhere unseen — "Girls can never tag me!"

Hannah and Cheryl run toward the Millers' house, avoiding Big Ben's and the Jenners' lawns, but for different reasons.

Missy Grossman stands at her screen door looking like she wants to go out, and I have to move my butt to give the door enough room to open. Even from where I'm sitting, she looks short to me, and her face scrunches together like she's contemplating something serious, or she's expecting me to break something on her property. She always looks that way. Even now, when she sits beside me on the top step of her stoop, handing me the envelope, she seems ready to accuse me of something.

The envelope, with its *Loblolly Avenue loves the Rosenbergs*, feels more like a curse in my hands than a blessing. It's a reminder of my situation, of Mom's situation, that maybe we're not supposed to live on Loblolly Avenue anymore, or maybe not even in Skokie at all. It reminds me, too, that the Hydra Glide will be Kelly Kinder's pretty soon.

"You look awful, Jeremy," Missy Grossman says.

"Right," I say.

Missy Grossman's eyes are deep brown, almost black, and she blinks at the obvious bruises on my face.

"I don't want you to think that the money's all from me and Arnold," she says. "There's fifteen fives in there, one from each house on the block."

I know, from counting things when I've got nothing better to do, that there's ten steps to my basement, four on the pinners porch, one hundred fifteen sidewalk squares on my side of Loblolly Avenue and seventeen houses on the block, not including my own house. I figure fifteen houses gave fives, two gave ones. The two houses only gave ones for a while then stopped. Maybe they *liked* the Rosenbergs, or thought we were okay, but they didn't *love* the Rosenbergs. Missy Grossman corrects me.

"The Millers don't have much money. Bup told his parents to give his allowance — the two ones. Of course with Bup in the hospital, you know, they can't give it now."

Missy Grossman's arm goes over my shoulders and rests at my waist. Her hand twitches a bit like it doesn't know what to do at first, then squeezes me toward her. I bend into her, shaped like the letter *C*, my waist having no choice about it, but my head and feet trying to stay away by habit. "The goddamn Jenners refused to give anything, those bastards. Every last one of them outright refused. They're so cheap and nasty, and they act like they're Ozzie and Harriet."

"They're mere fractions," I say.

"'Survival of the fittest,' is what the Jenners told me," Missy Grossman says, and again, "Those bastards, those goddamn cheap sons of bitches."

"Call them fractions," I say. "It's the Sabbath."

"Fractions," Missy Grossman says.

I squeeze the envelope tight in my hands and smell the musty odor so special to paper money. Sixteen out of seventeen houses isn't bad, I guess. And I wonder about the Jenners 'cause I know what 'survival of the fittest' means. It means the Rosenbergs need fifteen fives every month to survive, and that sixteen out of seventeen houses want to give it to us. So we survive. If more houses were like the Jenners', we would have stopped surviving long ago.

I say to Missy Grossman, "You're a good *tuchas.*"

For the first time I've ever heard, Missy Grossman laughs. It makes the makeup around her eyes crack.

David appears running from the Kinders' house past the Lipshilts' sidewalk. Cheryl, Hannah, and Charlie are after him, screaming *Get him!* David turns to look back at them and doesn't see he's run across the Jenners' lawn.

"You're poisoned!" Cheryl shouts.

"Poisoned!" Hannah and Charlie agree, laughing at David as hard as they can.

David falls to his knees and gives up, realizing what he's done.

"Get off! I'll sue!" Skyler Jenner says, still watching from his window screen.

Missy Grossman throws her evil-eye glare at the Jenners'

house. "Fractions!"

I wish Bup Miller were back on Loblolly Avenue. I think now, I really do, that Loblolly Avenue could love the Millers.

• • •

This early evening, Cheryl, David, and I wait for the arrival of Cantor Morton. Cheryl and I wear our jeans and T-shirts from it-kid tag. David's changed into his dressy black pants and white shirt. He's saved the knot in his black real tie and only has to slip the loop over his head and shirt collar, then slide the knot up to his throat.

"It's the simple way," he explains. "I'm surprised Dad didn't tell you."

David doesn't notice how his tie's been wrecked, the middle of the fat end smashed and shrunk like the narrow of an hourglass after being squeezed in the knot for months and months. I leave him alone about it 'cause he has some new confidence showing on his face, that he might've discovered something clever, something not even his brother or father had ever known.

"This feels weird," Cheryl says.

"I've got my tie on," David says.

"It's for Mom," I say, and we wait in the living room, hearing the ticking of the sunburst clock on the east wall.

Cadillacs aren't motorcycles. They're the opposite of motorcycles. They're built to surround you with as much metal as a battleship, to make the feeling of driving down a road go away as much as possible. Cantor Morton parks his black Cadillac behind Big Ben's broken yellow Cadillac, now wired around the front end to keep its cock-eyed front bumper off the street. The two Cadillacs take up the same space as would three of our Chevy Bel-Airs, and out comes Cantor Morton in his wide-rimmed hat, wearing a turtleneck sweater under a suit coat that's under a long businessy trench coat. He walks to our front door with his head and shoulders moving level and perfectly postured as if sliding along on a wire. It's an easy comparison, he's the opposite of Dad.

When the doorbell rings, we freeze.

"You get it, Jeremy," Cheryl says, tapping her saddle shoes on the wood floor. "He's *your* cantor."

"Let's wait for Mom to get it," I say.

"But he's seen us through the window, I'm sure."

"He can see us through bricks," I say.

"I'll let him in," David says. He slips his black *kipah* from his front pocket and puts it on his head with a firm pat, but it's inside out and the seams poke up thick and crossed, like X marks the spot.

"Flip it," I tell David, but he skips to the door without flipping it.

With the rush of air through the front door carrying the smell of Cantor Morton's cologne to our noses, David says, "Shalom!"

"Why Sha-lom ah-lech-em, young man." And like he knew all along, Cantor Morton reaches in and flips David's *kipah.*

"Sees through bricks," Cheryl mutters.

"Hears, too," I warn.

Cantor Morton steps into our house and removes his hat. His overcoat, his sports suit coat and his turtleneck sweater make him loom large in our little entrance hall, filling it up as David steps back to give him room. David's busy inspecting him and gapes at Cantor Morton's head.

"Where's your *kipah*?"

"I am on a date, young man. And I have nice thick hair." Cantor Morton eyes me with his odd rectangle smile that reminds me of hospitals. "Nice thick hair is ah-bout all that I have go-ing for me."

He's got his neck glob tucked in beneath his turtleneck.

"The Waxbergs don't drive on Saturdays," David says. "Mookie and Dah-veed and Mr. Waxberg wear their *kipahs* all the time."

"That is their choice," Cantor Morton says, playing with his hat. "I am a re-formed can-tor."

David works his tongue against the corner of his mouth. "Re-formed from what?"

"It is a type of Ju-dee-is-um, young man. Orth-ah-dox, con-ser-vah-tive, re-formed."

"What type am I?"

"Which do you want to be?"

"What's the easiest?"

"That is not how you should choose."

"Which is the quickest?"

"Choose own-lee what you be-lieve in."

"The easiest and quickest. I want to be Jewish right away."

"You are all-red-ee, young man."

"But I can't speak Hebrew too good."

"You will."

"Jeremy hardly can, and Karl Grossman can't at all."

"Jare-ah-mee has been stud-ee-ing his He-brew."

"I don't hear it, and we live in the same bedroom."

"I am sure," Cantor Morton says, "that your bruth-er has been stud-ee-ing and will do more stud-ee-ing as his bar mitz-vah nears."

"Yes, sir," I say. "I have been stud-ee-ing."

"I don't go to Hebrew school at all," Cheryl says as if boasting. "And I don't have to get bat mitzvahed either."

"She's not Jewish," David insists.

"Yes, she is, young man."

"But that's not fair at all. I don't know what she does when I'm in Hebrew school, but I know she's not learning Hebrew."

"I read my *Archies*," Cheryl says so serious. "It's about high school."

"Where is your muh-ther?" Cantor Morton says, looking over our heads, squeezing his hat.

"She is get-ting red-ee, sir," I say.

"I thought you said he can see through bricks," Cheryl says.

"Quiet," I say.

David persists, "So I don't have to wear a *kipah* all the time?"

"What?" Cantor Morton says.

"Aren't *kipahs* required hats?"

"I am re-formed."

David sighs. He knows when he's being ignored.

"Why do you talk like that?" Cheryl says.

"How soon will your muh-ther be red-ee?"

"Like *that*," Cheryl says, pointing at Cantor Morton's mouth. "'Muh-ther' —why not 'mother?'"

"He ee-nun-see-ates," I say.

"Now you're doing it. It sounds funny."

"It is re-qui-erd," I say.

"Nothing's required to be Jewish anymore," David whines.

"I am go-ing on a date, young man, and my hair is the best thing I have got."

"But it's lost its color," Cheryl says.

"Gray is a kuh-ler," Cantor Morton says, "and I have not lost it."

"Mr. Waxberg never had hair on his head as far as I know," David says.

"May-be that is why he likes to wear his *kee-pah* all the time," Cantor Morton says.

"Mookie and Dahveed and Mr. Waxberg wear theirs all the time," David says, "especially on Sabbath. And the sun's still up on Sabbath and you're not wearing one."

"I am re-formed, I am on a date with your muh-ther, and I have my good hair."

"I hate the 'muh-ther' stuff," Cheryl says, clicking her tongue.

"I am sah-ree," Cantor Morton says. "This is how I talk."

"That's *sorry*. Stop ee-nun-see-a-ting!"

"Why'd you bring that hat if you want Mummy to see your hair?" David says. "A *kipah* doesn't cover nearly as much."

Cantor Morton says, "This might be too soon, Jare-ah-mee."

Cheryl snaps her fingers, "That's *Jeremy.*"

Mom wants to know why we've got Cantor Morton trapped at the front door. She's dressed in her business suit, the stiff one with the skirt that goes below her knees. The coat makes her body look packaged in a box, and she wears her oldest pair of glasses— black and thick-framed, with butterfly wings stretching out to her hair, speckled with heavy, fake diamonds that certainly would keep any real butterfly from flying. She's uglied herself up for Cantor Morton. He's done his best to make himself look good for her. They seem to match a bit that way, although he seems disappointed and can hardly look at her, and Mom only looks at him for a second before turning away.

"We're seeing *A Fistful of Dollars,*" Mom says. "It's at the Old Orchard Theater."

They leave in a hurry, the powerful Cantor Morton defeated by the Rosenberg children, and Mom maybe thinking the sooner started, the sooner done.

David folds his *kipah* and drops it on the television set. "I'm not wearing it no more," he says.

"He'll never be like Dad," Cheryl says.

"He's like us," I say.

"Nuh-uh," David whines.

"No way," Cheryl tsks and tongue clicks.

My voice fills the house. "He saw his wife die. He's a lot like us."

Cheryl and David watch me like they're waiting to hear me shout *April fool.* But I don't 'cause I'm certain he saw her die. Anybody who's watched him hover over Bup knows I'm right.

"Are we strange like him?" David says.

"We pee in our toilet from the bathroom scale," I say.

"Not me," Cheryl says.

"'Cause you can't," I say. "You would if you could."

David reaches for his *kipah* and inspects it, pets its black shine, and places it carefully and correctly, with a light pat, on his head. "Mummy isn't sleeping in front of her TV tonight," he says.

"She made a real dinner for us," Cheryl says. "Franks and beans."

"Is Mummy gonna marry him?"

"Please, David," I say, groaning.

"Maybe he's like us," Cheryl says, "in some ways. But he's nothing like Dad."

"I look like Dad," David reminds her.

I say, "We all do."

"Nobody looks like Cantor Morton," Cheryl says. "We'll have to find Mom somebody else."

"Who wants a cantor in the house anyway?" David says. "That's like being in Hebrew school all the time."

"It's a good plan, Jeremy," Cheryl says. "I like franks and beans, and she's not watching TV in her room, but let's pick somebody else."

"There's nothing strange about peeing off a bathroom scale," David says. "I'm only eight years old!"

I have become a defender of Cantor Morton, but I say nothing. My silence is not 'cause of him. I think I'm understanding him. But anybody who's thinking about marrying Mom will also have us forever looking at him through our memories of our father. I doubt there's a man alive who will stick around for that.

•   •   •

Baby-sitting Saturday nights isn't so hard. I just can't say *baby-sitting* so David and Cheryl won't go nuts. David wants to watch *Flipper* but changes his mind when Cheryl says *Flipper*'s for silly boys. *The Jackie Gleason Show* starts. Then they have *Get Smart* to watch, *Mission Impossible*, and *Gunsmoke*. I stay with them on the couch until halfway through *The Jackie Gleason Show*, their eyes glazed over even during commercials, and leave to study my bar mitzvah portion in my bedroom.

I've been studying, just not as often as I should, and I don't practice my portions out loud like I'm supposed to 'cause David's a spy, and Cheryl's likely to torture me. I hear the TV going in the living room even though my bedroom door's closed, and I've set up my Wildcat record player so it plays *Happy Together* over and over again. I've locked the door and practice my *Aliyah*, the blessing before and after reading from the Torah.

Ba-rah-chu et ah-do-nai ha-mai-vo-rach

I close my eyes and imagine the congregation responding, and I sing beneath the volume of *Happy Together*.

Ba-rah-chu et ah-do-nai ha-mai-vo-rach lai-oh-lahm vah ed.

The *Aliyah* is as familiar to me as a nursery rhyme. All bar mitzvah boys, with the exception of Karl Grossman, can't help but memorize its words and simple melody for life. Turning my bar mitzvah pamphlet to Leviticus twenty-six three, while the Turtles sing on about how happy they are together, I whisper-sing my Torah portion. My memorization of the Hebrew letters and their sounds has been an unavoidable accident of attending Hebrew school for six years. But correctly *singing* from the Torah is another matter. My Leviticus portion is nine *Pentateuch* pages long, and I've counted the words— nine hundred fifty-nine words— each with its own trope, its own melody, as chaotic as static. I'm lost!

I count the words in my Leviticus portion again and get nine hundred forty-seven words, and I wonder whether another count might shrink it up even more. But a third count gives me nine hundred sixty-two words. I stop counting before Leviticus overruns me. If only the Turtles had written the Torah, I'd sing through Leviticus as easy as Mookie Waxberg. Leviticus to the tune of *Happy Together* would make things so simple. Why couldn't it be that simple? I decide to try it, turning to Leviticus twenty-six three.

> *. . . the only one for me is you,*
> *and you for me, so happy together!*

Enter Leviticus!— and how wonderful the Hebrew words become! It's a game to make them fit, but they do, and it's easy. I sing the bright *Happy Together* melody using the words of Leviticus, stopping only three times to let the Wildcat stylus reset itself at the beginning. Even the spitty words do all right with *Happy Together*. Cantor Morton and Rabbi Abrahms might not bless me as a bar mitzvah boy, and I might shock the regular congregation people, but I'd be a hit with everyone else, maybe even Melinda Levinberg, if she shows up. And why wouldn't the Cantor and Rabbi bless me? They let Karl Grossman get away with not knowing anything at all. I know my bar mitzvah well enough for the Cantor and Rabbi and Mr. Trauby to be less disgusted with me than with Karl Grossman.

I flop back on my bed and try to run through Leviticus the correct way. It's not nearly as much fun.

The Wildcat needle gets stuck at the end of the record, swaying side to side where there's no music. *Mission Impossible's* starting up, and I hear Cheryl explaining to David that he'll turn on *The Lawrence Welk Show* only after he's able to beat her up first. There's no fight, just the rest of the frantic-sounding *Mission Impossible* song. It's good to hear them getting along so well.

● ● ●

I must've fallen asleep, and I think I might've been snoring 'cause I woke myself up hearing the suspicious end of a snore gurgle rumbling in the back of my throat. There's that repeated *flap flap flap* going beside my bed. In the darkness, with only the glow of David's clock radio light, my bar mitzvah pamphlets slide off my belly to the floor as I reach to feel for the reel-to-reel. I'm thinking David the snore detective finally got me. But the recorder's not here. It's with Bup.

My jeans and T-shirt feel heavy on me, pinching me in my crotch and behind my knees and under my armpits. As I rest my head on my pillow, wriggling to loosen my clothes, sleep's heaviness begins to go away. The Wildcat's still spinning, making its own *flap flap flap* rhythm in that shiny, music-less strip.

I haven't washed up, I haven't brushed my teeth, and I didn't watch the news. I went to sleep without the usual habits happening first, and way too early for my responsibilities as the baby-sitter. This kinda sleep leaves me wondering what time it might be. It could be almost any hour of the night. I worry what condition David and Cheryl have left the house in, or each other. Standing from my bed, I tiptoe toward David's clock radio, knocking my Keds against the Wildcat, sending the needle scratching across the record as loud as a microphoned zipper zipping up.

"Sorry," I say. But by his bed, I see David's gone, and it's ten minutes to midnight.

What dangers await me in this house? What booby-traps? Is it just a coincidence that the hallway lights flash on then off with a quick sizzle— both of them!— when I flip the wall switch? I hate it when that happens at night, and it's happened to me only once before, when I was five, braving the basement gargoyles climbing up from hell to our furnace. I reached to the landing light switch, the basement's darkness swirling below me, and I raised the toggle to catch those gargoyles, 'cause little kids know that light fries gargoyles, and to prove to myself once and for all that Dad was right, that our furnace was not the door to hell. *Flash, sizzle, back to black*— and I ran, thinking I saw something evil, and sang *I'm a little teapot* 'cause little kids know that gargoyles stay away from singing children.

As I stand in the hallway, surrounded by black, I hear soft pounding beneath my feet. I'm ready to become a bar mitz-vah, I'm thinking, but the noise, beating like footsteps, shrinks me down to five years old— *They're coming from the furnace!*— and I prepare to sing my childhood song.

I reach for the kitchen light switch— *flash, sizzle, back to black.*

The glow from the Ellerson Street light lands on the kitchen floor at my feet. I'm floating over storm clouds, I'm thinking, when the moon's full, soaring along before dropping beneath the cloud cover into a storm. I turn to the landing doorway and fall toward that soft pounding— *from the furnace!*

Standing at the basement staircase, I reach for the toggle. The soft pounding stops and David sniffles below me.

"Jeremy?"

David turns on one of Dad's old workshop flashlights under his chin and the tiny bulb struggles to glow. It throws eerie orange and black streaks across his face, turning him into what a gargoyle might truly look like, and fades away until only the bulb's dimming wire remains.

"I've run the batteries down," David says.

David has never admitted that he believed in gargoyles. There couldn't be anything bad coming up through our furnace, he explained once when he was five— *'Cause Santa Claus comes through the furnace to get into our house, the gargoyles wouldn't dare try. Like Dad says, it's the metal stretching.* Still, until he was almost seven, in the cold of winter when the furnace shut off and the pops and banging below us began, David huddled his head beneath the protective powers of his magical blankets and hummed his song, *Five little ducks that I once knew, tall ones, short ones, skinny ones, too...*

"What're you doing down there?"

The pounding returns, and David cries and whimpers, and I switch on the basement light. The light works, vaporizing my childish fears, and our poor basement is once again cement walls and floor, and the wall studs Dad never got to finish. Our basement in the light is just a sad place to be.

David leans against a wall stud in front of the furnace,

beneath the telephone cord jack Big Ben wired in. He's still in his dress pants, white shirt, and tie, loosened as I had taught him, a businessman's tie. The kitchen phone sits on David's lap, his left hand pounding the earpiece against his knee and the flashlight rolling away on the floor. There's a white sheet of paper at his feet.

"I've been snooping," David cry-talks. "I know it already, so don't yell at me."

As I walk down the stairs, David's eyes follow me, flooded in tears. His head begins to shake side to side, and his face becomes flush with anger or disappointment or frustration, it's hard to tell exactly. Maybe it's all of them. I sense a warning from him that I'm not gonna like something, but just the same, I need to know.

The paper's creased like it had been in an envelope. The serious businessy print at the top reads, *Jerome Yellen, Attorney at Law, 180 N. LaSalle St., Chicago. Contracts, Real Estate, Wills, Civil and Criminal Litigation.* The writing below it is by hand and seems large and messy, like it had been written in a hurry. There's no date on it, and I can barely read some of the letters, but it's easy to make out the important words— *Dear Grace: There's nothing I can do. I'm truly sorry. However, the monthly envelopes will continue for as long as need be. Here's the information in case you want to talk to another lawyer. With love and compassion, Jerome Yellen.* A line of numbers at the bottom begins with the same area code I had dialed to call the Atlanta police.

"A boy answered," David says, wiping his tears as new ones fall. "A boy sounding no bigger than me. Then his father started yelling at me— his *father!* He cursed at me, Jeremy. He cursed and said it was all Dad's fault and told me to go away and swore at me again and hung up on me harder than banging a hammer!"

David's shoulders heave and he curls into a rocking ball on the floor, holding the telephone on his lap. His grip around the receiver tightens. There's a rumbling going on inside him, I sense it, feel it, and share it. David's body snaps straight and his lungs gather up all the air they can. He roars into our basement and my own heart, the words I wish to say, our final truth we know about our father.

Nothing's Dad's fault!

"You've broken enough phones," I say as David raises the receiver over his head. I take the receiver from his hand and speak into the mouthpiece.

"It wasn't our dad's fault."

I settle down beside David. He's hotter than the furnace behind us. Our own monstrous thoughts climb up from within our bodies, like the gargoyles we imagine in the night. David twitches herky jerky beneath my arm as I hold him. How hard is it for an eight-year-old to hear such cruel things, for a boy who saw his father die? I can only imagine my own thoughts, how powerful they've been, how much they've confused me, packed into a smaller boy. I pull him closer, and he seems to melt against me.

"What have you done now?" Cheryl says in her pajamas at the top of the stairs. Her curls are flat on one side and puffed out big on the other. She wipes sleep from her eyes. Mom stands beside her. I see the high heels and long skirt and the bottom of her boxy jacket, but the basement ceiling blocks the rest of her. I'm certain Mom's not looking too pleased.

Mom's voice echoes sharp against the cement walls and floor.

"That letter!"

She falls to her knees on the landing, her face cupped in her hands.

"What have you done? What?" Cheryl repeats, balling her hands into fists. "What have you done to Mom?"

"It's not Dad's fault," David cries. "It's not!"

"I know it," I say.

Cheryl brings her fists to her ears and orders us to stop.

Through the yelling and crying, Mom says so soft, "It was his fault." Raising her face from her hands, her eye makeup streaking black to the corners of her mouth, she says louder,

"It *was* his fault." We stare at our mother, silenced by her words, our jaws drooped as large as caves. Her heavy butterfly glasses fall to her chin, then to the landing floor.

"It was his fault— it *was* your father's fault."

David won't believe it, and he says so as he cries beside me, and Cheryl rapid-fires out for everybody to stop talking, just stop talking. Mom settles to her hip on the landing. Beneath David and Cheryl's racket, Mom thanks me, I think, and whisper-talks to herself, *I've finally said it.*

I feel as hollow inside as this basement that Dad left unfinished, and my heart pounds low over my stomach. But there's Mom's face, smeared in black tears, smiling her almost forgotten smile that I love and miss. Like a mouse-squeak, I say, "Will you tell me how?" Her blue eyes fixed on mine, Mom keeps her pretty smile pushing out against that awful running makeup.

•   •   •

David kneels at my bedside, wearing his BVDs as pajamas and nothing else. His hands are palms down and flat at the edge of my mattress, and his chin strains up to rest on his fingers. His desk reading lamp warms around him, like fireplace light, I think, and his pouty lips have been holding back a question for a while now. I pull my sheet cover beneath my chin and roll on my side to face him. I'm so tired, but I can't fall asleep. Finally, he speaks like he's apologizing ahead of time for his question, "Do you think Mummy's told us the truth?"

"Yes."

"It could be just one big April fool."

"Not Mom, not about this."

David lowers his cheek to his wrist. "No, I guess not."

"Go to sleep."

"I can't sleep. I won't. I don't know what to think about Dad."

"I don't either, but we have to go to sleep."

"Dad didn't make mistakes, Jeremy. He's Dad."

"You're too little to remember any."

"Did you see Dad make mistakes?"

"Never."

"Told you so."

David's eyelids flutter long and black to his cheek. He scratches his tangled hair and tucks his fingers back beneath his chin. "I don't know," he says. "I guess Dad made this one."

"I know."

"It's almost been a year," he says real soft.

"Go to bed."

David stands and slides his bare feet along the floor toward my head. "I'll go to bed but I won't go to sleep," he says as if making a promise.

"It's all right if you do," I say, and I close my eyes to prove it.

He breathes shallow and quick, watching me for a moment, I know, 'cause I sense him examining my fake sleep. His feet thud on the floor as he turns and goes to his bed. After the click of his desk lamp and the rustle of his covers, David falls asleep. Soon the snore detective himself is snoring.

Beyond our closed bedroom door, footsteps make their way down the hall, slow and uneven, as if somebody's feeling their way along the floor in the darkness. The footsteps stop short of my room, unexpectedly, 'cause I always think the gargoyles are after me and nobody else. Tonight would be a good night for the gargoyles, I think.

"Mommy?" Cheryl whispers, and taps on Mom's bedroom door.

Daddy's Little Girl creaks open Mom's door and puts herself on the bed with no mattress. In the night, with Mom's television set off, box spring squeaks and soft voices are loud through my closet and walls. "I can't sleep," Cheryl says.

"I know, honey," Mom says, hushing her. "I'll hold you."

And they squeak and adjust themselves and hold each

other close. These are the sounds I fall asleep to.

• • •

I wake up feeling that I might be able to lose two pounds peeing off the bathroom scale, and I rush out my room, down the hall. Mom's sitting on a dining room chair turned to face the east wall. She's watching a blank white light shining against it, but I can't wait to investigate just yet. I've got to go.

"Did you wash your hands?" Mom says when I return. Our clunky projector clicks along on the dining room table, the film spinning over the machine between reels, rewinding. "Be honest with me— did you just run the water?" I go back to wash my hands for real.

Mom's not wearing her glasses, and her beehive hair has fallen completely flat and straight, like a Beatle, I'm thinking. I have no idea what time it is 'cause Mom's taken the sunburst clock off the wall so she can use the wall as a movie screen. It's still black outside and in the house, but Mom's eyes look at me blue, clear, and rested. In her old pajamas, the white ones with little blue dots, she pats a chair she has pulled alongside her. "Sit," she says, and begins to loop the rewound film through the projector.

Dad loved his Hydra Glide, but it wasn't for racing. He raced dirt bikes, which fit 'cause they always looked like bugs caked in dirt. He stopped racing them about a year or two after David was born 'cause Mom decided it was too dangerous for a married man with three kids. There wasn't a fight about it. Dad knew she was right. And it gave him more time to work at his two gas stations and drive his truck and give us Saturday morning rides on the Hydra Glide— he was never gonna stop doing that.

He loved his dirt bike racing and sometimes borrowed a movie camera so he could see himself race and make himself better at it. Dad used to borrow a movie projector from a friend before he bought his own one spring, without Mom's permission, I figured out. They had a fight, a loud argument, about needing a new car and wasted money and all that. But like Mr. Grossman said, it was only their *tuchas* passion, and David was born the next January. That old projector is responsible for David, I guess.

I never could figure out how that movie camera would do any good. No matter who worked it for him, it was impossible to see where Dad was. The movies are black and white and grainy and have no sound, and the camera could never get too close anyway. It's hard to pick out anybody in particular at the start, and the mud and dirt soon make it completely impossible.

Mom flips a silver toggle and the film begins to go. "There's not much to it," she says along with the clicks of the projector. "It's the only one I didn't throw out."

A row of dirt bikes, maybe fifty of them, face an open field lining some woods. It's hard to tell exactly 'cause the horizon's tilted so bad and the picture jumps around. When the camera's on them, I see the racers facing away and straddling their bikes with their heels dug into the ground.

"He's ninth on the right," Mom says so certain. "Look at the shape of his back."

I can't tell.

The picture steadies, and at once the racers lift their left boots to their shifters and smoke blows dirty out the tail pipes. One bike isn't blowing smoke. The rider dismounts and starts kicking at it, the ninth man on the right.

"Your father hated this reel." Mom's eyes fill with the light off the wall. "It's the only one I like to watch."

A man standing at the far end raises his arm. He's so far away, it looks like the puff of smoke comes out of his hand. The racers are off, up a rise and down it, disappearing into the woods in seconds. It's hard to imagine how Dad got any use out of these movies.

The ninth man on the right wheels the dirt bike around and rolls it, standing on a pedal, swinging one leg against the ground like a boy riding a scooter. The picture begins to fill

with him and the bike, and Dad flings off his goggles and helmet. Bending low and bringing his nose close to the lens,
Dad mouths something broad and big.

"Burt, your dirt bike sucks," Mom says beside me, matching Dad's lips.

And then Mom appears next to Dad. The camera points
up at them. They look so much like they did in that photograph on the Hydra Glide before riding it to Niagara Falls.
She slaps Dad on the shoulder and points to the camera.

"Shh, Al, your oldest is watching," Mom says.

Dad takes his riding gloves off and reaches so his palm
fills the picture and his fingertips grab it around the edges.
The picture spins around and zips by a boy, then slowly shifts
back to him. I look littler than David, and just as stupid.

"You loved to wear Dad's leather jacket," Mom says.

"I look like a tent."

My eyes look up, and Dad's shadow and the shadow of
the camera fall over my little-boy face on the wall. I try to run
to him, but I trip and fall to my belly and begin to cry. Again
the camera spins around, and the grass and trees whiz by in
a blur. There's Mom and Grandpa Erwin behind her.
Grandpa Erwin's smoking a cigar and holding Cheryl packed
up in puffy baby clothes, her hair curling out around the
edges of her drawstring hood. Grandpa Erwin looks exactly
the same. Exactly. Just as bald, wearing those gray slacks and
button-down white shirt over an undershirt. He's got Cheryl
on one arm, bouncing her, and her head bops about as loose
as wiggling Jell-O. She's got that silly baby look on her face,
a look that says she won't remember anything of the day.

Mom's face fills the picture, then the world blurs by
again, landing on Dad as he lifts me off the ground to coo
over me, to soothe me. His hair is thick and short, with a
small pompadour mussed up from the helmet. He can't take
his eyes off me as he kisses me and kisses me until my tears
become laughter as quick as a finger-snap. We're in our
leather jackets, Dad in his tough and roughed-up racing jacket, and me in his shiny Hydra Glide riding one. We stare into

the camera, making tough-guy faces and mouthing, *Burt, your dirt bike sucks.*

"So much like your father," Mom says.

• • •

My mother explained to David, Cheryl, and me, huddled with her on the landing floor, that on October 9, 1965, our father traveled late at night to return home after delivering pallets of refrigerated fruit to a plant in Atlanta. He had two gas stations to manage, a wife and three kids, and rides on the Hydra Glide to give. He did so much, he was tireless and never needed much sleep. *The candle was burning at both ends*, Mom said often as she talked. Those words seemed familiar to her, an old warning, I suspect, that she had often said to Dad.

Dad didn't drink coffee when he drove. Said it soured his mouth, and he couldn't stop a truck to brush his teeth with all of us waiting for him. He drank ice water. Late at night, starting out to come home to us, burning the ends of his candle, he reached to shift gears and spilled his ice water on his lap at fifty miles an hour. He didn't see he had veered toward the shoulder. He didn't see the back end of the tow truck, barely moving with its lights out, and Dad only remembered lights and the screech of metal folding in on him, and the pain and the dark.

"You don't know that's true," Cheryl said.

David and I remembered the Atlanta policeman and had our doubts, too.

"Mr. Yellen explained the police reports and hospital records to me," Mom said. "The police found the cup."

"But you can't be sure," Cheryl pleaded.

"Your father told me," Mom said, reaching deep into Cheryl's hair. "He apologized so much for it, I can't forget. He told me."

"So that's it?" David said.

Mom said, "The accident led to the aneurysm, eventually. That's what the doctors decided."

David raised his stare to me slow, like a secret, and I knew immediately that he'd want my help with the *A* Volume World Book Encyclopedia in the morning.

My father, the man who managed two gas stations, drove his wonderful interstate truck and never left us feeling lonely, only longing for more of him, lived his life like those performers on *Ed Sullivan* spinning all those plates on sticks, dozens of them at once, so it seems to me. Until one of the plates fell, then they all fell.

When Mom finished, she reached to hug us all at once. We're not much to look at, I thought at that moment, a fatherless family in our unchanging house, with our scratched floors, our old furniture and old pictures, and our mother without a mattress, collecting monthly charity from the neighbors. But I thought harder about it, sitting on our landing above the basement Dad left unfinished. Half past midnight, there was no other family in the world sitting together like us, huddled and hugging and crying together.

• • •

The reel runs low on film as I watch my father's face on our dining room's east wall. The dusty outline the sunburst clock left behind on the white paint frames him. He's smiling at me, and I feel my eyes begin to grow. They grow as large as the light shining against the wall that shows my father moving and talking. I surround him and keep him for myself even after the film ends and the wall goes blank.

I turn to Mom as she reaches toward the projector. Beside it rests the sunburst clock, unplugged and perfectly set at eight a.m., the second hand exactly on the twelve.

"Cantor Morton is not at all like your father," she says, "but he's a good man." She reaches to the clock, her fingers steady, her eyes thoughtful, and pushes the second hand to the right, if only by a minute.

May 19, 1990
Leviticus Revisited

Ever since I turned thirty-six last January, David keeps bugging me about the same thing— "You're as old as Dad ever was." He'll call me from the teacher's lounge at Eisenhower K-8, where he teaches math and history, and say, "If you count up the months and days after your birthday, you know, you're *older* than Dad ever was."

"I know."

"Be careful," he says.

"Don't be ridiculous, David."

"I'm sorry. I think about it a lot. When I turned fourteen, I realized I had lived as long without him as with him, and at twenty-one twice as long without him. I can't help it sometimes. It's strange math, I suppose." David ends all our conversations with, "Are you all right?"

"I'm fine. And you?"

"I'm good."

This Saturday morning, he sits in my living room waiting for our mother and Cheryl to arrive, asking me about his *Aliyah* portion for my son's bar mitzvah that starts in two hours. "Which version should I use?" he says.

"How many are there?"

"Two that I know of."

"Use the one you know best."

"I've forgotten them both."

"There'll be cheat sheets."

And then he gets to his real question— "Are you all right?"

"I'm fine. And you?"

"I'm good— but now you're older than he ever was, by four months to the day."

"Stop it with your strange math."

"I know. But I like to talk to you about this, you know? It's something other people might find strange."

"It's strange to think about it."

"It's even harder when you feel it."

I give my patience to David. He's the youngest. Sitting there on my couch wearing Dad's old Hydra Glide riding coat over his dress shirt and tie, David looks so much like our father. He keeps staring at the end table, even as his little boy pulls at his knees like he will never let go.

"Why do you keep that picture out?" he says, and he reaches to the end table, to the old photograph I've put in a marble frame, of Mom and Dad dressed in their leathers sitting on the Hydra Glide before riding to Niagara Falls.

"To remind me," I say.

"Do you really need a reminder?"

"No, David. I just like the way they look in the picture."

He holds the photograph and smiles and I offer to let him take it, to keep with Dad's Hydra Glide riding jacket and cycle hat and mitts, and Dad's cufflinks and a pair of his shoes, and everything else he snooped out of Mom's bedroom before she threw our father's things in the trash so long ago.

"That's all right, Jeremy. You keep it. I just can't imagine that in less than five years, I'll be older than he ever was."

I'm not surprised he's a teacher at our old school. Even with his own wife and son, and his wife pregnant again, I

think he wants to be a father to as many children as possible.
He returns the photograph to the end table and lifts his
boy to his chest.

And he says to me, "How are you?"

"I'm fine, David. And you?"

•   •   •

Cheryl remains tough. She always has been. She says it
has something to do with the way she watched Mom lift herself up from *woman's wages.* "Like a bulldog with its teeth in
Mr. Man's fat ass," Cheryl says. "It was the sixties, after all.
What a time to be a single mother."

On her office door on the fifth floor of the Old Orchard
Professional Building, Cheryl's business plaque logo used to
read:

The No-Bullshit Marriage Counselor

It was the only office plaque of its kind in the building
and caused the Fifth Floor Therapists Association to petition
the tenant management office to force Cheryl to remove the
profane plaque. "I think I would've won that battle," she
insists. "But I only fought it long enough to get the newspaper coverage. It was great free advertisement."

Now her office entrance door plaque reads:

The Amazing No-Bull Marriage Counselor
(For Bull, Go Down the Hall)

"The 'Amazing' part is just to get me listed first in the
Yellow Pages," Cheryl says, and it might only be a coincidence that Dr. Bondurant's office is down the hall. It's clear,
however, that she is successful. Cheryl's clients wrote letters
to the editor in her defense and against the Fifth Floor
Therapists Association's petition. They praised Cheryl's
amazing psychotherapeutic marriage counseling abilities,

often noting that she's a marriage counselor who actually expects therapy to *end* on a date certain, and sooner rather than later, unlike other marriage counselors, whose programs seem to meander along with their clients' abilities to pay billable hours.

"I make my clients search for their *tuchas* passion. If they can't find it after grabbing each other's ass for five minutes, it's probably never going to be there."

"Interesting," I tell her. "Is that from your college training?"

"You know better," she says.

Her clients leave her office, their clothes rumpled and askew, said one letter to the editor, *and often arm-in-arm after the first session. It's wonderful! She's wonderful!*

Cheryl married a mechanic with strength in his hands and dirt under his nails. He smells of motor engines, exhaust, and gasoline, and they live together raising two children not far from her office.

•   •   •

David, Cheryl and I have often encouraged Mom to sell the house and move into a condo or town house. It'd be so much easier for her now with all of us moved out. The old house, in spite of the changes inside, and a new mattress, is still the place where our father died. "It's where I survived," Mom always says, "and Ben and Ida and Missy and Arnold. I'm staying where I'm loved."

It seems no coincidence that the Jenners sold their house the day we received our last monthly envelope. After twenty-five months, we didn't need the fifteen fives anymore, with Mom promoted to *Executive Assistant to the Personnel Director of International Minerals, Incorporated.* It was a long title, worthy of doubling her income. "Almost man's wages," Mom said, "and good enough to end the envelopes." When the movers hauled the Jenners' last piece of property away, Mom gathered the twenty-five envelopes, each proclaiming their love for the Rosenbergs, and burned them in a barbecue grill. "Don't get me wrong," she said as David, Cheryl and I gathered with her around the flames wearing party hats and blowing our kazoos. "I love Loblolly Avenue back. But this is something I need to do."

"Steaks?" Big Ben said, walking by with his cane.

"Burnt offerings," Mom said.

"Let me know when you're making steaks."

We blew our kazoos at Big Ben.

After our envelope barbecue, Mom had a party for us. Not for anybody's birthday, "Just for us," Mom said, and she set up streamers and my Wildcat record player in the kitchen, and brought out a double-layer white cake with some Neapolitan ice cream.

"I have a present for Cheryl," David said. "I made it," and he ran off to our bedroom.

"Better run away now," Mom said, and Cheryl laughed a little and itched at her head like she was thinking the same thing, too.

"Probably pet worms," I said.

Skipping back, David handed Cheryl a box the size of a deck of cards, and I started saying *Tick, Tick, Tick,* and Cheryl only opened it because Mom insisted.

Cheryl opened the box saying, "What's it for?" but David couldn't stop giggling and slipping to the edge of his chair. A folding twin picture frame is all it was.

"That's your picture," David said, pointing to the one on the right.

"Look at that smile," Mom said. "She's going to need braces."

"But what's this one on the left?" Cheryl said. "It's just a drawing."

"I did it," David said. "I drew it from the picture. It's you."

David's drawing did look like Cheryl's picture, the one the school took in the fall for her fifth-grade class, her hair poofed up in curls, and her face spotted with leftover summer freckles.

"But it doesn't look like my picture at all. You drew me with my mouth shut."

David smiled and said, "I know. It's something I've always wanted to see."

Cheryl, so silent and blank-faced, folded the picture frame and set it by her dish of ice cream. David froze, his big smile gone, looking like he expected to get hit. "I thought it was funny," he said.

Chewing some cake, Cheryl turned to him and stared sharp into his eyes. "It *is* funny," she said, and they started to laugh together like they were never going to stop.

Skokie is no longer the world's largest village, and it's hardly the New Neighborhood anymore, but it's where the Rosenberg children live with our families, not too far from each other, and where our mother remains on Loblolly Avenue.

•　•　•

The Millers moved away before Bup died, if he died. I still don't know. I don't ask about it and I don't want to find out. I prefer to think he's alive, that the consummate liar lied his way out of juvenile leukemia. Although I may never see Bup again, I know I kept my promises to him before he left me.

Passover came late in April 1967, and Bup complained throughout our bar mitzvah training that he still wanted it to be Purim. Passover, he thought, was a sad holiday. Too much killing and dying and hatred just so people can be free and believe in God. "And besides," he confided in me and Cantor Morton, "they killed the first male born and I have no lamb's blood."

"Geez, Bup," I said. "I'm the first male born, too."

"We're a lot alike," Bup said, and then, "but we're not alike at all, are we?"

Cantor Morton stayed with Bup and washed him and

wiped him down. Even as we made our way through
Leviticus, Cantor Morton stopped to lift Bup to the commode chair for him to use, and cleaned him up afterwards
and got right back to Leviticus. Cantor Morton was more
delicate about it than the nurses, and he knew it and helped
Bup out whenever he could.

"Your muh-ther does not care for me in *that* way," Cantor
Morton said, sitting with me in the visitor's lounge while Bup
went down for x-ray treatment. "Tell me the truth. It is all
right."

"She says you are a good man. I know she likes you."

"But not in *that* way."

"I do not see it, sir."

"Not like with your fah-ther."

"No, sir."

"It will neh-ver be like how it was with your fah-ther.
Your muh-ther will learn."

Cantor Morton placed his pale hand on mine. It felt
warm and gentle. His looks deceive him, I thought. "I am not
go-ing to make a pest of my-self," he said. "I can neh-ver replace your fah-ther."

I invited all the neighbors on Loblolly Avenue to a
Passover Seder in Bup's room in the Juvenile Ward, dropping
notices in mailboxes. Then I followed up by going to each
house to remind them. I brought David with me, practicing
first to teach him how to beg pitifully. "Remember Opie
Taylor's face after he accidentally slingshot that mother
bird?" and David knew exactly what I was talking about.

"Please come, won't you?" he said, and his eyebrows
twisted up, and his eyes glistened, and his face filled up with
straining, merciless pity. Refusal was futile. Even the Jenners
came.

Cantor Morton provided the Seder meal and brought the
traditional lamb's leg bone used to protect the firstborn male
child from the Angel of Death. The hospital staff began to
line up to warn us about the number of people in Bup's room
and then called security. But Loblolly Avenue, and Grandma

Elaine and Grandpa Erwin, and Mr. Trauby and Mary
Trauby, soon had them outnumbered. A college student part-
timing as a hospital security guard said he was going to call
the police and Cantor Morton pulled him to the side.

"Will I have to call your muh-ther?"

The security guard enunciated, "No, Can-tor."

"He was one of my worst num-ber twos," Cantor Morton
said to me, setting out the Passover meal. "But I still neh-ver
beat him. I neh-ver beat an-ee bah-dee."

"I know," I said.

Mr. Waxberg ran the Passover Seder. Bup's bed, with Bup
in it, became a buffet table filled with the traditional
Passover Seder plate symbols— bitter herbs, roasted
shankbone, charoses (chopped apples), chazeres (horserad-
ish), karpas (parsley), and hard-boiled eggs. His blankets
crumbed up from cracking matzos as Mr. Waxberg led us
through the service and guided us with our Seder plates:

Blessed art Thou, O Eternal, our God, King of the
Universe, who hast preserved us alive; sustained us,
and brought us to enjoy this season.

"Take your matzos," Mr. Waxberg said, and he raised a
plate of three above his head for us to see:

This is the bread of affliction which our ancestors ate
in the land of Egypt; let all those who are hungry
enter and eat thereof; and all who are in distress,
come and celebrate it here, but the next year we hope
to celebrate it in the land of Israel. This year we are
servants here, but next year we hope to be free men
in the land of Israel.

"We're not moving to Israel," Mom whispered reassuringly.

"Oh," David peeped.

Loblolly Avenue moved in on Bup as he chanted
Passover's traditional four questions from his bed in Hebrew.

Mr. Trauby answered them, petting Bup's head as if Bup needed to hear the answers personally. It was troublesome going through the ten plagues God cast upon ancient Egypt and the pharaoh, dripping our sweet wine, plague by plague, onto our plastic Seder plates, until the last. And Bup joined us, saying, *Slaying of the first-born.* "Don't worry," Bup said about himself. "I've got the lamb's leg bone for now." We ate our Seder meal quickly, chicken and *kishke* and gefilte fish and the chicken soup with *k'naidelakh* that I didn't dare eat and that Bup couldn't. Bup said he'd stick with his I.V. and nothing-good tube.

When Loblolly Avenue left, along with Cantor Morton, the Traubys, and my grandparents, their heat and moisture stayed behind in Bup's room. Mr. and Mrs. Miller thanked me and hugged me between them, sweaty and hot and for as long as eternity.

The Millers asked Mom to let them drive me home, there was something we had to do alone. Mom didn't ask any questions, and Cheryl and David wanted to stay but were easily coaxed home by a promise of Jiffy Pop popcorn.

Alone with the Millers, I learned I was going solo on my bar mitzvah. "We're moving," Mr. Miller said. "We're taking Bup to New York for a new treatment program they have there."

"He won't be here for the bar mitzvah," Mrs. Miller said. "We have to take him right away."

"Let me do the bar mitzvah now," Bup said. "The recorder's under the bed."

I plugged the old reel-to-reel in and rewound it to the beginning, recording over our practice sessions and what was left of Mookie's *Stupid* song. Bup sang his Torah portion, from Leviticus twenty-seven one to Leviticus twenty-seven thirty-four. His soft voice, though confident singing the Hebrew words, wavered weak and tired. I read in his face, his eyes squeezed shut, his brow furrowed, that he understood the Hebrew words he sang. He sang them to his parents, to me, to his faith, and held the little microphone close

to his dry, cracked lips so the recorder wouldn't miss a word.
He told us upon finishing his Haftorah portion in Hebrew,
from the prophet Jeremiah, exactly what he had said. And he
finished in English:

Thou hope of Israel, the Lord! All that forsake Thee
shall be ashamed; They that depart from Thee shall
be written in the earth, because they have forsaken
the Lord, the fountain of living waters. Heal me, O
Lord, and I shall be healed; Save me, and I shall be
saved; for Thou art my praise.

Still holding the microphone near his chin, letting it
slowly fall away, Bup said, "The synagogue was opening the
new sanctuary for us, Jeremy. We were to be the first."

"I didn't know."

The microphone slipped to his blankets, but Bup's fingers
remained curled as if he still imagined holding it in his hand.
"Play it for the congregation so I can become a bar mitzvah."

I knew then that Bup had already transformed into a bar
mitzvah, I suppose more than I did or ever could. He took
his faith with him to New York, and I sang my bar mitzvah
part, according to Cantor Morton, *sa-tis-fac-tor-ah-ly.*

Bup's voice carried through the new sanctuary's powerful
microphone and speakers, filling the sanctuary with his sadness and earnest belief in his faith. The reel-to-reel spun on
the lectern set beside the Torah as Bup brought the congregation to its knees, perhaps the largest congregation the new
sanctuary has ever held.

The reel-to-reel's tape neared its end as Bup said, *The*
synagogue was opening the new sanctuary for us, Jeremy. We
were to be the first . . . Bup's final words faded away in the
sanctuary as if Bup himself walked to take his seat beside
Cantor Morton. I turned off the reel-to-reel and peered
behind me to the towering, silo-shaped Ark that keeps the
Torahs. There, in his great leather chair, his famous posture
collapsed, Cantor Morton slumped and began to cry.

I think I would have accepted Cantor Morton as my step-
father. Sometimes I wished for that to happen. But my mother had already had her marriage, her *tuchas* passion marriage, and she didn't want to try a second time.

• • •

I didn't want a bar mitzvah party, the after-service snacks
were enough, and it was too uncomfortable to celebrate. For
my bar mitzvah present, I wanted only one thing. After I
carefully removed the tape from the reel-to-reel and stored it
in its tin case, tucked away in a shoe box in my dresser drawer, I hurried to the front closet to find the jacket, the hat, the
gloves, and the goggles. I collected Cheryl and David and
asked them to stand on the pinners porch with me. The
Rosenberg children stood there and waited.

From our garage, a roar arose, grumbling and revving.
Sounds of acceleration split through alley stones bearing past
the Jenners' and the Millers'. A squeal shot off the Ellerson
Street asphalt. This long-absent music roused the neighbors,
and they began to peer through their front doors. Mom
leaned the Hydra Glide around the corner, in her leathers,
the Hydra Glide spewing out tawny smoke as if clearing its
insides of rust. She brought the Hydra Glide to rest in front
of our house, and David and Cheryl leapt over the pinners
porch steps and rushed down the sidewalk.

"For Jeremy," Mom said, raising her goggles to her
leather helmet.

I waited on the porch for the right moment as Mom
revved the throttle and smiled at me. Karl Grossman was the
first to arrive, then Charlie and Bobby and Mookie and
Dahveed and Hannah. Then the parents started coming out
in a rush, Ida Lipshilts puff-puffing her cigarette jaunted up
toward her nose. As they crowded around the Hydra Glide,
I waited. Skyler Jenner, with his father looming over his
shoulder, opened his front screen door and leaned forward. I
flew over the pinners porch.

While the neighbors around us took turns deciding who should go next, Mom directed me to sit up front. "I still have to sell it," she said in my ear.

"I know. It's all right."

The power under me seemed to load up as Mom gripped the throttle and shifted into first. I lowered Dad's goggles over my eyes and pulled back the cuffs on his leather jacket as I settled my hands on the handlebars.

Mom drove to Rural Beckwith Road. She eased control of the Hydra Glide to me, guiding my right hand to the throttle, my left hand to the tank-shifter, and held me close as I shifted into fourth and leaned the Hydra Glide's power to follow the narrow road's gentle curve. Skyward-leaping trees, their young leaves green and vibrant, branched together overhead like interlacing fingers. We dashed through the forest tunnel, Mom's arms tight around my waist, and she whispered among the Hydra Glide's rumblings, "You're a man now, Jeremy. You've become a man."

•   •   •

It took me several years to find another 1949 Hydra Glide, and more to restore it and make it look as much like my father's as possible. And it took another year or two during college to find Melinda Levinberg and convince her to marry me.

"Stop sending me Valentine's Day cards! It's spring!"

"Forgetting Valentine's Day is how I lost you to Leonard Schlictman," I said.

"Who's Leonard Schlictman?"

So I married Melinda after a year of convincing her that a ride on the Hydra Glide to Niagara Falls would be a perfect honeymoon.

Melinda thinks it's odd how I emulate my father's life as much as I can, that I married her, my grammar school sweetheart, and ride my Hydra Glide, and insist that the ancient Cantor Morton schedule our son's bar mitzvah for the same

Leviticus reading I had with Bup Miller.

"You're not going to play that old tape, are you?"

"I might," I say, and she rolls her eyes about until I grab her and kiss her and *tuchas* passion her into putting up with me and my neurosis.

I ride my Hydra Glide when I can, even this early Saturday morning as my son busies himself dressing for his bar mitzvah. I roll it down the driveway and rev it at the street curb, where my mother, Cheryl and David gather close, and the neighbors pile out to surround me and ask for their turns on the old bike, and one neighbor scolds how dangerous it is for children to ride on motorcycles. Below me, I hear the sweet little girl's voice that shakes my heart.

Me, Daddy!

I raise my daughter to the seat and set her close in front of me, removing my helmet and lowering it over her uncountable bazillion brown curls. With her bewitching smile and sweet face, she controls me, ties my insides in knots.

We ride the streets of my childhood, and I feel my father's strength within me, like a bird with one wing flying straight and true.

Acknowledgments

Rob, Bob, and Carol Harrsch and the entire Harrsch-McHugh-Fries clan, Judi and Steve Zeal, D.C. Brod, Susan Kraykowski, Bonnie Harm-Pechous, Kitty Jarman, Kevin Burris, Paul Cook, Dean Pannell, Sue Balik, Fran Fredricks, Nancy Wedemeyer, Todd Possehl, Joselle Kehoe, Maryann Durland, Kim Dechert, John Buckley, Laurie Bohlke, Dave Barrows, Sherry Miller, Sue Glavin, Adrienne Lee, Shari Bertane, Pat Dixon, Sandi Byrd, Philip DiMarzio, Paul Glaser, Dr. Timothy Brown, Bruce Currie, Neil Chethik, Sheldon and Charolette Siegel, Halle Cox, NancyLee Browne, Gloria Carr, Victoria Camron, the Women of the St. Charles Library Reference Desk, and Rabbi Neil Brief.

Special Thanks:

To my handsome nephew Sam, his equally dashing brother, Evan, and their amazed parents, Elaine and Larry. To my always interesting sister, Lois, and to the memories and lives of Elaine and Erwin Krawitz, Professor Albert Tilman, and Hildegard Landmark.

To the Ewen family for including me in that category.

To the St. Charles Writers Group and Writers Anonymous, and our fearless, talented leader, Rick Holinger; and to Rose M. Kennedy, Mary Sanders Smith, and Mary Cella, all of whom I owe tremendously for this novel.

To Bob and Elizabeth Collins for their confidence in this novel and me.

To Hazzan Alan Smolen and Congregation Knesseth Israel for being put to the test by "Jeremy" and for providing invaluable guidance.

To Mike and Eileen Balcom-Vetillo, as well as John Adams, for showing that amazing people and talent, and friendship are often in our midst.

And to Donna Church, not just my editor, but a new friend to this novel and me.